MW00633034

Functional Memory Manual

Jean Elbaum, Ph.D.
Peggy Kramer, M.S., CCC-SLP
Deborah Benson, Ph.D.
Carrie Dulaski, OTR/L

pro·ed
An International Publisher
8700 Shoal Creek Boulevard
Austin, Texas 78757-6897
800/897-3202 Fax 800/397-7633
www.proedinc.com

pro·ed
An International Publisher

8700 Shoal Creek Boulevard
Austin, Texas 78757-6897
800/897-3202 Fax 800/397-7633
www.proedinc.com

These pharmaceutical products are registered trademarks of the following companies:

Aricept: Eisai, Inc., and Pfizer, Inc.
Ativan: Wyeth-Ayerst Laboratories
Buspar: Bristol-Meyers Squibb Co.
Dantrium: Proctor and Gamble Pharmaceuticals
Depakote: Abbott Laboratories
Dilantin: Parke-Davis
Effexor: Wyeth-Ayerst Laboratories
Flexeril: Merck and Co, Inc.
Halcion: Pharmacia
Haldol: McNeil Pharmaceuticals
Lioresal: Medtronic, Inc., Neurological Division
Neurontin: Parke-Davis
Paxil: Glaxo-SmithKline
Prozac: Dista
Restoril: Novartis
Risperdal: Janssen Pharmaceuticals
Ritalin: Novartis
Tegretol: Novartis
Tizanidine: Athena Neurosciences
Valium: Roche Products
Xanax: Pharmacia
Zoloft: Roerig
Zyprexa: Eli Lilly & Company
Neuropage® is a registered trademark of N.A. Hersh and L. G. Treadgold

Library of Congress Cataloging-in-Publication Data

Goldstein, Trudy Sandler.
Functional rehabilitation in orthopaedics / Trudy Sandler Goldstein.
p. ; cm.
Originally published: Gaithersberg, Md. : Aspen Publishers, 1995, in series: Rehabilitation of Institute of Chicago publication series.
Includes bibliographical references and index.
ISBN-13: 978-094448039-7 (alk. paper)
ISBN-10: 0-944480-39-X (hard)
1. Orthopaedics. 2. People with disabilities--Rehabilitation. I. Title.
[DNLM: 1. Disabled Persons--rehabilitation. 2. Patient Care Planning. 3. Physical Therapy Techniques--methods. WB 320 G624f 1995a]
RD732.G59 1995
617'.03--dc21

203046860

Printed in the United States of America

4 5 6 7 10 09 08

Acknowledgments

We acknowledge and would like to thank
all past and current clients and
Transitions of Long Island for supporting this project.

Contents

Chapter 1

The Importance of a Functional Memory System

Impaired memory is one of the most persistent and pervasive deficits after injury to the brain (Parente and DiCesare 1991). A reliable memory system is vital for independent living. Memory difficulties may create more challenging barriers to independent functioning, social adaptation, family life and school or work endeavors than do physical deficits (Vogenthaler 1987).

A functional memory system provides a sense of continuity in the environment. Without it, daily events are disconnected, distorted or forgotten. The individual lives from moment to moment, and there is a loss of control over oneself and the environment (Toglia 1993).

Therapists working with clients who have short-term memory difficulties must find systems and strategies that match the clients' specific needs.

Clients with significant memory difficulties who are not able to develop compensatory systems become dependent on others to make sure they follow through on important activities. They may demonstrate significant difficulty in recalling basic information, such as meals they have eaten, phone conversations they have had, activities they have participated in or people they have seen recently. This confusion leads to repetition of activities that may lead to weight gain, reduced sense of self and extraordinary frustration. Family members may be overwhelmed.

The process leading to retrieval of new information involves attending to relevant stimuli, registering the stimuli, storing the information effectively and then being able to retain the information.

Using *Functional Memory Manual*

This manual is written for members of the interdisciplinary neurorehabilitation team: neuropsychologists, speech-language pathologists, occupational and physical therapists, and cognitive therapists. Special education teachers also may apply the strategies discussed here to improve recall in students with memory deficits.

Functional Memory Manual is designed primarily for clients with memory deficits due to acquired brain injury as a result of motor vehicle, bicycle or pedestrian accidents, stroke, aneurysm or anoxia, work-related brain injury, assault, encephalitis, meningitis and brain tumor. It also may be used with clients with dementia and other types of memory impairments.

The exercises contained in *Functional Memory Manual* are appropriate for clients with mild, moderate and severe memory deficits.

With more than 30 years of combined experience in the area of neurorehabilitation, the authors have tested these exercises clinically with clients at three different levels of functioning: mild, moderate and severe. The authors have modified the exercises to meet the needs of clients at each level. They also have extensive experience with clients at Level 4 (high) with subtle memory deficits requiring more advanced challenges. Some of these clients may have had superior memories prior to their injuries and currently are adapting to a memory system that is still within normal limits yet reduced from pre-injury levels.

Instructions at the beginning of each chapter provide guidance in selecting activities for individual clients. Evaluation results, discussion with family members and significant others, performance in individual and group sessions, and clinical experience all provide the information necessary for selecting appropriate exercises for each client.

Before beginning any memory exercise with a client, review and suggest appropriate strategies to help the client encode and retrieve the information you will present. Specific strategies are discussed in Chapter 2, and clear examples are provided. Additional examples of strategy application are presented at the beginning of each chapter.

The rationale for the hierarchy of exercises is explained at the beginning of each chapter or activity.

Terms Associated with Memory Functioning

The following terms define various aspects of memory. Discuss and review these terms frequently with clients.

Sensory memory. The registration of new information through a selecting and recording process by which perceptions enter the memory system.

Short-term memory (STM). The first stage of short-term memory is immediate recall, in which information is held for approximately 30 seconds to several minutes. The second stage is a limited-capacity, temporary store in which information is held from several minutes to two days. It also is called *primary memory* or *working memory.*

Long-term memory (LTM). A large-capacity store that is considered a more permanent "filing cabinet" of the memory system. Information is continually processed in the two stages of short-term memory and saved in long-term memory for future reference. Long-term memory involves storage of both semantic and episodic memories. It is also called *secondary memory.*

> *Semantic memory.* Memory for knowledge, such as knowing that an apple is a fruit and the earth is a planet.
>
> *Episodic memory.* Memory for events that occurred at a particular time and place, such as recalling what you ate for breakfast.

Procedural memory. The ability to reproduce an action or procedure, which includes the following two subcategories:

> *Implicit memory.* The ability to reproduce an action, although the individual does not recall having learned a certain skill. However, when presented with the task, the person is able to reproduce it.
>
> *Explicit memory.* The ability to reproduce an action or procedure, with the client's awareness that he or she is able to recall the specific activity.

Prospective memory. The ability to remember to do something at a future time, such as remembering to take medications at a certain time.

Retrieval. The ability to recall or recover information from long-term memory when needed.

Recognition. The ability to identify a person, thing or experience as being known or familiar from the past.

Chapter 2
A Comprehensive View of Memory Rehabilitation

Various compensatory strategies are available to facilitate improvements in memory functioning. Individuals whose short-term memory has been significantly impaired by traumatic brain injury require the use of these techniques so that they may develop effective memory systems to work around their difficulties. These strategies and techniques will be discussed later in this chapter. (See pages 9–14.)

But, in addition to teaching clients how to become expert compensators, it also is important to teach them about the influence of physical, chemical, emotional, attitudinal and motivational factors on memory. This multimodal approach is a comprehensive approach to memory rehabilitation (Herrmann and Parente 1994).

Influences on Memory Performance

Physical Condition

An individual's physical condition and general health can have a major influence on memory performance (Fisher and Reason 1986). Even routine disruptions of health (such as the common cold) impair cognitive functioning. Sleep loss generally impairs cognition (Herrmann and Searleman 1990). Montgomery (1995) suggested that physical symptoms influence an individual's cognitive functioning indirectly by competing for attention and interfering with concentration and work efficiency. Clients need counseling on how to maintain a healthy diet, exercise regularly consistent with medical recommendations and address sleep disorders that may result from their injury.

Anatomical Correlates

Because memory is an extremely complex concept, it is overly simplistic to try to localize memory functions to one or two areas of the brain. It is important to realize that these brain regions are not storage sites in themselves but are areas that provide access to information that probably is stored elsewhere, perhaps in multiple sites (Heilman and Valenstein 1993).

In particular, the hippocampus is thought to record the context in which events relate to each other and to the individual. Thus, individuals with medial temporal damage generally retain the gist of information but fail to recall details, context and associations related to those memories. Because the hippocampus has a limited capacity, eventually information processed there is lost or consolidated in different brain regions. Thus, the hippocampus is not required for retrieval of remote memories. The cortical area overlying the hippocampus, known as the temporal neocortex, also contributes to memory functioning. In animal studies and in human case studies, lesions to this area (which spare the hippocampus) have been found to result in memory impairment. The amygdala, situated anterior to the hippocampus in the temporal lobe, also has been implicated in memory functioning. While the exact nature of the amygdala's involvement in memory is uncertain, the amygdala is important in mediating the emotional aspects of memory.

Diencephalic structures (that is, mammillary bodies, thalamus) also are involved in memory functioning. Damage to these areas most often has been found in individuals with Wernicke-Korsakoff disease (a disease resulting from thiamine deficiency, often associated with chronic alcoholism). It has been proposed that the mammillothalamic region and associated tracts serve as connection pathways for other areas important in memory.

The basal forebrain is the third major region considered important in memory functioning. The significant memory loss that occurs following ruptured anterior communicating artery aneurysms has been attributed to disruption in this region. The massive cholinergic projections (neurons within the pathways that release acetylcholine) from this area (to hippocampus, amygdala and neocortex) have been implicated in memory dysfunction associated with Alzheimer's disease.

The frontal lobes have been associated with memory functioning. In particular, frontal lobe damage is likely to produce impairment in *prospective* memory functioning ("remembering to remember"). This form of deficit can have enormous functional implications; individuals may not remember to go to work or keep appointments. Frontal lobe damage also interferes with the individual's capacity to organize learned information. Sensitivity to interruptions, a tendency to confabulate (that is, unconsciously invent fictitious detail about events due to inability to fill in missing gaps in recall) and inability to use context to facilitate recall also are characteristic of memory impairments related to frontal lobe damage (Lezak 1995).

Medications and Side Effects

Following a brain injury, individuals often are prescribed various medications as a part of the treatment plan. Some of these medications are designed to assist with the healing process of the brain itself; others are designed to alleviate secondary complications that can occur related to the brain injury; still others are needed to deal with other injuries the individual may have sustained in addition to the brain injury. While the use of medication to assist in recovery after brain injury often is an important aspect of treatment, many of these medications have unwanted side effects. Some of these side effects are particularly problematic in the brain-injured person, given the physical, cognitive, emotional and behavioral symptoms that already may exist. The following is a review of several categories of medications commonly used to treat people with brain injury (or associated illnesses and injuries) and associated side effects (Braunling-McMarrow et al. 1998).

- *Anticonvulsant/Antiseizure medications.* These include carbamazepine (Tegretol), phenytoin (Dilantin), valproic acid (Depakote), gabapentin (Neurontin) and phenobarbital. These medications are known for causing drowsiness, dizziness and reduced speed of cognitive processing. Phenobarbital has been found to produce the most significant negative side effects and therefore is usually the last drug of choice in this category for individuals with brain injury.

- *Antispasticity agents.* These include dantrolene (Dantrium), cyclobenzaprine (Flexeril), baclofen (Lioresal) and zanaflex (Tizanidine). These medications are used primarily to reduce muscle tone and spasm. Major side effects include drowsiness and dizziness.

- *Antipsychotics.* These include haloperidol (Haldol), risperidone (Risperdal) and olanzepine (Zyprexa). They are prescribed to combat psychosis and sometimes are used to deal with agitation following brain injury. Common side effects include low blood pressure and sedation. Recent evidence suggests that some antipsychotic medications can interfere with recovery following brain injury and should be used only when absolutely necessary.

- *Antidepressants.* Commonly prescribed categories include tricyclics (for example, imipramine, nortriptyline, amitriptyline) and specific serotonin reuptake inhibitors (SSRIs) including Prozac, Zoloft, Paxil and Effexor. These are used in treatment of depression, headache (tricyclics) and panic and obsessive-compulsive disorder. Cognitive/behavioral side effects can include sedation, drowsiness, headache or agitation.

- *Antianxiety medications.* Benzodiazepines include lorazepam (Ativan), diazepam (Valium), alprazolam (Xanax), temazepam (Restoril) and triazolam (Halcion). These are commonly used in treatment of anxiety, insomnia and agitation following brain injury. Significant cognitive side effects can include impaired short-term memory and drowsiness. Buspirone (Buspar) has been used more recently as an alternative with fewer reported cognitive side effects, although headache and dizziness have been reported.

- *Cardiac/Hypertensive medications.* It is not uncommon for individuals with brain injury (particularly resulting from stroke or anoxia) to take medications related to their cardiovascular functioning. Examples of these include Vasotec for the treatment of hypertension and digoxin for treatment of cardiac failure. Potential side effects of these medications are confusion, anxiety and depression.

- *Antibiotics.* Even medications routinely used to treat common infections (for example, urinary tract infection, bronchitis and ear infections) can have potentially disruptive effects in individuals with brain injury. These can include dizziness, confusion, fatigue, restlessness and agitation.

A number of medications have been used to enhance cognitive functioning in individuals with brain injury. Results have been mixed. Methylphenidate (Ritalin) has been used to improve attention and concentration and reduce fatigue. Potential side effects include agitation, decreased appetite and insomnia. Aricept has been used specifically to improve memory functioning in dementia and memory impairment associated with acquired brain injury. Potential side effects of this medication include delusions, irritability, aggression and aphasia.

Recently, a number of herbs have received attention for reported positive effects on cognition. These include ginkgo biloba (Ginkgo) and ginseng. Biloba has been indicated for use in organic brain dysfunction and demonstrated to improve concentration and memory deficits resulting from arterial occlusion. Ginseng reportedly has been used to improve stamina and increase energy and concentration (Fleming 1998). Vitamin E also has been purported to improve memory functioning in individuals with organic brain dysfunction.

Chemicals found in tobacco smoke, coffee, tranquilizers and sedating antidepressants have been shown to impair cognition and lessen memory performance. O'Shanick (1991) stated that despite many past attempts and current efforts to search for a chemical agent to enhance memory after brain injury, researchers thus far have failed to describe a consistent compound that works in all clinical situations.

Other Influences on Memory Functioning

Emotional states such as anxiety and depression also have been shown to interfere with memory functioning (Hertel 1994). Individuals with traumatic brain injuries may feel depressed not only because they cannot function as before, but also because the injury has damaged areas of the brain that directly mediate mood (Mayes 1988). A depressed mental state reduces the amount of attention that otherwise could be paid to ongoing experiences.

Counseling and pharmacotherapy may be critical to improve clients' moods so they can focus more effectively on getting better.

Cognitive performance also is affected by attitudinal state. People are likely to perform more effectively when their attitude toward a task is positive (Gruneberg 1992; Wyer and Srull 1989). If a situation entails incentives for good task performance, clients' motivational states often result in improved cognitive performance. If they can be made to feel in control of the goals and rewards of their efforts to improve cognitive function, clients become motivated toward acquiring the knowledge and methods that will produce better cognitive performance (Parente and Stapleton 1993).

A Combined Approach to Memory Rehabilitation

A critical component of memory rehabilitation involves three factors:

- Educating clients on all available compensatory strategies (that is, techniques to work around impairments)
- Facilitating practice of various strategy uses. If clients are presented with various memory exercises without emphasis on practicing strategy use, the exercises will have only limited effectiveness.
- Identifying the specific strategies that are most appropriate for each client

Compensatory Strategies

Memory rehabilitation exercises can be categorized in three groups: *stimulation therapy, internal strategies* and *external strategies.* A combined approach including all three will allow clients to feel that they are really "working on" their memory while also having the external aid as a backup system if they need it.

A word of caution: Be aware that clients may resist learning strategies to improve their memory function. Their resistance may be due to denial or lack of awareness of their difficulties, unfamiliarity with compensatory strategies or the feeling that use of strategies is a sign of weakness. Working with clients to break down that resistance is an extremely important component of rehabilitation. Providing feedback from the neuropsychological evaluation and input and examples from significant others about everyday memory failures can provide a basis for helping clients understand the need to address memory problems.

Stimulation Therapy

Stimulation therapy is the oldest form of memory retraining (Parente and DiCesare 1991) and is still used widely in rehabilitation units (Harris 1992). This therapeutic mode is based on the assumption that memory responds like a mental muscle and that exercising one's memory on a given task will strengthen it for use on other tasks and generalize to the requirements of everyday life. Harris demonstrated that mental exercise during a period of neural regeneration may enhance the regeneration. However, Hersh and Treadgold (1994) indicated that the restorative approaches in cognitive rehabilitation may have limited effectiveness.

Stimulation therapy focuses on the value of practice. For example, when you present stories for clients to recall, the expectation is that by reviewing the stories, the individual's ability to process and recall information will be strengthened. Also, if clients are working on memory exercises presented on the computer, the actual process of concentrating and responding to the exercise is believed to enhance memory. This type of memory rehabilitation is passive, unlike the reinforcement of strategy use which is an active form of neurorehabilitation and which is linked to better clinical outcomes.

Internal Strategies

Individuals with traumatic brain injury can benefit from the use of various *internal strategies.* These are mentally employed techniques, invisible to others, that allow the individual to process information more actively in order to facilitate retrieval. Internal strategies include *association, imagery, rehearsal, chunking, mnemonics* and other techniques (Parente and DiCesare 1991). Harris (1992) indicated that the benefits derived from mental strategies are related to the fact that individuals learn to encode information more effectively.

Internal strategies are most useful for clients with mild to moderate difficulties. For clients with moderate to severe memory deficits, external strategies are recommended. (See page 14.)

Association

Association involves encoding information to be learned by connecting it to information that already exists in memory. This type of meaningful processing and connecting allows the information to stand out more vividly and be more accessible when the client searches for it during the retrieval process.

Association can take place by either:

- Connecting information to be learned with similar information that already has been stored.

  Examples of this type of association may include the following:

  1. Associating an already familiar name, such as grandfather's name of Jeremiah, with the title of a movie, *Jeremiah Johnson*

  2. Associating ingredients needed with someone's favorite recipe

3. Associating names of places already visited or familiar with when receiving directions

4. Associating familiar product names when shopping or going on errands

- Creatively imposing an association between information to be learned and some other piece of information that will enable the information to stand out in a striking manner.

  It is easier to associate two related items than two unrelated items. When you encounter unrelated items that you must remember, it is important to creatively link the two items to aid storage and recall of the information. For instance, when recalling the word "physiatry," link with an amusing phrase such as "fuzzy eye in a tree" to boost recall.

  Another example would be associating a technical term or learning specific vocabulary related to a school subject with already known names such as the spelling for Missouri: "Miss, oh you are I."

Association can be used to assist in the recall of specific bits of information such as names, ages, occupations and the current month.

Personalization is a subcomponent of association, wherein the client recalls new information by connecting the information directly to specific personal information such as the client's name, age or occupation.

Using association as a strategy requires the ability to remember to use it, highlight a connection that already exists or actively impose a connection between two items.

Clients with severe memory difficulties have trouble with the complex encoding demands involved in this strategy use. These clients may be able to use this strategy with cues, and they may be better able to recognize the specific information that was presented to them following strategy use. However, they may require verbal cues to access the information (for example, "Isn't the name in this story the same as your brother's name?").

This strategy will best benefit clients who are easily able to see connections between items and who have the flexibility and creativity to impose connections between disparate items.

Imagery

Imagery is a strategy that involves forming a mental picture of information to be remembered as a means of facilitating better encoding and retrieval of new information. It is important to train clients to encode information into meaningful visual bits of information so they can improve access to stored information during the retrieval process. This is a particularly good strategy for clients with reduced auditory recall and strong visual skills. For example, in the case of information that is presented verbally or in writing, instruct the client to form mental pictures of relevant details and to encode the imagery so that the relevant bits of information stand out in a meaningful way.

Instruct clients to imagine relevant details when they are listening to information presented verbally. For example, they may imagine an office number by forming a mental picture of it. Clients also can learn to use visual landmarks to recall new places and orient themselves in space (for example, to remember where they have parked the car).

Following a traumatic brain injury, clients initially may be confused and unable to process details effectively. It is important to emphasize the usefulness of attending to landmarks in the environment and visualizing them in association with surrounding items. For example, clients can learn to recall the location of the clinician's office by relating it to such features as proximity to a certain picture on the wall or a row of chairs of a particular color.

Rehearsal

Rehearsal involves repeating (either aloud or to oneself) the information to be recalled in the immediate or near future. It is a form of feeding information into short-term memory by keeping it actively in mind and more accessible when needed.

Rehearsal is used for immediate recall of information such as names. For example, a man joins a discussion at a party where he knows only a few people. After meeting three new people, he rehearses their names several times, then begins conversing with those people and immediately using their names aloud, which reinforces their names in short-term memory.

Using rehearsal as a strategy requires basic attentional and language skills such as repetition. Being skilled at tuning out extraneous noise also is essential, because information frequently is presented in less than perfect environments.

Chunking

Chunking is the practice of grouping information into smaller segments to facilitate immediate recall so more data can be stored effectively. Common uses of chunking include recall of telephone numbers and social security numbers. By chunking a seven-digit phone number (say, 5553478) into three chunks (555-34-78), only three sets of numbers must be recalled instead of seven separate numbers. This strategy leaves more "room" in short-term memory.

Skills necessary for chunking include basic attention, categorization and organization.

First-Letter Mnemonics

This strategy involves forming a word by using the first letters of words to be recalled. For example, STOP can represent the items to be purchased at the grocery store:

Spaghetti

Toothpaste

Onions

Potatoes

The word STOP acts as a retrieval cue for the different items that the letters in the word represent. This strategy allows the individual to reduce the amount of information to be encoded. It is especially useful in learning a certain sequence (for example, WDCR, which represents the steps involved in keeping track of tasks to be completed):

Write task to be completed

Do the task when scheduled.

Check off when completed.

Refer to memory book to see what you've done or still need to do.

Categorization

Categorization involves encoding information in meaningful clusters. For example, if clients need to memorize lists of different items, instruct them to organize the information in distinct categories (for example, items to be purchased at the grocery store: dairy, meat, fruits and vegetables; or items to pack for a trip: toiletries, footwear, clothing).

Semantic Elaboration

This is the process by which an individual encodes information to be learned by creating a story or adding information to link unassociated bits of information in a cohesive, meaningful way. This strategy is most helpful for clients who are re-entering the academic setting; when encoding technical, detailed and complex information; or when learning a new task or trying to master a technical article from a magazine or newspaper.

Verbal Labeling

This strategy involves associating something abstract and ambiguous with a label that is concrete and clear. It is particularly useful in helping clients who are returning to an academic setting in which technical information is being encoded. For example, a student is required to memorize a list for anatomy class. Having difficulty with recalling the name of a muscle in the ear, a student renames it "the Italian muscle" because its anatomical name resembles an Italian-sounding name, Sal Pingo Pharyngeus.

External Strategies

External strategies are techniques that make use of tangible tools to provide visual or auditory reminders (or both) to boost memory. These strategies are essential for clients with moderate to severe memory deficits who are unable to initiate use of internal strategies.

External strategies include establishing motor routines and using checklists, logbooks including memory books, electronic signaling devices and tele-memo devices. These external memory strategies are usually designed to cue the person to some future activity (Parente and Parente 1989). Lists, timetables, plans and diagrams are inexpensive and effective ways to help people with memory deficits (Harris 1992).

Motor Routines

In this strategy, clients are taught to develop certain consistent habits such as putting keys or glasses in the same place all the time.

Checklists and Memory Books

Any checklist may be developed with an individual client to provide cues to start and complete certain activities at designated times. For example, on a morning checklist, clients enter a check on the list after they have brushed their teeth, showered, changed clothing and eaten breakfast.

Memory books or specialized logbooks provide a system for keeping track of information by date in an organized fashion. They include calendar books, planners and organizers.

The authors have developed a color-coded organizer, *Mempal: A Novel Compensatory Tool. Mempal* is designed to record the day's events and enter follow-up items and notes regarding meals, medications, appointments, visitations and calls. See Elbaum et al. 1999.

Tele-Memo Devices

These are devices with which one simply hits a button to record a message that can be played back after another button is pushed. These devices are particularly helpful for keeping track of brief bits of information, such as directions while driving, instructions from significant others and school assignments. The clients who benefit most from this device are best able to process information auditorily, especially with review.

Alphanumeric Paging System

Neuropage®, described in detail by Hersh and Treadgold (1994), is a system that allows a therapist, family member or friend to compose a written message that is transmitted to the pager worn by the client. In this way, the client is cued to respond.

In Conclusion

Therapists need to be aware of the comprehensive factors that influence memory, and they must educate clients and significant others about those factors. In this chapter, we have reviewed the multimodal aspects of memory and explained various internal and external strategies that are available to improve recall. The following chapters, prepared by an interdisciplinary team, provide practice of these strategies using original exercises that are appropriate for clients with mild, moderate and severe deficits.

Chapter 3

Improving Attention

The purpose of this chapter is to provide a basic review of attentional processes and describe several approaches to remediation, targeting different levels of attention and progressing from more basic (focused attention) to complex (divided attention) levels of difficulty.

The chapter is organized by levels of attention, with different types of suggested exercises targeting each level. Strategies to facilitate performance are described. Introduce and reinforce these strategies to clients who are unable to efficiently perform the tasks without using them.

Cancellation exercises, commonly used to assess and provide training in visual attention, are provided in the Appendixes (pages 359–381).

Attention deficits are extremely common following many types of brain injuries and can be an underlying factor contributing to memory failure. If a person is unable to attend to a given stimulus, he or she is not likely to be able to recall or retrieve it at a later time because it may not have been stored adequately to begin with. Thus, attention deficits can have a profoundly negative impact on memory and can interfere with functional independence following brain injury. Attentional difficulties include an inability to focus, distractibility, becoming overwhelmed in stimulating environments and having difficulty performing multiple tasks.

Sohlberg and Mateer (1989) and Lezak (1995) conceptualize attention as a multidimensional capacity. These dimensions can be considered hierarchically, from the most basic to highest levels, as outlined below.

- Immediate span of attention
- Focused attention
- Sustained attention
- Selective attention
- Alternating attention
- Divided attention

In this chapter, we will discuss deficits in each of these attention areas and provide exercises and strategies for remediation.

Deficits in Immediate, Focused and Sustained Attention

Immediate span of attention refers to how much information can be held at once. It is a relatively automatic and effortless process and often is resistant to the effects of brain injury. The ability to repeat a series of verbally presented numbers is an example of immediate attention span.

Focused attention involves the ability to focus on and "respond discretely to" one or more aspects of the environment (Sohlberg and Mateer 1989). This aspect of attention is commonly known as concentration. The ability to track a moving target or orient to a person speaking are examples of focused attention.

Sustained attention, also known as *vigilance,* involves the maintenance of continuous attention over a period of time. The ability to remain focused on a movie or throughout a conversation are examples of sustained attention.

Deficits in focused and sustained attention are commonly observed in clients who are emerging from coma or severe brain injury. Various coma stimulation techniques attempt to gain the client's focus and orientation. They involve input from various sensory modalities: playing music (auditory), using colored lights and photos (visual) and light touch and massage (kinesthetic).

The computer can be a useful tool in remediating these basic attention deficits. A number of computer programs have been developed for this purpose (New York University Head Trauma Program 1987; Rattok 1988). Typically, these programs require the client to focus on the computer screen and respond when a target appears, or track a target across the screen over a period of time. These exercises are intended to improve accuracy of responding (focused attention) and to increase the length of time over which the client must attend before a response is indicated (sustained attention).

Strategies

You may want to provide compensatory strategies or cues to help the client perform focused or sustained attention tasks. These include:

- Pointing to the area of the computer screen in which the target is expected to appear
- Giving an auditory cue that precedes the appearance of the visual target
- Directing the client to continuously and silently repeat the task instructions (for example, "Press ENTER when the red light appears.") while waiting for the target

Deficits in Selective Attention

Selective attention refers to the ability to ward off distractions. Individuals with this difficulty are easily drawn off task by extraneous stimuli (including external sounds or visual distractions) and internal distractions (such as anxiety or depressed mood). Two examples of selective attention are the ability to focus on a phone conversation while the television is on, or to track one particular item among a display of similar items.

Selective attention deficits are a common target of remediation efforts. Typically, these are approached through various visual or auditory modalities.

The Use of Cancellation Exercises

Cancellation exercises are useful for global selective attention deficits and focal (for example, hemi-inattention) impairments. Hemi-inattention (the failure to attend to stimuli on one side of space) is most common following right-hemisphere stroke (with corresponding left-hemi-inattention, or left neglect).

Present visual stimuli across a page, and instruct the client to cross out (or point to) a target stimulus. Stimuli can be letters, numbers or other symbols or pictures. (See Appendixes 3 and 4, pages 359–381.) They can be sized according to the level of difficulty desired. For higher-level clients, present brief news articles and ask the client to read the article and circle any instance of a certain word (for example, the word "the"). Materials for these exercises are easily generated with any word-processing program or by using articles from newspapers and magazines.

Strategies

Train the client to use compensatory strategies or cues to help performance on cancellation tasks. These include:

- Anchors. Draw thick, noticeable lines down the left side of the page (or the right side in the case of right hemi-inattention). Orient clients to the anchor and instruct them to find the anchor when moving from one line of text to another. This cue can facilitate clients' awareness of the neglected side of space in instances of hemi-neglect.

- Scanning aids. Have the client use a ruler, point or employ other visual aids to improve the ability to scan across an array systematically (for example, right to left, line by line).

- Timing devices. Use an egg timer to set speed goals. Begin with untimed trials focused on accuracy. Once the client masters accuracy, proceed to trials requiring increased speed. In most cases, however, the goal is to achieve high accuracy, followed by increased speed without reducing accuracy.

Use the reproducible cancellation exercises in Appendix 3 (359–368) with clients who are working on deficits in selective attention.

The Use of Distractor Tasks

Present a task such as making simple calculations, copying an exercise, filing or reading. Add environmental distractors (for example, white noise, radio playing or telephone ringing). Vary both the level of task difficulty and the salience of the distractor according to the desired level of demand on attention. Mastery typically is measured by high accuracy on the designated task. For example, have the client achieve consistent accuracy levels of 85% or above before introducing a more complex task.

As with all remedial tasks, determine the baseline level at which the client can achieve mastery. Then introduce increasingly difficult tasks or distractors until the client's maximal level of performance is attained.

Strategies

Some clients may not be able to achieve a functional level of selective attention; that is, they may be unable to perform tasks when certain levels of distraction are presented. For these individuals, explore and discuss compensatory strategies that modify the environment (that is, limit distractions) in order to facilitate task performance. Strategies include:

- Wearing earplugs or headphones to minimize auditory distractions
- Wearing sunglasses or tinted lenses to reduce light sensitivity
- Modifying the work or study environment to obtain more distraction-free conditions (for example, working in a private office or cubicle versus working in a large room with others, or studying in a designated distraction-limited space versus a living room or dorm room)
- Determining times to perform certain tasks (for example, shopping or driving) when crowds and traffic are at a minimum

Deficits in Alternating Attention

Alternating attention involves mental flexibility: the ability to shift focus from one activity or task to another. An example of alternating attention is being able to stop typing a letter to answer a ringing telephone, take a message, then go back to the letter without losing track of where one left off.

Alternating attention exercises may be set up in two ways:

- Cued set-shifting exercises, in which the therapist structures when the shift in attention will take place
- Independent set-shifting exercises, in which the client initiates the shift

The Use of Cued Set-Shifting Exercises

Design alternating attention tasks from any two activities that the client is able to work on sequentially. Choose activities that are mildly to moderately challenging to the client. The goal of the exercise is to challenge the alternating attention system, not to improve the skill required by the activity. For example, present a series of basic calculations and a typing task. Instruct the client to begin with one task. After a certain amount of time, cue the client to switch to the other task. Have the client spend the same amount of time on the alternate task. Then cue the client to switch back to the original task. Continue to provide periodic cues to switch tasks. Choose a length of time (for example, 15 minutes) that will result in a mild attention-shifting challenge. When the client has mastered that level, systematically decrease the length of time on task over subsequent trials, thus increasing the demand on the client's alternating attention abilities.

Some clients may be unable to achieve the ability to shift between tasks independently at a functional level. In this case, you may need to provide more substantial support and cuing to facilitate the client's ability to shift focus before switching tasks. For example, offer a five-minute break, or spend a few minutes discussing the upcoming task and its demands, thereby "priming" the client for the new task. These modifications may need to be carried over to the work or academic environment in clients who have persistent difficulties in alternating attention.

The Use of Independent Set-Shifting Exercises

This is a higher-level version of the cued set-shifting exercise. Give the client two or more tasks that compete for attention. For example, seat the client at a desk with a telephone. Ask the client to take phone messages while working on another task such as typing a letter or reading and summarizing a news article. In this exercise, there is no "coaching" regarding when to switch tasks or "priming" to facilitate attention shifting. The client must shift as required by task demands and across variable time intervals.

Deficits in Divided Attention

Divided attention involves the capacity to respond to more than one task at a time or to multiple demands within a given task. The ability to divide one's attention may reflect either the ability to rapidly and continuously alternate attention between two or more tasks, or to rely on "automatic" processing of one or more tasks while actively attending to others. Examples of divided attention are participating in a cocktail party conversation while simultaneously listening to another conversation or driving while listening to the news on the radio.

Once a client demonstrates the ability to alternate attention between tasks, you can begin to remediate divided attention deficits. In large part, this represents an extension of the work done on alternating attention; the time frames between shifts in task become so short that the tasks become virtually simultaneous and the person is doing both at the same time.

The Use of Complex Cancellation Exercises

Complex versions of cancellation tasks tap into more advanced levels of attentional processing. (See Appendix 4, pages 369–381.)

Modify the cancellation exercises described above, increasing task demands so that the client is required to attend and respond simultaneously to more than one stimulus in the array. For example, instruct the client to "Cross out every k and r," thus requiring simultaneous attention to two letters. Vary the level of difficulty by stimulus size, type and number. Also increase task demands by increasing the complexity of the processing demands. For example, instruct the client to "Circle every 2 that is preceded by an 8."

> ***Note:*** Some clients will turn this into an alternating attention task. First they will proceed through the array crossing out each k, then begin again searching for every r. This may be an appropriate starting point if the client is unable to perform the task simultaneously, with the ultimate goal to build up to the simultaneous "double cancellation" mode.

The Use of Simultaneous Task Exercises

These exercises represent an extension of the set-shifting exercises described previously in that they require simultaneous attention to more than one task rather than sequential or alternating attention. For example, instruct the client to:

- Listen to a radio news broadcast and discuss highlights with you while performing repetitive upper-limb exercises
- View an episode of a television news program (such as *20/20*) while filling out an application form
- Read a paragraph while listening and responding to your intermittent commands (for example, "Raise your right hand.")

During these tasks, engage the client's active attention. After the client has performed the tasks, determine the amount of information processed on each task.

Other Approaches

Other approaches to attentional training have been described elsewhere. See Robertson et al. (1998) for a description of techniques targeting neglect (hemi-inattention) of the affected limb in clients who have had strokes. Also see Robertson et al. (1995) for discussion of sustained attention training in clients who have had strokes. Mateer (2000) and Sohlberg and Mateer (1989) also have described a systematic approach to attention training (attention process training) for brain-injured individuals. These investigators have generated data supporting the effectiveness of their approaches.

Please note: The cancellation exercises are in Appendixes 3 and 4 beginning on page 359.

Chapter 4

Auditory Recall Exercises

These auditory recall exercises provide practice in strategy use to facilitate recall of verbally presented information of increasing length and complexity.

Contents

Auditory Recall Sentences

The purpose of this exercise is to serve as a warm-up activity at the beginning of the memory therapy session to provide clients with strategy use to improve immediate recall.

The passages become more lengthy and complex as the exercise continues.

Strategies

Clients can incorporate several strategies to aid with recall of these sentences. Strategies include *visualization, association, rehearsal* and *writing the information.* See pages 9–14 for more information on strategies.

Give the client a copy of the worksheet (page 31) that accompanies the sentences. At Level 1, begin by reviewing strategies, including *writing* the information. Give the worksheet to the client, who can write in the information as you are reading the sentence aloud. The client can refer to the worksheet when using *rehearsal* as a strategy. Then ask the client to turn over the worksheet and retell the sentence without using the written aid.

Instructions

1. Present the sentences according to client level, based on clinical judgment and the following guidelines:

Skill Level	**Presentation**
Level 1—Severe impairment	Sentences 1-10, one at a time
Level 2—Moderate impairment	Sentences 11-30, one or two at a time
Level 3—Mild impairment	Sentences 31-50, two or more at a time

2. Begin the session by reviewing the strategies that can be used to improve recall. To help the client comprehend the strategies, provide examples, such as *associating* a name with another name that is in the client's personal memory (for example, Sam is the name of someone the client already knows).

3. At Level 1, read one sentence (from sentences 1 through 10) aloud to the client; then immediately ask the client to repeat the sentence. If the client is unable to recall the sentence, repeat the sentence several times (which is a form of rehearsal). If the client continues to have difficulty with recall, cue the client to listen for names, time, dates and other specific information.

At Levels 2 (sentences 11–30) and 3 (sentences 31–50), read the sentence aloud; then ask the client to retell the entire sentence. As the client becomes more proficient, read two sentences aloud; then ask the client to retell both sentences. In some cases the client will be able to do three sentences.

The worksheets that accompany the sentences can also be used to help the client recall the information. At Level 1, the activity can start with the clinician reviewing strategies, including writing the information. The worksheets can be given to the client, who can write in the information as the clinician is reading the sentence aloud. The client can then refer to the worksheet when using rehearsal as a strategy. Turning the worksheet over, the client can then be asked to retell the sentence without the aid of the worksheet.

The activity becomes more challenging when clients are asked to recall several sentences. To increase the challenge, provide a delay (5 to 10 minutes) before asking the client to retell several sentences. For an additional challenge, read the sentences aloud, provide a short discussion on another topic, and then have the client fill in the worksheet. In group sessions, have clients form teams and work together to see who can recall the verbally presented sentences with the greatest speed and accuracy.

Auditory Recall Sentences

1. Come over tomorrow at 2:00 p.m.
2. Yesterday was Ed's birthday.
3. I need to buy some fruit.
4. May I go over to Jean's house?
5. Boston, Massachusetts, is a college city.
6. Remind me to go to the drugstore today.
7. Annette's 80th birthday party is on Sunday.
8. Will you bring some watermelon for dessert?
9. Let's meet for lunch at Rosa's.
10. I need a ride to school this morning.

---

11. Your interview is on Wednesday, the 25th, at 2:00 p.m.
12. Remember to vote next Tuesday between the hours of 6:00 a.m. and 7:00 p.m. at your local fire station.
13. Karen said she is able to begin working the first week in July, provided her occupational therapy license arrives by then.
14. Tai and Jeansun have been accepted to Columbia University in New York City.
15. Tell Jose his cousin Roberto will be coming to the celebration next Thursday.
16. Please remember to bring your birth certificate, photo identification and a credit card.
17. The concert tickets can be charged on a credit card, or you may pay cash at the box office.
18. On Monday morning, call Lamont at his office to confirm the interview at 11:00 a.m.
19. Please tell Rick that the reservations at the Japanese restaurant are for six people at 7:00 p.m.
20. Tammy and Kris will be joining us for our trip to Texas next June for Megan's graduation.
21. Mai and Saburo became engaged last night at the New Year's party at the Palace of the Arts in San Francisco.

22. I'm calling from Dr. Jasper's office to confirm your appointment for next Tuesday, the 15th, at 4:30 p.m.

23. Warren called to say he and Jackie will be over for dinner on Saturday at 7:00 p.m.

24. Josh and Matt got a golden retriever puppy they named Wally.

25. On Wednesday, the annual alumni party at Transitions Rehabilitation will be held in the Community Room on the third floor.

26. For her birthday, Alice called Philip to invite him to the opera at Symphony Hall in Springfield.

27. I'm calling from Tom Brown's Butcher Shop to say your order will be ready for pickup on Friday afternoon after 2:00 p.m.

28. Last Tuesday, I called my dance instructor to find out when the classes for the winter will be starting.

29. Please tell Marge the bingo game has been changed from 3:00 p.m. to 7:30 tonight.

30. Kathy and Pat will be visiting from Greensboro, North Carolina, on the third weekend in May.

---

31. Deb left a message saying she and Rebecca are going to a garage sale on Saturday morning and would like to have you join them.

32. I'm calling from Dr. Larson's office to remind you that your cat, Lucky, needs to have her shots updated before the end of this month.

33. Can you meet me at the polar bear exhibit at the Museum of Natural History near Central Park around 1:00 p.m.?

34. Please tell Julianne that Mrs. Witherspoon will be arriving for speech therapy on Wednesday at noon.

35. Tomorrow's weather will be cloudy with a 90% chance of late-day thunderstorms north and west of the city.

36. I cannot attend the meeting of the quilting group tomorrow because I have an appointment with the dentist at 2:15.

37. Next Monday, March 15th, the meeting of the college alumni group will be held from 10:00 a.m. to 12:00 noon.

38. Lucas told Hugo that the phone number for the junior high school has been changed to 555-9898.

39. I have tickets to the hockey game on Saturday afternoon at 2:00 p.m. between the Islanders and the Bruins.

40. When you get to the Wilson Bridge, bear to the right toward Route 193 south until you see Exit 19, where you'll make a left turn into our community.

41. When you hear the beep, please leave your name, phone number where you can be reached during the evening, the time of your call and a brief message.

42. The next time we're in St. Louis, please make sure we get to see the Arch and the paddle boats on the Mississippi, get in a game of golf with my brother, Bill, and visit the aquarium to see the new shark exhibit.

43. If you would like to place an order, please press 3 and listen to our lovely musical selection while the next available representative waits on someone else.

44. Rubin's physical therapist, Harry, is out today, so Christina will see him at 5:00 p.m. instead of 3:30.

45. If it rains tomorrow, Wendy would like to have you pick her up by 7:30 a.m. at the corner of Northern Boulevard and Shelter Rock Road.

46. Please tell Mr. McAndrews that his tulip order can be picked up at Marty's Nursery in Brookville any time on Thursday afternoon after 2:00.

47. Josh phoned from Tokyo before he departed for the next leg of his business trip to say he will be stopping in Singapore, Bangkok and Taiwan before returning to Los Angeles.

48. Can you stop at the cleaners to pick up my shirts, red blazer, black trousers and your tan raincoat before picking up a chicken at the market?

49. Aunt Sylvia called for Leah's phone number in Miami so when she visits there in February they can get together and see Aunt Mildred and Uncle Herbie.

50. Our menu has changed. Please listen to the following options:

    Press 1 to hear the visiting hours.

    Press 2 to request your records.

    Press 3 to make an appointment.

    Press 4 to speak to someone for a referral.

    Press 5 to confirm an appointment.

    For all other matters, please press 0.

Name____________________ Date____________________

Auditory Recall Sentences Worksheet

Instructions

As you listen to the sentences, fill in the blanks. Read the sentences one at a time as a form of rehearsal to help your memory.

Sentences

1. Come over tomorrow at _____ _____.
2. Yesterday was Ed's ____________.
3. I need to buy some _________.
4. May I go over to _________ house?
5. Boston, ______________, is a college city.
6. Remind me to go to the _____________ today.
7. Annette's 80th ___________ ________ is on __________.
8. Will you bring some _____________ for ___________?
9. Let's meet for __________ at _________.
10. I need a ______ ____ ___________this morning.
11. Your _____________ is on Wednesday, the ______, at ______.
12. Remember to ______ ______ ___________ between the hours of 6:00 a.m. and ______ at your _________ ________ ___________.
13. Karen said she is able to begin working the ________ _______ in July, provided her _______________ ___________ license arrives by then.
14. Tai and ____________ have been accepted to _______________ _______________ in New York City.
15. Tell ________ his cousin Roberto will be coming to the _______________ next Thursday.
16. Please remember to bring your _________ ___________________, ________ identification and a credit card.

17. The __________ tickets can be charged on a __________ ________, or you may pay cash at the ______ __________.

18. On Monday morning, call __________ at his ________ to confirm the interview at 11:00 a.m.

19. Please tell __________ that the reservations at the Japanese restaurant are for _____ people at _____ p.m.

20. Tammy and Kris will be joining us for our trip to _________ next June for ___________ ________________.

21. _______ and __________ became engaged last night at the New Year's party at the Palace of the Arts in ______ ______________.

22. I'm calling from Dr. __________'s office to confirm your appointment for next ___________, the 15th, at _______ p.m.

23. Warren called to say he and Jackie will be over for ___________ on ______________ at 7:00 p.m.

24. Josh and ______ got a ________ retriever puppy they named _______.

25. On ___________, the annual alumni party at Transitions Rehabilitation will be held in the _______________ ________ on the _______ floor.

26. For her ____________, Alice called Philip to invite him to the __________ at Symphony Hall in _______________.

27. I'm calling from ______ ___________ Butcher Shop to say your order will be ready for pickup on ___________ afternoon after ________.

28. Last Tuesday, I called my _________ _____________ to find out when the classes for the winter will be starting.

29. Please tell Marge the _________ _________ has been changed from ____ p.m. to 7:30 tonight.

30. ________ and ______ will be visiting from _______________, North Carolina, on the third weekend in May.

31. Deb left a message saying she and ______________ are going to a garage sale on morning and would like to have you join them.

32. I'm calling from Dr. Larson's office to remind you that your _____, ________, needs to have her shots updated before the ______ of this __________

33. Can you meet me at the ________ _______ exhibit at the Museum of Natural History near __________ _______ around ___ p.m.?

34. Please tell ____________ that Mrs. ________________ will be arriving for __________ therapy on Wednesday at ________.

35. Tomorrow's _____________ will be _________ with a 90% chance of late-day __________________ north and ________ of the city.

36. I cannot attend the meeting of the __________ group tomorrow because I have an appointment with _____ __________ at ______.

37. Next Monday, _________ ______, the meeting of the _________ _________ group will be held from _____ a.m. to 12:00 noon.

38. Lucas told Hugo that the _________ __________ for the junior high school has been __________ to 555-_______.

39. I have tickets to the _________ ________ on ___________ afternoon at 2:00 p.m. between the Islanders and the __________.

40. When you get to the __________ Bridge, bear to the ________ toward Route ______ south until you see Exit ___, where you'll make a _____ turn into our community.

41. When you hear the beep, please leave your ________, phone number where you can be reached ___________ _____ __________, the time of your call and a _________ message.

42. The next time we're in _____ _______, please make sure we get to see the __________ and the _________ ________ on the Mississippi, get in a game of ______ with my brother, ________, and visit the aquarium to see the new _________ exhibit.

43. If you would like to place an ________, please press ____ and listen to our lovely ____________ selection while the next available ____________________ waits on someone else.

44. Rubin's ____________ therapist, Harry, is ______ __________, so Christina will see him at ______ p.m. instead of _______.

45. If it ________ tomorrow, ___________ would like to have you pick her up by ______ a.m. at the corner of ______________ Boulevard and ____________ Rock Road.

46. Please tell Mr. McAndrews that his _________ order can be picked up at Marty's Nursery in ________________ any time on _______________ ________________ after 2:00.

47. Josh phoned from _________ before he departed for the next leg of his ____________ trip to say he will be stopping in Singapore, ____________ and Taiwan before returning to ______ ___________.

48. Can you stop at the _____________ to pick up my shirts, _____ blazer, black ____________ and your tan _____________ before picking up a ____________ at the market?

49. Aunt ___________ called for Leah's phone number in __________ so when she visits there in _____________ they can get together and see Aunt ___________ and Uncle ____________.

50. Our menu has changed. Please listen to the following options:

    Press 1 to hear the __________ __________.

    Press 2 to request your _____________.

    Press 3 to make an ____________________.

    Press 4 to speak to _____________ for a _____________.

    Press 5 to confirm an ____________________.

    For all other matters, please press _____.

Auditory Recall Stories

This section contains 32 auditory recall stories divided into four categories: Fiction, History, Health and Medicine, and Sports.

Each passage has four levels. Level 1 is a basic, less demanding format. As the levels increase, so do the length and complexity of the passages. Each level has a specific range of number of details. For instance, each Level 1 story contains only two to four bits of information.

Level 4 is intended for those clients who had superior memories prior to their injury and who currently demonstrate average memory capacities. Often it is difficult to challenge these clients in therapy sessions; they require an extra level of complexity to sharpen their skills.

The chart on the next page depicts the level of memory impairment and corresponding exercises for each level. When matching the level of the exercise to the client, please refer to this chart and use clinical judgment when determining the starting level and when advancing to more challenging levels.

The exercises are arranged in hierarchical order with three recall formats provided: multiple choice, open-ended questions and free recall.

- Multiple-choice questions assess recognition versus recall. Recognition is a less active process; simply ask the client to identify recently presented information from a list of choices.
- Open-ended questions require the individual to answer specific questions about the passage (for example, "In what month did Babe Ruth make his announcement?").
- Free recall is the most challenging level. In free recall, clients are asked to retrieve verbally presented information in entirety, without verbal clues.

The auditory recall passages on Health and Medicine and Sports contain more complex and detailed material than the sections on Fiction and History. It is not expected that clients will recall every detail from the passages, especially at Levels 3 and 4. The objective is to challenge clients to use strategies on elaborate passages that require much attention to detail.

Strategies

The client needs to use strategies in order to make the exercise meaningful and facilitate carryover of strategy use into daily life activities.

Instruct the client to use several strategies, such as *visualizing* the details of the story that you will read aloud. By using *association,* clients can connect the events in the story to events in their personal lives to highlight the information and facilitate encoding and retrieval.

During the learning phase of the exercise, encourage clients to *write* the information on a separate sheet of paper as a means of processing the information more actively and having a record to refer to and *rehearse* the important details and events to be recalled. *Chunking* is useful for encoding bits of information such as telephone numbers.

Instructions

Begin the exercise by reviewing strategies to be used to facilitate recall of these verbally presented stories. You may want to write the strategies on a chalkboard to reinforce their use during the exercise.

Determine the appropriate exercise level for the client, based on clinical judgment and the following guidelines:

Skill Level

Level 1—Severe impairment

Level 2—Moderate impairment

Level 3—Mild impairment

Level 4—Advanced skill level

Read the passage aloud at the appropriate level, and have the client respond verbally. For clients with severe impairment, begin with multiple-choice questions. Once the client has mastered the multiple-choice format, present challenge with open-ended questions, and then proceed to free recall.

Auditory Recall Stories – Fiction

Story 1
Tom and Ellen

Level 1

Tom is a police officer.

Level 1 Questions

A. Multiple-Choice Questions

1.What is the man's name?
   a. Frank
   b. Tom
   c. Bob
   d. Hank

2. What type of work does he do?
   a. Firefighter
   b. Social worker
   c. Engineer
   d. Police officer

B. Open-Ended Questions

1. What is the man's name?
2. What type of work does he do?

C. Free Recall

Level 2

Tom McPherson is a 28-year-old police officer who lives in Brooklyn.

Level 2 Questions

A. Multiple-Choice Questions

1. How old is the man?
   a. 28
   b. 30
   c. 40
   d. 38

2. Where does he live?
   a. Bronx
   b. Queens
   c. Brooklyn
   d. Long Island

3. What type of work does the man do?
   a. Police officer
   b. Firefighter
   c. Social worker
   d. Electrician

4. What is the man's full name?
   a. Tom McPherson
   b. Thomas McFinn
   c. Dennis McGlynn
   d. Robert Fellow

B. Open-Ended Questions

1. What is the man's full name?
2. How old is he?
3. What is his occupation?
4. Where does he live?

C. Free Recall

Level 3

Tom McPherson is a 28-year-old New York City police officer who lives in Sheepshead Bay, Brooklyn. He is engaged to be married to Ellen Forman, a transit police officer.

Level 3 Questions

A. Multiple-Choice Questions

1. How old is the man?
   a. 28
   b. 30
   c. 26
   d. 38
2. Where does he live?
   a. Bronx
   b. Queens
   c. Brooklyn
   d. Long Island
3. What type of work does he do?
   a. Police officer
   b. Firefighter
   c. Social worker
   d. Electrician
4. What is the man's full name?
   a. Tom McPherson
   b. Thomas McFinn
   c. Dennis McGlynn
   d. Robert Fellow
5. What is his fiancée's occupation?
   a. Secretary
   b. Cook
   c. Nurse
   d. Transit police officer
6. What is his fiancée's full name?
   a. Rona Forrest
   b. Sherrie Finn
   c. Ellen Forman
   d. Linda Frost

B. Open-Ended Questions

1. What is the man's full name?
2. How old is he?
3. What is his occupation?
4. Where does he live?
5. What is his fiancée's name?
6. What is his fiancée's occupation?

C. Free Recall

Level 4

Tom McPherson is a 28-year-old New York City police officer who lives in Sheepshead Bay, Brooklyn. He is engaged to be married to Ellen Forman, a transit police officer. Tom and Ellen both enjoy skiing and scuba diving. They plan to relocate to Florida six months after their wedding on February 12.

Level 4 Questions

A. Multiple-Choice Questions

1. How old is the man?
   a. 28
   b. 24
   c. 26
   d. 38
2. Where does he live?
   a. Bronx
   b. Queens
   c. Brooklyn
   d. Long Island
3. What type of work does the man do?
   a. Police officer
   b. Firefighter
   c. Social worker
   d. Electrician
4. What is the man's full name?
   a. Tom McPherson
   b. Thomas McFinn
   c. Dennis McGlynn
   d. Robert Fellow
5. What is his fiancée's occupation?
   a. Secretary
   b. Cook
   c. Nurse
   d. Transit police officer
6. What is his fiancée's full name?
   a. Rona Forrest
   b. Sherrie Finn
   c. Ellen Forman
   d. Linda Frost
7. What are the couple's two favorite hobbies?
   a. Bowling and tennis
   b. Skiing and swimming
   c. Tennis and golf
   d. Skiing and scuba diving
8. When is the couple's wedding date?
   a. 2/12
   b. 2/22
   c. 3/20
   d. 3/02
9. To which state does the couple plan to relocate?
   a. Arizona
   b. California
   c. New Jersey
   d. Florida
10. When does the couple plan to relocate?
    a. The day after their wedding
    b. Three months after their wedding
    c. Six months after their wedding
    d. One year after their wedding

B. Open-Ended Questions

1. What is the man's full name?
2. How old is he?
3. What is his occupation?
4. Where does he live?
5. Who is he going to marry?
6. What are the couple's favorite hobbies?
7. What is his fiancée's occupation?
8. When does the couple plan to get married?
9. Where does the couple plan to relocate?
10. When does the couple plan to relocate?

C. Free Recall

Story 2
Lolita

Level 1

Lolita is 75 years old.

Level 1 Questions

A. Multiple-Choice Questions

1. The woman's name is:
   a. Laura
   b. Lolita
   c. Linda
   d. Lena

2. The woman's age is:
   a. 65
   b. 75
   c. 78
   d. 55

B. Open-Ended Questions

1. What is the woman's name?
2. How old is she?

C. Free Recall

Level 2

Lolita is a 75-year-old widow. She lives in Denver and spends her free time volunteering at a local nursing home.

Level 2 Questions

A. Multiple-Choice Questions

1. The woman's name is:
   a. Laura
   b. Lolita
   c. Linda
   d. Lena

2. The woman's age is:
   a. 65
   b. 75
   c. 78
   d. 55

3. Where does the woman live?
   a. Manhattan
   b. Denver
   c. Huntington
   d. Los Angeles

4. How does the woman spend her free time?
   a. Shopping
   b. Volunteering
   c. Swimming
   d. At the Senior Center

B. Open-Ended Questions

1. What is the woman's name?
2. How old is she?
3. Where does she live?
4. How does she spend her free time?

C. Free Recall

Level 3

Lolita is a 75-year-old widow. She lives in Denver and spends her free time volunteering. On Tuesdays and Thursdays, she spends her time playing pool and rummy with her two closest friends, Sally and Sharon.

Level 3 Questions

A. Multiple-Choice Questions

1. The woman's name is:
   a. Laura
   b. Lolita
   c. Linda
   d. Lena
2. The woman's age is:
   a. 65
   b. 68
   c. 80
   d. 75
3. Where does the woman live?
   a. Manhattan
   b. Denver
   c. Huntington
   d. Los Angeles
4. How does the woman spend her free time?
   a. Shopping
   b. Volunteering
   c. Swimming
   d. At the Senior Center
5. What are the names of her closest friends?
   a. Sharon and Sally
   b. Shelley and Sandy
   c. Shana and Shaun
   d. Robin and Sharon
6. What activities does she participate in besides volunteering?
   a. Swimming and golf
   b. Rummy and pool
   c. Blackjack and tennis
   d. Aerobics and walking

B. Open-Ended Questions

1. What is the woman's name?
2. How old is she?
3. Where does she live?
4. How does she spend her free time?

5. What activities does she participate in on Tuesdays and Thursdays?
6. What are the names of her closest friends?

C. Free Recall

Level 4

Lolita is a 75-year-old widow who lives alone in Denver. She spends her free time volunteering. On Tuesdays and Thursdays, she plays pool and rummy with her two closest friends, Sharon and Sally. Lolita has one daughter, who is 50 years old, and a 45-year-old son. Her daughter lives in Switzerland and her son lives in White Plains, New York.

Level 4 Questions

A. Multiple-Choice Questions

1. The woman's name is:
   a. Laura
   b. Lolita
   c. Linda
   d. Lena
2. The woman's age is:
   a. 65
   b. 68
   c. 80
   d. 75
3. Where does the woman live?
   a. Manhattan
   b. Denver
   c. Huntington
   d. Los Angeles
4. How does the woman spend her free time?
   a. Shopping
   b. Volunteering
   c. Swimming
   d. At the Senior Center
5. What are the names of her closest friends?
   a. Sharon and Sally
   b. Shelley and Sandy
   c. Shana and Shaun
   d. Robin and Sharon
6. What activities does she participate in besides volunteering?
   a. Swimming and golf
   b. Rummy and pool
   c. Blackjack and tennis
   d. Aerobics and walking
7. Who does the main character live with?
   a. Alone
   b. With her son
   c. With her daughter
   d. With her two closest friends
8. Where does her son live?
   a. Zurich
   b. White Plains
   c. London
   d. Denver
9. Where does her daughter live?
   a. Switzerland
   b. England
   c. New York
   d. France
10. How old are her two children?
   a. 50 and 55
   b. 50 and 45
   c. 40 and 45
   d. 52 and 55

B. Open-Ended Questions

1. What is the woman's name?
2. How old is she?
3. How does she spend her free time?
4. Where does she live?
5. What activities does she participate in on Tuesdays and Thursdays?
6. What are the names of her closest friends?
7. What are the ages of her children?
8. Where does her daughter live?
9. Where does her son live?
10. Who does the main character live with?

C. Free Recall

Story 3
Carmen

Level 1

Carmen is a 15-year-old high school student.

Level 1 Questions

A. Multiple-Choice Questions

1. What is the girl's name?
   a. Tina
   b. Jean
   c. Lisa
   d. Carmen

2. How old is she?
   a. 15
   b. 18
   c. 16
   d. 13

B. Open-Ended Questions

1. What is the girl's name?
2. How old is she?

C. Free Recall

Level 2

Carmen is a 15-year-old high school student. Her favorite subject is social studies and her least favorite subject is science.

Level 2 Questions

A. Multiple-Choice Questions

1. What is the girl's name?
   a. Tina
   b. Jean
   c. Lisa
   d. Carmen

2. How old is she?
   a. 15
   b. 18
   c. 16
   d. 13

3. Her favorite subject is:
   a. Math
   b. English
   c. Science
   d. Social studies

4. Her least favorite subject is:
   a. Math
   b. English
   c. Science
   d. Social studies

B. Open-Ended Questions

1. What is the girl's name?
2. How old is she?
3. What is her favorite subject?
4. What is her least favorite subject?

C. Free Recall

Level 3

Carmen is a 15-year-old high school student. Her favorite subject is social studies and her least favorite subject is science. Her favorite hobby is dancing. She is the youngest of six siblings. Both of her parents are accountants.

Level 3 Questions

A. Multiple-Choice Questions

1. What is the girl's name?
   a. Tina
   b. Jean
   c. Lisa
   d. Carmen
2. How old is she?
   a. 15
   b. 18
   c. 16
   d. 13
3. Her favorite subject is:
   a. Math
   b. English
   c. Science
   d. Social studies
4. Her least favorite subject is:
   a. Math
   b. English
   c. Science
   d. Social studies
5. She is the youngest of how many siblings?
   a. Four
   b. Six
   c. Two
   d. Five
6. What is her mother's occupation?
   a. Homemaker
   b. Nurse
   c. Accountant
   d. Doctor

B. Open-Ended Questions

1. What is the girl's name?
2. How old is she?
3. What is her favorite subject?
4. What is her least favorite subject?

5. What is her favorite hobby?

6. What are her parents' occupations?

C. Free Recall

Level 4

Carmen is a 15-year-old high school student. Her favorite subject is social studies and her least favorite subject is science. Her favorite hobbies are tennis and dancing. She is the youngest of six siblings. Both of her parents are accountants. Carmen is planning to spend the summer working as an assistant counselor at Brook's Camp in Rhode Island.

Level 4 Questions

A. Multiple-Choice Questions

1. What is the girl's name?
   a. Tina
   b. Jean
   c. Lisa
   d. Carmen

2. How old is she?
   a. 15
   b. 18
   c. 16
   d. 13

3. Her favorite subject is:
   a. Math
   b. English
   c. Science
   d. Social studies

4. Her least favorite subject is:
   a. Math
   b. English
   c. Science
   d. Social studies

5. She is the youngest of how many siblings?
   a. Four
   b. Six
   c. Two
   d. Five

6. What is her mother's occupation?
   a. Homemaker
   b. Nurse
   c. Accountant
   d. Doctor

7. What is her father's occupation?
   a. Lawyer
   b. Nurse
   c. Accountant
   d. Teacher

8. What type of work will she be doing in the summer?
   a. Cashier
   b. Assistant counselor
   c. Lifeguard
   d. Salesperson

9. In what state will she be working during the summer?
   a. New Jersey
   b. Rhode Island
   c. Maine
   d. Vermont

10. What is the name of the place where she will be employed?
    a. Andrew's
    b. Brian's
    c. Brook's
    d. Kurt's

B. Open-Ended Questions

1. What is the girl's name?
2. How old is she?
3. What is her favorite subject?
4. What is her least favorite subject?
5. What are her hobbies?
6. What is her mother's occupation?
7. What type of work will she be doing in the summer?
8. In what state will she be doing this work?
9. What is the name of the place where she will be working?
10. What is her father's occupation?

C. Free Recall

Story 4
Nancy Wu

Level 1

Nancy Wu is a 5-year-old kindergartner.

Level 1 Questions

A. Multiple-Choice Questions

1. What is the girl's name?
   a. Sandra
   b. Ivanna
   c. Jessie
   d. Nancy

2. What grade is she in?
   a. Third
   b. Kindergarten
   c. First
   d. Second

B. Open-Ended Questions

1. What is the girl's name?
2. What grade is she in?

C. Free Recall

Level 2

Nancy Wu is a 5-year-old girl who just started kindergarten. She was born in China and moved to the United States at age 2. She has three older brothers and one younger brother.

Level 2 Questions

A. Multiple-Choice Questions

1. What is the girl's name?
   a. Sandra
   b. Ivanna
   c. Jessie
   d. Nancy

2. What grade is she in?
   a. Third
   b. Kindergarten
   c. First
   d. Second

3. How old was she when she moved to the U.S.?
   a. 1
   b. 2
   c. 3
   d. 4

4. How many brothers does she have?
   a. None
   b. Three
   c. Two
   d. Four

B. Open-Ended Questions

1. What is the girl's name?
2. What grade is she in?
3. How many siblings does she have?
4. When did she move to the United States?

C. Free Recall

Level 3

Nancy Wu is a 5-year-old girl who just started kindergarten. She was born in China and moved to the United States at age 2. She has three older brothers and one younger brother. Her maternal grandparents and paternal uncle live with her family. Nancy loves to draw and sing.

Level 3 Questions

A. Multiple-Choice Questions

1. What is the girl's name?
   a. Sandra
   b. Ivanna
   c. Jessie
   d. Nancy
2. What grade is she in?
   a. Third
   b. Kindergarten
   c. First
   d. Second
3. How old was she when she moved to the U.S.?
   a. One
   b. Two
   c. Three
   d. Four
4. How many brothers does she have?
   a. None
   b. Three
   c. Two
   d. Four
5. Who lives with her family?
   a. Her three cousins
   b. Her paternal uncle
   c. Her aunt
   d. Her paternal grandparents
6. What does she like to do?
   a. Dance
   b. Bowl
   c. Sing
   d. Run

B. Open-Ended Questions

1. What is the girl's name?
2. What grade is she in?
3. How many siblings does she have?
4. When did she move to the United States?
5. Who lives with her family?
6. What does she like to do?

C. Free Recall

Level 4

Nancy Wu is a 5-year-old girl who just started kindergarten. She was born in China and moved to the United States at age 2. She has three older brothers and one younger brother. Her maternal grandparents and paternal uncle live with her family. Nancy loves to draw and sing. Nancy's mother is an artist and her father is a businessman. Nancy's closest friend at school is Helen.

Level 4 Questions

A. Multiple-Choice Questions

1. What is the girl's name?
   a. Sandra
   b. Ivanna
   c. Jessie
   d. Nancy

2. What grade is she in?
   a. Third
   b. Kindergarten
   c. First
   d. Second

3. How old was she when she moved to the U.S.?
   a. One
   b. Two
   c. Three
   d. Four

4. How many siblings does she have?
   a. None
   b. Three
   c. Two
   d. Four

5. Who lives with her family?
   a. Her three cousins
   b. Her paternal uncle
   c. Her aunt
   d. Her paternal grandparents

6. What does she like to do?
   a. Dance
   b. Bowl
   c. Sing
   d. Run

7. How many older brothers does she have?
   a. None
   b. Three
   c. Two
   d. Four

8. How many brothers are younger than she?
   a. None
   b. One
   c. Two
   d. Four

9. What type of work does her father do?
   a. Artist
   b. Film producer
   c. Banker
   d. Businessman

10. What type of work does her mother do?
    a. Artist
    b. Therapist
    c. Banker
    d. Salesperson

B. Open-Ended Questions

1. What is the girl's name?
2. What grade is she in?
3. How many siblings does she have?
4. How many older brothers does she have?
5. How old was she when she moved to the United States?
6. Who lives with her family?
7. What does she like to do?
8. What is her mother's occupation?
9. What is her father's occupation?
10. What is her closest friend's name?

C. Free Recall

Story 5
Miguel

Level 1

Miguel is a 34-year-old architect.

Level 1 Questions

A. Multiple-Choice Questions

1. How old is he?
   a. 30
   b. 40
   c. 52
   d. 34

2. What is his occupation?
   a. Architect
   b. Accountant
   c. Taxi driver
   d. Maintenance worker

B. Open-Ended Questions

1. What is his name and age?
2. What is his occupation?

C. Free Recall

Level 2

Miguel Hernandez is a 34-year-old architect. One Saturday in May, he woke up early and had blueberry pancakes for breakfast.

Level 2 Questions

A. Multiple-Choice Questions

1. How old is he?
   a. 30
   b. 40
   c. 52
   d. 34

2. What is his occupation?
   a. Architect
   b. Accountant
   c. Taxi driver
   d. Maintenance worker

3. What day and month were mentioned?
   a. Saturday and May
   b. Sunday and May
   c. Thursday and April
   d. Saturday and April

4. What did he have for breakfast?
   a. Corn flakes
   b. Blueberry pancakes
   c. Waffles
   d. French toast

B. Open-Ended Questions

1. What is his name and age?
2. What is his occupation?
3. What day and month were mentioned?
4. What did he have for breakfast?

C. Free Recall

Level 3

Miguel Hernandez is a 34-year-old architect. One Saturday in May, he woke up early and had blueberry pancakes for breakfast. He then played 36 holes of golf with his brother, Jose. After golf, he took his son, Jake, to the movies.

Level 3 Questions

A. Multiple-Choice Questions

1. How old is he?
   a. 30
   b. 40
   c. 52
   d. 34
2. What is his occupation?
   a. Architect
   b. Accountant
   c. Taxi driver
   d. Maintenance worker
3. What day and month were mentioned?
   a. Saturday and May
   b. Sunday and May
   c. Thursday and April
   d. Saturday and April
4. What did he have for breakfast?
   a. Corn flakes
   b. Blueberry pancakes
   c. Waffles
   d. French toast
5. How did he spend his time with his brother?
   a. Movies
   b. Having breakfast
   c. Golf
   d. Gardening
6. What did he and his son do?
   a. Movies
   b. Breakfast
   c. Golf
   d. Tennis

B. Open-Ended Questions

1. What is his name and age?
2. What is his occupation?
3. What day and month were mentioned?
4. What did he have for breakfast?

5. How did he spend his day?
6. What are the names of his brother and son?

C. Free Recall

Level 4

Miguel Hernandez is a 34-year-old architect. One Saturday in May, he woke up early and had blueberry pancakes for breakfast. He then played 36 holes of golf with his brother, Jose. After golf, he took his son, Jake, to the movies. Miguel's wife, Lillian, also 34, is a school secretary. She is an avid reader and excellent cook.

Level 4 Questions

A. Multiple-Choice Questions

1. How old is he?
   a. 30
   b. 40
   c. 52
   d. 34
2. What is his occupation?
   a. Architect
   b. Accountant
   c. Taxi driver
   d. Maintenance worker
3. What day and month were mentioned?
   a. Saturday and May
   b. Sunday and May
   c. Thursday and April
   d. Saturday and April
4. What did he have for breakfast?
   a. Corn flakes
   b. Blueberry pancakes
   c. Waffles
   d. French toast
5. How did he spend his time with his brother?
   a. Movies
   b. Having breakfast
   c. Golf
   d. Gardening
6. What did he and his son do?
   a. Movies
   b. Breakfast
   c. Golf
   d. Tennis
7. What is his wife's name?
   a. Lillian
   b. Lucy
   c. Leah
   d. Lorraine
8. How old is his wife?
   a. 30
   b. 24
   c. 34
   d. 28
9. What is her occupation?
   a. School secretary
   b. Nurse
   c. Therapist
   d. Bus driver
10. What is one of her hobbies?
    a. Boating
    b. Biking
    c. Cooking
    d. Skating

B. Open-Ended Questions

1. What is his name and age?
2. What is his occupation?
3. What day and month were mentioned?
4. What did he have for breakfast?
5. How did he spend his day?
6. What are the names of his brother and son?
7. What is his wife's occupation?
8. What are her hobbies?
9. What is his wife's name?
10. How old is his wife?

C. Free Recall

Story 6
Tom and Patricia

Level 1

Tom was in a boating accident when he was 22.

Level 1 Questions

A. Multiple-Choice Questions

1. What is the man's name?
   a. Bob
   b. Tim
   c. Tom
   d. Bill

2. What happened to him?
   a. Pneumonia
   b. Car accident
   c. Lyme disease
   d. Boating accident

B. Open-Ended Questions

1. What is the man's name?
2. What happened to him?

C. Free Recall

Level 2

Tom Cohen was in a boating accident when he was 22. He had just received his master's degree in business, and his accident occurred one week before he was to begin a new job.

Level 2 Questions

A. Multiple-Choice Questions

1. What is the man's name?
   a. Bob
   b. Tim
   c. Tom
   d. Bill

2. What happened to him?
   a. Pneumonia
   b. Car accident
   c. Lyme disease
   d. Boating accident

3. What level of school had he completed?
   a. High school
   b. College
   c. Graduate school
   d. Military school

4. What was he about to start when his accident occurred?
   a. Law school
   b. Medical school
   c. A new job
   d. Working with his best friend

B. Open-Ended Questions

1. What is the man's name?
2. What happened to him?
3. What level of education does he have?
4. What was he about to start when his accident occurred?

C. Free Recall

Level 3

Tom Cohen was in a boating accident when he was 22. He had just received his master's degree in business, and his accident occurred one week before he was to begin a new job. Tom broke his right arm and right leg. His fiancée, Patricia, took off 10 days of work to help Tom.

Level 3 Questions

A. Multiple-Choice Questions

1. What is the man's name?
   a. Bob
   b. Tim
   c. Tom
   d. Bill
2. What happened to him?
   a. Pneumonia
   b. Car accident
   c. Lyme disease
   d. Boating accident
3. What level of school had he completed?
   a. High school
   b. College
   c. Graduate school
   d. Military school
4. What was he about to start when his accident occurred?
   a. Law school
   b. Medical school
   c. A new job
   d. Working with his best friend
5. What were his injuries?
   a. Head injury
   b. Broke two ribs
   c. Broke left leg and right arm
   d. Broke right arm and right leg
6. What is his fiancée's name?
   a. Patricia
   b. Elizabeth
   c. Lorraine
   d. Rosemary

B. Open-Ended Questions

1. What is the man's name?
2. What happened to him?
3. What level of education does he have?
4. What was he about to start when his accident occurred?

5. In what way was Tom injured?
6. What is his fiancée's name?

C. Free Recall

Level 4

Tom Cohen was in a boating accident when he was 22. He had just received his master's degree in business, and his accident occurred one week before he was to begin a new job. Tom broke his right arm and right leg. His fiancée, Patricia, took off 10 days of work to help Tom. Tom and Patricia are engaged to be married on the first Saturday of June. They met three years ago in the school library.

Level 4 Questions

A. Multiple-Choice Questions

1. What is the man's name?
   a. Bob
   b. Tim
   c. Tom
   d. Bill
2. What happened to him?
   a. Pneumonia
   b. Car accident
   c. Lyme disease
   d. Boating accident
3. What level of school had he completed?
   a. High school
   b. College
   c. Graduate school
   d. Military school
4. What was he about to start when his accident occurred?
   a. Law school
   b. Medical school
   c. A new job
   d. Working with his best friend
5. What were his injuries?
   a. Head injury
   b. Broke two ribs
   c. Broke left leg and right arm
   d. Broke right arm and right leg
6. What is his fiancée's name?
   a. Patricia
   b. Elizabeth
   c. Lorraine
   d. Rosemary
7. What did his fiancée do to help him after his accident?
   a. Bought him an expensive gift
   b. Agreed to marry him
   c. Took time off to be with him
   d. Cleaned his house
8. Where did they meet?
   a. A club
   b. The library
   c. The gym
   d. The grocery store
9. How many years ago did they meet?
   a. One
   b. Five
   c. Three
   d. Eight
10. When do they plan to get married?
    a. October
    b. April
    c. September
    d. June

B. Open-Ended Questions

1. What is the man's name?
2. What happened to him?
3. What level of education does he have?
4. What was he about to start when his accident occurred?
5. In what way was Tom injured?
6. What is his fiancée's name?
7. How did she help him following the accident?
8. Where did they meet?
9. When do they plan to be married?
10. When did they meet?

C. Free Recall

Story 7
Joseph

Level 1

Joseph has worked as a carpenter for 30 years.

Level 1 Questions

A. Multiple-Choice Questions

1. What is the man's name?
   a. Joseph
   b. Jonathan
   c. Ronald
   d. Maxwell

2. What type of work has he done?
   a. Fisherman
   b. Taxi driver
   c. Carpenter
   d. Butler

B. Open-Ended Questions

1. What is the man's name?
2. What type of work experience does he have?

C. Free Recall

Level 2

Joseph Stone has worked as a carpenter for 30 years. He started working for Starr Builders when he was just 20, and at age 50 he has remained a loyal employee. Joseph works 35 hours a week.

Level 2 Questions

A. Multiple-Choice Questions

1. What is the man's name?
   a. Joseph
   b. Jonathan
   c. Ronald
   d. Maxwell

2. What type of work has he done?
   a. Fisherman
   b. Taxi driver
   c. Carpenter
   d. Butler

3. How old was he when he started working?
   a. 20
   b. 50
   c. 30
   d. 25

4. What is the name of the company where he works?
   a. Jones Builders
   b. Stone Builders
   c. Starr Builders
   d. Gold Builders

B. Open-Ended Questions

1. What is the man's name?
2. What type of work experience does he have?
3. How old was he when he started his job?
4. What is the name of the company where he works?

C. Free Recall

Level 3

Joseph Stone has worked as a carpenter for 30 years. He started working for Starr Builders when he was just 20, and at age 50 he has remained a loyal employee. Joseph works 35 hours a week. He plans to retire in five years. He will move from New York to San Diego, California. His two sisters live there. Joseph was divorced 15 years ago and has not remarried.

Level 3 Questions

A. Multiple-Choice Questions

1. What is the man's name?
   a. Joseph
   b. Jonathan
   c. Ronald
   d. Maxwell
2. What type of work has he done?
   a. Fisherman
   b. Taxi driver
   c. Carpenter
   d. Butler
3. How old was he when he started working?
   a. 20
   b. 50
   c. 30
   d. 25
4. What is the name of the company where he works?
   a. Jones Builders
   b. Stone Builders
   c. Starr Builders
   d. Gold Builders
5. When does he plan to retire?
   a. Never
   b. In 10 years
   c. In five years
   d. At age 65
6. Where does he want to relocate?
   a. Florida
   b. California
   c. Hawaii
   d. Alaska

B. Open-Ended Questions

1. What is the man's name?
2. What type of work experience does he have?
3. How old was he when he started his job?
4. What is the name of the company that he works for?

5. When does he plan to retire?
6. Where would he like to move?

C. Free Recall

Level 4

Joseph Stone has worked as a carpenter for 30 years. He started working for Starr Builders when he was just 20, and at age 50 he has remained a loyal employee. Joseph works 35 hours a week. He plans to retire in five years. He will move from New York to San Diego, California. His two sisters live there. Joseph was divorced 15 years ago and has not remarried. Joseph has no children. When he retires, he would like to marry again and perhaps have children. He plans to spend his retirement writing novels.

Level 4 Questions

A. Multiple-Choice Questions

1. What is the man's name?
   a. Joseph
   b. Jonathan
   c. Ronald
   d. Maxwell
2. What type of work has he done?
   a. Fisherman
   b. Taxi driver
   c. Carpenter
   d. Butler
3. How old was he when he started working?
   a. 20
   b. 50
   c. 30
   d. 25
4. What is the name of the company where he works?
   a. Jones Builders
   b. Stone Builders
   c. Starr Builders
   d. Gold Builders
5. When does he plan to retire?
   a. Never
   b. In 10 years
   c. In five years
   d. At age 65
6. Where does he want to relocate?
   a. Florida
   b. California
   c. Hawaii
   d. Alaska
7. What is his marital status?
   a. Engaged
   b. Married
   c. Divorced
   d. Widowed
8. Whom does he know in the state where he plans to retire?
   a. His mother
   b. His former wife
   c. His sisters
   d. His high school sweetheart

9. How does he plan to spend his retirement?
   a. Golfing
   b. Taking courses
   c. Traveling
   d. Writing novels

10. What are his family plans for the future?
    a. Staying single
    b. Getting married again
    c. Not having children
    d. Adopting many children

B. Open-Ended Questions

1. What is the man's name?
2. What type of work experience does he have?
3. How old was he when he started his job?
4. What is the name of the company where he works?
5. When does he plan to retire?
6. Where would he like to move?
7. What is his marital status?
8. How many children does he have?
9. What does he want to do when he retires?
10. Whom does he know in the state where he plans retire?

C. Free Recall

Story 8
Charles and His Brother

Level 1

Charles has been a public school bus driver for the last 14 years.

Level 1 Questions

A. Multiple-Choice Questions

1. What is the man's name?
   a. Not stated
   b. Brian
   c. Charles
   d. Jason

2. What is his occupation?
   a. Taxi driver
   b. Bus driver
   c. Limo driver
   d. Sanitation worker

B. Open-Ended Questions

1. What is the man's name?
2. What is his occupation?

C. Free Recall

Level 2

Charles Longworth has been a bus driver for the last 14 years. After graduating from high school, he landed a job at a local car dealership. He stayed there for 10 years before deciding on a career change. He then began working as a public school bus driver.

Level 2 Questions

A. Multiple-Choice Questions

1. What is the man's name?
   a. Not stated
   b. Brian
   c. Charles
   d. Jason

2. What is his occupation?
   a. Taxi driver
   b. Bus driver
   c. Limo driver
   d. Sanitation worker

3. What was his first job after high school?
   a. In real estate
   b. At school
   c. In insurance
   d. At a car dealership

4. How many years was he there?
   a. 10
   b. 6
   c. 14
   d. 20

B. Open-Ended Questions

1. What is the man's name?
2. What is his occupation?
3. What was his first job out of high school?
4. How long did he work there?

C. Free Recall

Level 3

Charles Longworth has been a bus driver for the last 14 years. After graduating from high school, he landed a job helping out at a local car dealership. He stayed there for 10 years before deciding on a career change. He then began working as a bus driver. Charles spends his free time helping his younger brother, Paul, who is blind. Charles likes to help Paul clean his apartment.

Level 3 Questions

A. Multiple-Choice Questions

1. What is the man's name?
   a. Not stated
   b. Brian
   c. Charles
   d. Jason
2. What is his occupation?
   a. Taxi driver
   b. Bus driver
   c. Limo driver
   d. Sanitation worker
3. What was his first job after high school?
   a. In real estate
   b. At school
   c. In insurance
   d. At a car dealership
4. How many years was he there?
   a. 10
   b. 6
   c. 14
   d. 20
5. How does he spend his free time?
   a. Reading
   b. Helping his brother
   c. Playing tennis
   d. Running
6. What is his brother's name?
   a. Paul
   b. Robert
   c. Aaron
   d. Dillon

B. Open-Ended Questions

1. What is the man's name?
2. What is his occupation?
3. What was his first job out of high school?
4. How long did he work there?

5. How does he spend his free time?
6. What is his brother's name?

C. Free Recall

Level 4

Charles Longworth has been a bus driver for the last 14 years. After graduating from high school, he landed a job helping out at a local car dealership. He stayed there for 10 years before deciding on a career change. He then began working as a bus driver. Charles spends his free time helping his younger brother, Paul, who is blind. Charles likes to help Paul clean his apartment. Charles had a problem with alcohol in high school, but he has been sober since age 18. He still attends Alcoholics Anonymous (AA) meetings two times a week. Charles is a volunteer for the church on Sunday mornings.

Level 4 Questions

A. Multiple-Choice Questions

1. What is the man's name?
   a. Not stated
   b. Brian
   c. Charles
   d. Jason
2. What is his occupation?
   a. Taxi driver
   b. Bus driver
   c. Limo driver
   d. Sanitation worker
3. What was his first job after high school?
   a. In real estate
   b. At school
   c. In insurance
   d. At a car dealership
4. How many years was he there?
   a. 10
   b. 6
   c. 14
   d. 20
5. How does he spend his free time?
   a. Reading
   b. Helping his brother
   c. Playing tennis
   d. Running
6. What is his brother's name?
   a. Paul
   b. Robert
   c. Aaron
   d. Dillon
7. What type of problem did he have in high school?
   a. Recurring headaches
   b. A learning disability
   c. Alcohol abuse
   d. Difficulty making friends
8. What meetings does he attend during the week?
   a. Church meetings
   b. Bowling meetings
   c. Bus driver meetings
   d. Alcoholics Anonymous meetings

9. How often does he attend these meetings?
   a. Every day
   b. Weekends
   c. Sunday mornings
   d. Twice a week

10. What does he do on Sunday mornings?
   a. Jog
   b. Drive his bus
   c. Attend AA meetings
   d. Volunteer for the church

B. Open-Ended Questions

1. What is the man's name?
2. What is his occupation?
3. What was his first job out of high school?
4. How long did he work there?
5. How does he spend his free time?
6. What is his brother's name?
7. What type of problem did he have in high school?
8. What meetings does he attend each week?
9. How often does he attend these meetings?
10. How does he spend Sunday mornings?

C. Free Recall

Auditory Recall Stories – History

Story 1
Christopher Columbus

Level 1

Christopher Columbus discovered America in 1492.

Level 1 Questions

A. Multiple-Choice Questions

1. This story is about:
   a. Amerigo Vespucci
   b. Robinson Crusoe
   c. Christopher Columbus
   d. Magellan

2. Columbus discovered America in:
   a. 1776
   b. 1492
   c. 1215
   d. 1525

B. Open-Ended Questions

1. Who is this story about?
2. What year is mentioned?

C. Free Recall

Level 2

In 1492, Christopher Columbus discovered America. He was exploring on behalf of Queen Isabella of Spain.

Level 2 Questions

A. Multiple-Choice Questions

1. This story is about:
   a. Amerigo Vespucci
   b. Robinson Crusoe
   c. Christopher Columbus
   d. Magellan

2. Columbus discovered America in:
   a. 1776
   b. 1492
   c. 1215
   d. 1525

3. Columbus was exploring on behalf of:
   a. England
   b. Italy
   c. Brazil
   d. Spain

B. Open-Ended Questions

1. Who is this story about?
2. What year is mentioned?
3. What country was Columbus exploring on behalf of?

C. Free Recall

Level 3

In 1492, Christopher Columbus discovered America. Although he was Italian, he was exploring on behalf of Queen Isabella of Spain. There were three ships in his fleet: the *Niña*, the *Pinta* and the *Santa Maria,* which was the ship Columbus sailed on.

Level 3 Questions

A. Multiple-Choice Questions

1. This story is about:
   a. Amerigo Vespucci
   b. Robinson Crusoe
   c. Christopher Columbus
   d. Magellan
2. Columbus discovered America in:
   a. 1776
   b. 1492
   c. 1215
   d. 1525
3. Columbus sailed as an explorer for the country of:
   a. England
   b. Italy
   c. Brazil
   d. Spain
4. The queen of Spain, when Columbus sailed to America, was:
   a. Maria
   b. Elena
   c. Isabella
   d. Rosa
5. What was the name of the vessel Columbus sailed on?
   a. *Santa Maria*
   b. *Pegasus*
   c. *Nunda*
   d. *Hope*
6. What were the names of all three ships in Columbus' fleet?
   a. *Pegasus, Magellan, Cortez*
   b. *Santa Maria, Pinta, Niña*
   c. *Hope, Faith, Charity*
   d. *Niña, Pegasus, Santa Maria*

B. Open-Ended Questions

1. Who is this story about?
2. What year is mentioned?
3. What country was Columbus a native of?
4. Who was the queen of Spain when Columbus sailed to America?

5. What was the name of the ship Columbus sailed on?
6. What were the names of the other two ships?

C. Free Recall

Level 4

In 1492, Christopher Columbus, who was exploring on behalf of Queen Isabella of Spain, discovered America. There were three ships in the fleet: the *Niña,* the *Pinta* and the *Santa Maria,* which was the ship Columbus sailed in. Columbus had read stories written centuries before by Marco Polo about his travels to Asia. By sailing west from Spain, Columbus was looking for a faster route to China and India, where others had discovered tea, precious metals, spices and fine cloth. Seventy days after leaving Palos, Spain, Columbus thought they had reached Asia, although actually they had arrived in the Bahamas.

Level 4 Questions

A. Multiple-Choice Questions

1. This story is about:
   a. Amerigo Vespucci
   b. Robinson Crusoe
   c. Christopher Columbus
   d. Magellan
2. Columbus discovered America in:
   a. 1776
   b. 1492
   c. 1215
   d. 1525
3. Columbus sailed as an explorer for the country of:
   a. England
   b. Italy
   c. Brazil
   d. Spain
4. The queen of Spain, when Columbus sailed to America, was:
   a. Maria
   b. Elena
   c. Rosa
   d. Isabella
5. What was the name of the vessel Columbus sailed in?
   a. *Santa Maria*
   b. *Pegasus*
   c. *Nunda*
   d. *Hope*
6. What were the names of the three ships in Columbus' fleet?
   a. *Pegasus Magellan, Cortez*
   b. *Santa Maria, Pinta, Niña*
   c. *Hope, Faith, Charity*
   d. *Niña, Pegasus, Santa Maria*
7. What items did Marco Polo write about on his travels to Asia?
   a. Fruit, vegetables and spices
   b. Gold, silver and expensive cloth
   c. Tea, nuts and fruit
   d. Coal, steel and silver
8. Where did Columbus eventually land after leaving Spain?
   a. The United States
   b. Central America
   c. The Bahamas
   d. South America

9. How long after leaving Spain did Columbus arrive in the Bahamas?
   a. 1 year
   b. 6 months
   c. 70 days
   d. 93 days

10. From what city in Spain did Columbus depart?
   a. Madrid
   b. Seville
   c. Palos
   d. Barcelona

B. Open-Ended Questions

1. Who is this story about?
2. What year is mentioned?
3. What country was Columbus a native of?
4. Who was the queen of Spain when Columbus sailed to America?
5. What where the names of the ships in Columbus' fleet?
6. What other explorer is mentioned in this story?
7. How many days passed from setting sail to finding land?
8. What port in Spain did Columbus sail from?
9. What treasures did Columbus hope to obtain for Spain?
10. Where did Columbus' expedition eventually land?

C. Free Recall

Story 2
George Washington's Presidency

Level 1

During George Washington's first year in office, the first census was taken.

Level 1 Questions

A. Multiple-Choice Questions

1. This sentence is about:
   a. Counting people who live in Washington
   b. Washington, D.C.
   c. The first U.S. census
   d. Martha Washington

2. What U.S. president is mentioned in this sentence?
   a. Abraham Lincoln
   b. George W. Bush
   c. Andrew Jackson
   d. George Washington

B. Open-Ended Questions

1. What president was mentioned in this sentence?
2. What took place during Washington's first year in office?

C. Free Recall

Level 2

During George Washington's first year in office, the first census was taken. The total number of people in the U.S. was approximately 4 million in 1790.

Level 2 Questions

A. Multiple-Choice Questions

1. What is this paragraph about?
   a. Counting people who live in Washington
   b. Washington, D.C.
   c. The first U.S. census
   d. Martha Washington

2. What U.S. president is mentioned in this passage?
   a. Abraham Lincoln
   b. George W. Bush
   c. Andrew Jackson
   d. George Washington

3. Approximately how many people were counted in the U.S. census in 1790?
   a. 1 million
   b. 4 million
   c. 5 thousand
   d. 300,000

B. Open-Ended Questions

1. What president was mentioned in this passage?
2. What took place during Washington's first year in office?
3. In what year was the first U.S. census taken?

C. Free Recall

Level 3

During George Washington's first year in office, the first census was taken. The total number of people was approximately 4 million in 1790. Additional accomplishments during Washington's presidency included establishing the Bill of Rights, which are the first 10 amendments to the Constitution.

Level 3 Questions

A. Multiple-Choice Questions

1. What is this paragraph about?
   a. Counting people who live in Washington
   b. Washington, D.C.
   c. The first U.S. census
   d. Martha Washington
2. What U.S. president is mentioned in this passage?
   a. Abraham Lincoln
   b. George W. Bush
   c. Andrew Jackson
   d. George Washington
3. Approximately how many people were counted in the U.S. census in 1790?
   a. 1 million
   b. 4 million
   c. 5 thousand
   d. 300,000
4. What other accomplishment is mentioned in this passage?
   a. Washington crossing the Delaware
   b. Washington built the White House
   c. The Bill of Rights was written
   d. George married Martha
5. What is the Bill of Rights?
   a. Rights guaranteed to people living in Washington, D.C.
   b. The bill for the building rights to the White House
   c. The first 10 amendments to the Constitution
   d. A document that provides for U.S. currency
6. How many amendments are in the Bill of Rights?
   a. 15
   b. 5
   c. 25
   d. 10

B. Open-Ended Questions

1. What president was mentioned in this passage?
2. What took place during Washington's first year in office?
3. In what year was the first U.S. census taken?
4. Approximately how many people were in the U.S. in 1790?
5. What historical document was written during Washington's presidency?
6. How many amendments are contained in the Bill of Rights?

C. Free Recall

Level 4

During George Washington's first year in office, the first census was taken. In 1790, the total number of people counted was approximately 4 million. Some of the accomplishments during Washington's presidency included establishing the Bill of Rights, which are the first 10 amendments to the Constitution, and the formation of the Supreme Court. Congress established the Department of Treasury, headed by Alexander Hamilton; the Department of State, headed by Thomas Jefferson; and the War Department, headed by Henry Knox.

Level 4 Questions

A. Multiple-Choice Questions

1. What is this paragraph about?
   a. Counting people who live in Washington
   b. Washington, D.C.
   c. Washington's accomplishments
   d. Martha Washington
2. What U.S. president is mentioned in this passage?
   a. Abraham Lincoln
   b. George W. Bush
   c. Andrew Jackson
   d. George Washington
3. Approximately how many people were counted in the U.S. census in 1790?
   a. 1 million
   b. 4 million
   c. 5 thousand
   d. 300,000
4. What is the Bill of Rights?
   a. Rights guaranteed to people who live in Washington, D.C.
   b. The bill for the building rights to the White House
   c. The first 10 amendments to the Constitution
   d. A document that provides for U.S. currency

5. How many amendments are in the Bill of Rights?
   a. 15
   b. 5
   c. 25
   d. 10
6. What two accomplishments were mentioned in this paragraph?
   a. The Bill of Rights and formation of the Department of War
   b. Formation of the Supreme Court and the Department of Finance
   c. The Bill of Rights and formation of the Supreme Court
   d. Formation of the Department of State and Department of Taxation
7. Who headed the Department of State under George Washington?
   a. Alexander Hamilton
   b. Thomas Jefferson
   c. Benjamin Franklin
   d. George Washington
8. Who headed the Department of War under George Washington?
   a. Henry Knox
   b. Thomas Hamilton
   c. James Monroe
   d. John Adams
9. Who headed the Department of Treasury under George Washington?
   a. Alexander Bell
   b. Alexander Hamilton
   c. Adam Alexander
   d. Henry Hamilton
10. What branch of the U.S. Government formed the Departments of State, Treasury and War?
    a. The Senate
    b. The Judiciary
    c. The President
    d. The Congress

B. Open-Ended Questions

1. What president was in office in 1790?
2. What took place during Washington's first year in office?
3. In what year was the first U.S. census taken?
4. Approximately how many people were in the U.S. in 1790?
5. What historical documents were written during Washington's presidency?
6. How many amendments are contained in the Bill of Rights?
7. What departments did Congress form during Washington's presidency?
8. Who headed the first Department of Treasury?
9. Who headed the first Department of State?
10. Who headed the first War Department?

C. Free Recall

Story 3
The U.S. Constitution

Level 1

The Constitution of the United States was approved in 1790.

Level 1 Questions

A. Multiple-Choice Questions

1. This sentence is about the approval of:
   a. The Bill of Rights
   b. The U.S. Constitution
   c. The Articles of Confederation
   d. The Declaration of Independence

2. In what year was the Constitution approved?
   a. 1776
   b. 1785
   c. 1790
   d. 1800

B. Open-Ended Questions

1. What is this sentence about?
2. In what year was the U.S. Constitution approved?

C. Free Recall

Level 2

The Constitution of the United States was ratified by all 13 states in 1790. Nine of the original 13 states needed to vote for ratification for the Constitution to be adopted.

Level 2 Questions

A. Multiple-Choice Questions

1. This paragraph is about the approval of:
   a. The Bill of Rights
   b. The U.S. Constitution
   c. The Articles of Confederation
   d. The Declaration of Independence

2. In what year was the Constitution approved?
   a. 1776
   b. 1785
   c. 1790
   d. 1800

3. How may states needed to vote for ratification for the Constitution to be adopted?
   a. 6 of the 13
   b. 10 of the 13
   c. All 13
   d. 9 of the 13

B. Open-Ended Questions

1. What is this paragraph about?
2. In what year was the U.S. Constitution ratified?
3. How many states needed to vote for ratification for the Constitution to be adopted?

C. Free Recall

Level 3

The Constitution of the United States was ratified by all 13 states in 1790. Nine of the 13 states needed to ratify the Constitution for it to be adopted. The Constitution consists of 7 articles and 27 amendments. The first 10 amendments are known as the Bill of Rights.

Level 3 Questions

A. Multiple-Choice Questions

1. This paragraph is about the ratification of:
   a. The Bill of Rights
   b. The U.S. Constitution
   c. The Articles of Confederation
   d. The Declaration of Independence
2. In what year was the Constitution approved?
   a. 1776
   b. 1785
   c. 1790
   d. 1800
3. How many states needed to ratify the Constitution for it to become law?
   a. 9
   b. 13
   c. 10
   d. 8
4. How many articles are there in the Constitution?
   a. 27
   b. 13
   c. 7
   d. 50
5. How many amendments have been added to the Constitution?
   a. 50
   b. 15
   c. 27
   d. 33
6. What are the first 10 amendments called?
   a. The Bill of Rights
   b. The Preamble
   c. Articles
   d. The Articles of Confederation

B. Open-Ended Questions

1. What was this paragraph about?
2. In what year was the U.S. Constitution ratified?
3. How many states were required to ratify the Constitution?

4. How many articles are there in the Constitution?
5. How many amendments are there in the Constitution?
6. What are the first 10 amendments called?

C. Free Recall

Level 4

The Constitution of the United States was ratified by all 13 states in 1790. Nine of the 13 states needed to ratify the Constitution for it to be adopted. The Constitution consists of 7 articles and 27 amendments. The articles concern the establishment of division of power, states, amendment processes, legal status of the Constitution and ratification procedures. The amendments were written to update and change the laws of the nation as needed. The first 10 amendments are known as the Bill of Rights.

Level 4 Questions

A. Multiple-Choice Questions

1. This passage is about:
   a. The Bill of Rights
   b. The U.S. Constitution
   c. The Articles of Confederation
   d. The Declaration of Independence

2. In what year was the Constitution ratified?
   a. 1776
   b. 1785
   c. 1790
   d. 1800

3. How many states existed in 1790?
   a. 9
   b. 12
   c. 10
   d. 13

4. How many states needed to ratify the Constitution for it to become law?
   a. 9
   b. 13
   c. 10
   d. 8

5. How many articles are there in the Constitution?
   a. 27
   b. 13
   c. 7
   d. 50

6. How many amendments have been added to the Constitution?
   a. 50
   b. 15
   c. 27
   d. 33

7. What are some of the concerns of the articles?
   a. Ratification and states
   b. Legal status of the Constitution
   c. Division of power, amendment processes
   d. All of the above

8. What are the first 10 amendments more commonly knows as?
   a. The Bill of Rights
   b. The Preamble
   c. Articles
   d. The Articles of Confederation
9. What do amendments provide for?
   a. The Electoral College
   b. Responsibilities of the Judiciary
   c. Updating and changing laws as needed
   d. States' laws
10. When the U.S. Constitution was ratified in 1790, who was the president of the United States?
   a. John Quincy Adams
   b. Alexander Hamilton
   c. Thomas Jefferson
   d. George Washington

B. Open-Ended Questions

1. What was this paragraph about?
2. In what year was the U.S. Constitution ratified?
3. How many states existed in 1790?
4. How many states were required to ratify the Constitution?
5. How many articles are there in the Constitution?
6. How many amendments are there in the Constitution?
7. What do the articles concern?
8. What do the amendments accomplish?
9. What are the first 10 amendments called?
10. Who was the president of the United States in 1790?

C. Free Recall

Story 4
Lewis and Clark

Level 1

Lewis and Clark explored the Louisiana Territory.

Level 1 Questions

A. Multiple-Choice Questions

1. Who are the explorers mentioned in this sentence?
   a. Pike and Clark
   b. Lewis and Clark
   c. Columbus and Verrazano
   d. Williams and Meriwether

2. Where did Lewis and Clark explore?
   a. The Louisiana Territory
   b. Oregon Territory
   c. Mexico
   d. Florida Panhandle

B. Open-Ended Questions

1. What team of explorers is named in this sentence?
2. Where did they explore?

C. Free Recall

Level 2

Meriwether Lewis and William Clark began exploring the Louisiana Territory in 1804.

Level 2 Questions

A. Multiple-Choice Questions

1. Who were the explorers mentioned in this passage?
   a. Pike and Clark
   b. Lewis and Clark
   c. Lewis and Meriwether
   d. Williams and Pike

2. Where did Lewis and Clark explore?
   a. The Louisiana Territory
   b. Oregon Territory
   c. Mexico
   d. Florida Panhandle

3. In what year did their expedition begin?
   a. 1800
   b. 1904
   c. 1804
   d. 1850

B. Open-Ended Questions

1. What team of explorers is named in this passage?
2. Where did they explore?
3. In what year did they begin their journey?

C. Free Recall

Level 3

Meriwether Lewis and William Clark began exploring the Louisiana Territory in 1804. Along with approximately 40 men, they began their journey at the Missouri River in the spring. They arrived at the Pacific Ocean in December of 1805.

Level 3 Questions

A. Multiple-Choice Questions

1. Who were the explorers mentioned in this passage?
   a. Pike and Clark
   b. Lewis and Clark
   c. Lewis and Meriwether
   d. Williams and Pike
2. Where did Lewis and Clark explore?
   a. The Louisiana Territory
   b. Oregon Territory
   c. Mexico
   d. Florida Panhandle
3. In what year did their expedition begin?
   a. 1800
   b. 1904
   c. 1804
   d. 1850
4. Approximately how many men joined the expedition?
   a. 40
   b. 45
   c. 50
   d. 25
5. Where did the journey begin?
   a. The Mississippi River
   b. The Missouri River
   c. The Colorado River
   d. The Columbia River
6. When did they arrive at the Pacific Ocean?
   a. 1810
   b. 1804
   c. 1805
   d. 1820

B. Open-Ended Questions

1. What team of explorers is named in this passage?
2. Where did they explore?
3. In what year did they begin their journey?
4. How many men joined their expedition?

5. Where did they begin their journey?
6. When did they reach the Pacific Ocean?

C. Free Recall

Level 4

Meriwether Lewis and William Clark began exploring the Louisiana Territory in 1804. Along with approximately 40 men, they began their journey at the Missouri River in the spring. Thomas Jefferson, the president, secured funds from Congress to explore the newly purchased territory all the way to the ocean. They hired a French-Canadian trapper and his Shoshone Indian wife to guide them. They arrived at the Pacific Ocean in December of 1805.

Level 4 Questions

A. Multiple-Choice Questions

1. Who were the explorers mentioned in this passage?
   a. Pike and Clark
   b. Lewis and Clark
   c. Lewis and Meriwether
   d. Williams and Pike

2. Where did Lewis and Clark explore?
   a. The Louisiana Territory
   b. Oregon Territory
   c. Mexico
   d. Florida Panhandle

3. In what year did their expedition begin?
   a. 1800
   b. 1904
   c. 1804
   d. 1850

4. Approximately how many men joined the expedition?
   a. 40
   b. 45
   c. 50
   d. 25

5. Where did the journey begin?
   a. The Mississippi River
   b. The Missouri River
   c. The Colorado River
   d. The Columbia River

6. In what season did the journey begin?
   a. Summer
   b. Autumn
   c. Spring
   d. Winter

7. Who was the president when Lewis and Clark explored the Louisiana Purchase?
   a. George Washington
   b. John Adams
   c. Thomas Jefferson
   d. Andrew Jackson

8. Who funded the expedition?
   a. Congress
   b. The State Department
   c. The State of Louisiana
   d. The Treasury Department

9. How long did it take to get from the Missouri River to the Pacific Ocean?
   a. 3 years
   b. 1.5 years
   c. 14 months
   d. 2 years

10. When did they arrive at the Pacific Ocean?
    a. 1810
    b. 1804
    c. 1805
    d. 1820

B. Open-Ended Questions

1. What team of explorers is named in this passage?
2. Where did they explore?
3. In what year did they begin their journey?
4. How many men joined their expedition?
5. Where did they begin their journey?
6. At what time of year did the expedition begin?
7. Who was the president when Lewis and Clark explored?
8. Who funded the exploration of the Louisiana Purchase?
9. Who guided Lewis and Clark on the expedition?
10. When did they reach the Pacific Ocean?

C. Free Recall

Story 5
Inventors

Level 1

Alexander Graham Bell invented the telephone in 1876.

Level 1 Questions

A. Multiple-Choice Questions

1. Who invented the telephone?
   a. Alexander Hamilton
   b. Alexander Graham Bell
   c. Alexander Wilson
   d. Alexander Crater

2. In what year did he invent the telephone?
   a. 1927
   b. 1879
   c. 1876
   d. 1900

B. Open-Ended Questions

1. Who invented the telephone?
2. In what year did Alexander Graham Bell invent the telephone?

C. Free Recall

Level 2

Alexander Graham Bell invented the telephone in 1876. George Washington Carver, whose parents had been slaves, graduated from college and became a world-famous plant scientist who developed the idea of crop rotation.

Level 2 Questions

A. Multiple-Choice Questions

1. Who invented the telephone?
   a. Alexander Hamilton
   b. Alexander Graham Bell
   c. Alexander Wilson
   d. Alexander Crater

2. In what year did he invent the telephone?
   a. 1927
   b. 1879
   c. 1876
   d. 1900

3. What farming method did Carver develop?
   a. Crop rotation
   b. Crop dusting
   c. Crop fertilization
   d. Crop planting

B. Open-Ended Questions

1. Who invented the telephone?
2. In what year did Alexander Graham Bell invent the telephone?
3. Who was a famous plant scientist?

C. Free Recall

Level 3

Alexander Graham Bell invented the telephone in 1876. George Washington Carver, whose parents had been slaves, graduated from college and became a world-famous plant scientist who developed the idea of crop rotation. Thomas Edison had 1,093 patents issued to him by the U.S. government. This is a world record.

Level 3 Questions

A. Multiple-Choice Questions

1. Who invented the telephone?
   a. Alexander Hamilton
   b. Alexander Graham Bell
   c. Alexander Wilson
   d. Alexander Crater
2. In what year did he invent the telephone?
   a. 1927
   b. 1879
   c. 1876
   d. 1900
3. Who was a famous plant scientist?
   a. Eli Whitney
   b. Alexander Graham Bell
   c. George Washington Carver
   d. George Washington
4. What farming method did he develop?
   a. Crop rotation
   b. Crop dusting
   c. Crop fertilization
   d. Crop planting
5. Who holds the world's record for receiving the most patents?
   a. Eli Whitney
   b. Booker T. Washington
   c. Thomas Edison
   d. Luther Burbank
6. How many patents did Thomas Edison receive?
   a. 1,093
   b. 2,095
   c. 3,023
   d. 93

B. Open-Ended Questions

1. Who invented the telephone?
2. In what year did Alexander Graham Bell invent the telephone?
3. Who was a famous plant scientist?
4. What farming method did he develop?

5. Who holds the world's record for receiving the most patents?
6. How many patents did Thomas Edison receive?

C. Free Recall

Level 4

Benjamin Franklin is perhaps one of the most popular inventors in American history. His invention list includes a type of stove (1740), bifocal eyeglasses and the lightning rod. Alexander Graham Bell invented the telephone in 1876. George Washington Carver, whose parents had been slaves, graduated from college and became a world-famous plant scientist who developed the idea of crop rotation. Thomas Edison had 1,093 patents issued to him by the U.S. government. This is a world record.

Level 4 Questions

A. Multiple-Choice Questions

1. Who is one of the most popular American inventors?
   a. George Washington
   b. Benjamin Franklin
   c. Benjamin Harrison
   d. Franklin General
2. Name two items invented by Benjamin Franklin.
   a. The kite and string
   b. Bifocals and a type of stove
   c. The fountain pen and skates
   d. Eyeglasses and the light bulb
3. In what year did Franklin invent a type of stove?
   a. 1846
   b. 1749
   c. 1740
   d. 1854
4. Who invented the telephone?
   a. Alexander Hamilton
   b. Alexander Graham Bell
   c. Alexander Wilson
   d. Alexander Crater
5. In what year did Alexander Graham Bell invent the telephone?
   a. 1927
   b. 1879
   c. 1876
   d. 1900
6. Who was a famous plant scientist?
   a. Eli Whitney
   b. Alexander Graham Bell
   c. George Washington Carver
   d. George Washington
7. What farming method did he develop?
   a. Crop rotation
   b. Crop dusting
   c. Crop fertilization
   d. Crop planting
8. Who holds the world's record for receiving the most patents?
   a. Eli Whitney
   b. Booker T. Washington
   c. Thomas Edison
   d. Luther Burbank

9. How many patents did Thomas Edison receive?
   a. 1,093
   b. 2,095
   c. 3,023
   d. 93

10. Name the two inventors whose middle names are mentioned in this passage.
   a. Edison and Bell
   b. Carver and Franklin
   c. Franklin and Edison
   d. Carver and Bell

B. Open-Ended Questions

1. Who is one of the most popular American inventors?
2. Name two items invented by Benjamin Franklin.
3. In what year did Franklin invent a type of stove?
4. Who invented the telephone?
5. In what year did Alexander Graham Bell invent the telephone?
6. Who was a famous plant scientist?
7. What farming method did he develop?
8. Who holds the world's record for receiving the most patents?
9. How many patents did Thomas Edison receive?
10. Name all the inventors mentioned in this passage.

C. Free Recall

Story 6
The 19th Amendment – Women's Suffrage

Level 1

In 1920, the 19th Amendment to the U.S. Constitution was ratified.

Level 1 Questions

A. Multiple-Choice Questions

1. What year was mentioned in this sentence?
   a. 1915
   b. 1990
   c. 1920
   d. 1820

2. What happened in 1920?
   a. World War I ended
   b. The Constitution was ratified
   c. The 19th Amendment to the U.S. Constitution was ratified
   d. Prohibition ended

B. Open-Ended Questions

1. What is this sentence about?
2. When was the 19th Amendment ratified?

C. Free Recall

Level 2

In 1920, the 19th Amendment to the U.S. Constitution was ratified. This amendment provided voting rights to all adult women in the U.S.

Level 2 Questions

A. Multiple-Choice Questions

1. What year was mentioned in this passage?
   a. 1915
   b. 1990
   c. 1920
   d. 1820

2. What happened in 1920?
   a. World War I ended
   b. The Constitution was ratified
   c. The 19th Amendment to the U.S. Constitution was ratified
   d. Prohibition ended

3. What is the 19th Amendment about?
   a. Voting rights for adult women
   b. Abolishes slavery
   c. Prohibition
   d. States' rights

B. Open-Ended Questions

1. What is this passage about?
2. When was the 19th Amendment ratified?
3. What does the 19th Amendment provide?

C. Free Recall

Level 3

In 1920, the 19th Amendment to the U.S. Constitution was ratified. The idea of granting women the right to vote had been one of the results of the 1848 Women's Rights Convention in New York. After World War I, President Woodrow Wilson felt that women had provided the nation with great services during the war, and he supported the amendment.

Level 3 Questions

A. Multiple-Choice Questions

1. What years were mentioned in this passage?
   a. 1848 and 1915
   b. 1920 and 1990
   c. 1848 and 1920
   d. 1820 and 1948
2. What happened in 1920?
   a. World War I ended
   b. The Constitution was ratified
   c. The 19th Amendment to the U.S. Constitution was ratified
   d. Prohibition ended
3. What is the 19th Amendment about?
   a. Voting rights for adult women
   b. Abolishes slavery
   c. Prohibition
   d. States' rights
4. When was the Women's Rights Convention held?
   a. 1910
   b. 1915
   c. 1848
   d. 1850
5. Where was the Women's Rights Convention held?
   a. New York
   b. New London, Connecticut
   c. New Jersey
   d. New England
6. Why did President Wilson support the idea of women's suffrage?
   a. He felt they worked well with men
   b. He felt they had contributed enormously during World War I
   c. He wanted to be popular with women voters
   d. He supported the idea of his political party

B. Open-Ended Questions

1. What is this passage about?
2. When was the 19th Amendment ratified?
3. What does the 19th Amendment provide?
4. When was the Women's Rights Convention held?
5. Where was the Women's Rights Convention held?
6. Why did President Wilson support the idea of women's suffrage?

C. Free Recall

Level 4

In 1920, the 19th Amendment to the U.S. Constitution was ratified. Although the idea of granting women the right to vote had originally been one of the results of the 1848 Women's Rights Convention in New York, the idea was largely disregarded. After World War I, however, President Woodrow Wilson felt that women had provided the nation with great services during the war, and he supported the amendment. It took 14 months for the amendment to be ratified.

Level 4 Questions

A. Multiple-Choice Questions

1. What years were mentioned in this passage?
   a. 1848 and 1915
   b. 1990 and 1990
   c. 1848 and 1920
   d. 1820 and 1948
2. What happened in 1920?
   a. World War I ended
   b. The Constitution was ratified
   c. The 19th Amendment to the U.S. Constitution was ratified
   d. Prohibition ended
3. What is the 19th Amendment about?
   a. Voting rights for adult women
   b. Abolishes slavery
   c. Prohibition
   d. States' rights
4. When was the Women's Rights Convention held?
   a. 1910
   b. 1915
   c. 1848
   d. 1850
5. Where was the Women's Rights Convention held?
   a. New York
   b. New London, Connecticut
   c. New Jersey
   d. New England
6. What word was used in this passage to describe how the idea of women's right to vote was received after the Women's Rights Convention of 1848?
   a. Hopeful
   b. Disregarded
   c. Guaranteed
   d. Unbelievable

7. What war was mentioned in this passage?
   a. World War I
   b. Civil War
   c. World War II
   d. War of 1812

8. Who was the President when the 19th Amendment was ratified?
   a. Pete Wilson
   b. Woodrow Hale
   c. Woodrow Wilson
   d. Warren G. Harding

9. Why did President Wilson support the idea of women's suffrage?
   a. He felt they worked well with men
   b. He felt they had contributed enormously during World War I
   c. He wanted to be popular with women voters
   d. He supported the idea of his political party

10. How long did it take for the 19th Amendment to be ratified?
    a. 14 months
    b. 12 months
    c. 14 weeks
    d. 14 days

B. Open-Ended Questions

1. What is this passage about?
2. When was the 19th Amendment ratified?
3. What does the 19th Amendment provide?
4. When was the Women's Rights Convention held?
5. Where was the Women's Rights Convention held?
6. How was the idea of a woman's right to vote received in 1848?
7. After which war did the idea of granting women the right to vote become popular?
8. Who was the President when the amendment was ratified?
9. Why did President Wilson support the idea of women's suffrage?
10. How long did it take for the 19th Amendment to be ratified?

C. Free Recall

Story 7
The Great Depression

Level 1

October 29, 1929, was the date of the Great Crash at the New York Stock Exchange.

Level 1 Questions

A. Multiple-Choice Questions

1. What month is mentioned in this sentence?
   a. December
   b. November
   c. October
   d. May

2. What happened on that day?
   a. The stock yards in Iowa were full of cattle
   b. There was a train crash in New Jersey
   c. The New York Stock Market crashed
   d. The New York Yankees won the World Series

B. Open-Ended Questions

1. What month is mentioned in this sentence?
2. What crashed on October 29, 1929?

C. Free Recall

Level 2

Tuesday, October 29, 1929, was the date of the Great Crash at the New York Stock Exchange. Stock market prices had begun to drop seven weeks earlier.

Level 2 Questions

A. Multiple-Choice Questions

1. What day of the week is mentioned in this passage?
   a. Monday
   b. Tuesday
   c. Friday
   d. Saturday

2. What happened on that day?
   a. The stock yards in Iowa were full of cattle
   b. There was a train crash in New Jersey
   c. The New York Stock Market crashed
   d. The New York Yankees won the World Series

3. How many weeks earlier had the stock market shown signs of dropping prices?
   a. 12 weeks
   b. 7 weeks
   c. 8 weeks
   d. 2 weeks

B. Open-Ended Questions

1. What day of the week is mentioned in this passage?
2. What crashed on October 29, 1929?
3. Was this the first time the prices on the stock exchange had fallen?

C. Free Recall

Level 3

Tuesday, October 29, 1929, was the date of the Great Crash at the New York Stock Exchange. Stock market prices had begun to drop seven weeks earlier. With the fall of the stock market, people were not able to spend money, and goods began to accumulate, eventually causing many people to lose their jobs in factories.

Level 3 Questions

A. Multiple-Choice Questions

1. What day of the week is mentioned in this passage?
   a. Monday
   b. Tuesday
   c. Friday
   d. Saturday
2. What happened on that day?
   a. The stock yards in Iowa were full of cattle
   b. There was a train crash in New Jersey
   c. The New York Stock Market crashed
   d. The New York Yankees won the World Series
3. How many weeks earlier had the stock market shown signs of dropping prices?
   a. 12 weeks
   b. 7 weeks
   c. 8 weeks
   d. 2 weeks
4. What could people no longer spend?
   a. Time
   b. Money
   c. Retirement time
   d. Time with their families

5. What began to accumulate?
   a. Manufactured goods
   b. Debt
   c. Unemployment
   d. All of these

6. Why did people lose their jobs?
   a. Poor work
   b. Poor attendance
   c. Too many goods on hand
   d. Competition

B. Open-Ended Questions

1. What day of the week is mentioned in this passage?
2. What crashed on October 29, 1929?
3. Was this the first time the prices on the stock exchange had fallen?
4. What could people no longer spend?
5. What began to accumulate?
6. Why did people lose their jobs?

C. Free Recall

Level 4

Tuesday, October 29, 1929, was the date of the Great Crash at the New York Stock Exchange. Stock market prices had begun to drop seven weeks earlier. With the fall of the stock market, people were not able to spend money and goods began to accumulate, eventually causing many people to lose their jobs in factories. Twelve million Americans were unemployed by 1932 when the presidential election was held. Franklin D. Roosevelt won by a landslide and promised Americans a "New Deal," a financial and public program to turn around the depressed nation. Within two years, employment increased by 25 percent as programs to rebuild the nation's economy began to pay off.

Level 4 Questions

A. Multiple-Choice Questions

1. What day of the week is mentioned in this passage?
   a. Monday
   b. Tuesday
   c. Friday
   d. Saturday

2. What happened on that day?
   a. The stock yards in Iowa were full of cattle
   b. There was a train crash in New Jersey
   c. The New York Stock Market crashed
   d. The New York Yankees won the World Series

3. How many weeks earlier had the stock market shown signs of dropping prices?
   a. 12 weeks
   b. 7 weeks
   c. 8 weeks
   d. 2 weeks

4. What could people no longer spend?
   a. Time
   b. Money
   c. Retirement time
   d. Time with their families

5. What began to accumulate?
   a. Manufactured goods
   b. Debt
   c. Unemployment
   d. All of these

6. Why did people lose their jobs?
   a. Poor work
   b. Poor attendance
   c. Too many goods on hand
   d. Competition

7. What political event took place in 1932?
   a. Presidential election
   b. Elections of Congress
   c. Local elections
   d. The census

8. Who won the election?
   a. Herbert Hoover
   b. Theodore Roosevelt
   c. Franklin D. Roosevelt
   d. Dwight D. Eisenhower

9. What was the name of Roosevelt's program to help end the depression?
   a. The Farm Securities Plan
   b. The New Deal
   c. The Factory Deal
   d. The New Incentive

10. After Roosevelt was in office for two years, by what percentage did employment increase?
    a. 30%
    b. 10%
    c. 25%
    d. 55%

B. Open-Ended Questions

1. What day of the week is mentioned in this passage?
2. What crashed on October 29, 1929?
3. Was this the first time the prices on the stock exchange had fallen?
4. What could people no longer spend?
5. What began to accumulate?
6. Why did people lose their jobs?
7. What political event took place in 1932?
8. Who won the election?
9. What was the name of Roosevelt's program to help end the depression?
10. After Roosevelt was in office for two years, by what percentage did employment increase?

C. Free Recall

Story 8
Martin Luther King, Jr.

Level 1

Martin Luther King, Jr., was born in Atlanta in 1929.

Level 1 Questions

A. Multiple-Choice Questions

1. Who is mentioned in this sentence?
   a. Lewis Martin
   b. Martin Luther King, Jr.
   c. Martha Washington
   d. King Edward
2. When was Martin Luther King, Jr., born?
   a. 1900
   b. 1952
   c. 1929
   d. 1915

B. Open-Ended Questions

1. Who is mentioned in this sentence?
2. When was Martin Luther King, Jr., born?

C. Free Recall

Level 2

Martin Luther King, Jr., was born in Atlanta in 1929. He attended Morehouse College and received a doctorate in theology from Boston University.

Level 2 Questions

A. Multiple-Choice Questions

1. Who is this passage about?
   a. Lewis Martin
   b. Martin Luther King, Jr.
   c. Martha Washington
   d. King Edward
2. When was Martin Luther King, Jr., born?
   a. 1900
   b. 1952
   c. 1929
   d. 1915
3. What schools did Martin Luther King, Jr., attend?
   a. Harvard and Yale
   b. Michigan State and Boston College
   c. Morehouse and Princeton
   d. Morehouse and Boston University

B. Open-Ended Questions

1. Who is mentioned in this passage?
2. When was Martin Luther King, Jr., born?
3. What schools did Martin Luther King, Jr., attend?

C. Free Recall

Level 3

Martin Luther King, Jr., was born in Atlanta in 1929. He attended Morehouse College and received a doctorate in theology from Boston University. In 1956, the U.S. Supreme Court decision regarding segregation on buses was overturned.

Level 3 Questions

A. Multiple-Choice Questions

1. Who is this passage about?
   a. Lewis Martin
   b. Martin Luther King, Jr.
   c. Martha Washington
   d. King Edward
2. When was Martin Luther King, Jr., born?
   a. 1900
   b. 1952
   c. 1929
   d. 1915
3. What schools did Martin Luther King, Jr., attend?
   a. Harvard and Yale
   b. Michigan State and Boston College
   c. Morehouse and Princeton
   d. Morehouse and Boston University
4. What government branch is mentioned in this passage?
   a. The Supreme Court
   b. The Treasury
   c. The War Department
   d. The Labor Department
5. In what year did a change in a Supreme Court ruling take place?
   a. 1934
   b. 1960
   c. 1956
   d. 1900
6. What was the topic of the Court's decision?
   a. Women's rights
   b. Civil rights
   c. Animal rights
   d. Ecology

B. Open-Ended Questions

1. Who is mentioned in this passage?
2. When was Martin Luther King, Jr., born?
3. What schools did Martin Luther King, Jr., attend?
4. What government branch is mentioned in this passage?

5. In what year did a change in a Supreme Court ruling take place?
6. What was the topic of the Court's decision?

C. Free Recall

Level 4

Martin Luther King, Jr., a renowned civil rights leader, was born in Atlanta in 1929 and was assassinated in 1968 in Memphis, Tennessee. He attended Morehouse College and received a doctorate in theology from Boston University. In 1956, the U.S. Supreme Court decision regarding segregation on buses was overturned following a 382-day boycott in Montgomery, Alabama.

Level 4 Questions

A. Multiple-Choice Questions

1. Who is this passage about?
   a. Lewis Martin
   b. Martin Luther King, Jr.
   c. Martha Washington
   d. King Edward
2. When was Martin Luther King, Jr., born?
   a. 1900
   b. 1952
   c. 1929
   d. 1915
3. In what city was Martin Luther King, Jr., born?
   a. Memphis
   b. Washington, D.C.
   c. Atlanta
   d. St. Louis
4. When was he assassinated?
   a. 1960
   b. 1959
   c. 1972
   d. 1968
5. Where was he assassinated?
   a. Memphis, Tennessee
   b. Atlanta, Georgia
   c. Birmingham, Alabama
   d. Washington, D.C.
6. What schools did Martin Luther King, Jr., attend?
   a. Harvard and Yale
   b. Michigan State and Boston College
   c. Morehouse and Princeton
   d. Morehouse and Boston University
7. What degree did Martin Luther King, Jr., receive at Boston University?
   a. Doctorate in sociology
   b. Doctorate in theology
   c. Doctorate in law
   d. Doctorate in chemistry
8. What government branch is mentioned in this passage?
   a. The Supreme Court
   b. The Treasury
   c. The War Department
   d. The Labor Department

9. In what year did a change in a Supreme Court ruling take place?
   a. 1934
   b. 1960
   c. 1956
   d. 1900

10. What was the topic of the Court's decision?
    a. Women's rights
    b. Civil rights
    c. Animal rights
    d. Ecology

B. Open-Ended Questions

1. Who is mentioned in this passage?
2. When was Martin Luther King, Jr., born?
3. In what city was Martin Luther King, Jr., born?
4. When was he assassinated?
5. Where was he assassinated?
6. What schools did Martin Luther King, Jr., attend?
7. What degree did Martin Luther King, Jr., earn at Boston University?
8. What government branch is mentioned in this passage?
9. In what year did a change in a Supreme Court ruling take place?
10. What was the topic of the Court's decision?

C. Free Recall

Auditory Recall Stories – Health and Medicine

Topic 1
Anorexia Nervosa

Level 1

Anorexia nervosa is an eating disorder in which people starve themselves.

Level 1 Questions

A. Multiple-Choice Questions

1. An eating disorder in which people starve themselves is called:
   a. Anorexia
   b. Bulimia
   c. Binge eating disorder
   d. Aphasia

2. Anorexia nervosa is:
   a. A skin disorder
   b. A neurological disorder
   c. An eating disorder
   d. A gastrointestinal disorder

B. Open-Ended Questions

1. What is the name of the disorder in which people starve themselves?
2. What type of disorder is anorexia nervosa?

C. Free Recall

Level 2

Anorexia nervosa is an eating disorder in which people starve themselves. It causes extreme weight loss, which the National Institutes of Health (NIH) defines as at least 15 percent below the individual's normal body weight.

Level 2 Questions

A. Multiple-Choice Questions

1. An eating disorder in which people starve themselves is called:
   a. Anorexia nervosa
   b. Bulimia
   c. Binge eating disorder
   d. Aphasia

2. Anorexia causes:
   a. Mild weight loss
   b. Extreme weight loss
   c. Mild weight gain
   d. Extreme weight gain

Information in the Health and Medicine section is adapted with permission from North Shore-Long Island Jewish Health System (website: www.northshorelij.edu).

3. Extreme weight loss is defined as:
   a. 10% below normal body weight
   b. 15% below normal body weight
   c. 20% below normal body weight
   d. 25% below normal body weight

B. Open-Ended Questions

1. What is anorexia nervosa?
2. What does anorexia cause?
3. Extreme weight loss is defined as what, according to the NIH?

C. Free Recall

Level 3

Anorexia nervosa is an eating disorder in which people intentionally starve themselves. It causes extreme weight loss, which the National Institutes of Health (NIH) defines as at least 15 percent below the individual's normal body weight. Food and weight become obsessions. Compulsiveness may cause strange eating rituals or the refusal to eat in front of others. It is not uncommon for people with anorexia to collect recipes and prepare gourmet feasts for family and friends but not partake in the meals themselves. They may adhere to strict exercise routines to keep off weight.

Level 3 Questions

A. Multiple-Choice Questions

1. An eating disorder in which people intentionally starve themselves is called:
   a. Anorexia nervosa
   b. Bulimia
   c. Binge eating disorder
   d. Aphasia
2. Anorexia nervosa is:
   a. A skin disorder
   b. A neurological disorder
   c. An eating disorder
   d. A gastrointestinal disorder
3. Anorexia causes:
   a. Mild weight loss
   b. Extreme weight loss
   c. Mild weight gain
   d. Extreme weight gain
4. Extreme weight loss is defined as:
   a. 10% below normal body weight
   b. 15% below normal body weight
   c. 20% below normal body weight
   d. 25% below normal body weight
5. People with anorexia often do what in order to help keep weight off?
   a. Cook gourmet meals for others
   b. Engage in strict exercise routines
   c. Eat many vegetables
   d. Wear tight clothing

6. People with anorexia often become obsessed with:
   a. Food
   b. Weight
   c. Neither a nor b
   d. Both a and b

B. Open-Ended Questions

1. What is anorexia nervosa?
2. What does anorexia cause?
3. Extreme weight loss is defined as what, according to the NIH?
4. What things do people with anorexia become obsessed with?
5. Under what conditions can compulsiveness cause refusal to eat?
6. What types of routines may people with anorexia adhere to in order to keep off weight?

C. Free Recall

Level 4

Anorexia nervosa is an eating disorder in which people intentionally starve themselves. It causes extreme weight loss, which the National Institutes of Health (NIH) defines as at least 15 percent below the individual's normal body weight. Food and weight become obsessions. Compulsiveness may cause strange eating rituals or the refusal to eat in front of others. It is not uncommon for people with anorexia to collect recipes and prepare gourmet feasts for family and friends but not partake in the meals themselves. They may also adhere to strict exercise routines to keep off weight. Side effects of the disorder are many and may include a loss of monthly menstrual periods in women and impotence in men.

Level 4 Questions

A. Multiple-Choice Questions

1. An eating disorder in which people intentionally starve themselves is called:
   a. Anorexia nervosa
   b. Bulimia
   c. Binge eating disorder
   d. Aphasia

2. Anorexia nervosa is:
   a. A skin disorder
   b. A neurological disorder
   c. An eating disorder
   d. A gastrointestinal disorder

3. Anorexia causes:
   a. Mild weight loss
   b. Extreme weight loss
   c. Mild weight gain
   d. Extreme weight gain
4. Extreme weight loss is defined as:
   a. 10 percent below normal body weight
   b. 15 percent below normal body weight
   c. 20 percent below normal body weight
   d. 25 percent below normal body weight
5. People with anorexia often do what in order to help keep weight off?
   a. Cook gourmet meals for others
   b. Engage in strict exercise routines
   c. Eat many vegetables
   d. Wear tight clothing
6. People with anorexia often become obsessed with:
   a. Food
   b. Weight
   c. Neither a nor b
   d. Both a and b
7. Compulsiveness in anorexia can cause:
   a. Strange eating rituals
   b. Desire to eat with others
   c. Weight gain
   d. Failure to exercise
8. What might a person with anorexia do when having friends over for dinner?
   a. Serve only one course
   b. Serve extremely small portions
   c. Eat normally
   d. Serve a gourmet meal but not eat anything
9. A common side effect of anorexia in women is:
   a. Hair growth
   b. Excessive sweating
   c. Muscle cramping
   d. Loss of monthly menstrual cycle
10. A common side effect of anorexia in men is:
    a. Impotence
    b. Hair loss
    c. Excessive sweating
    d. Insomnia

B. Open-Ended Questions

1. What is anorexia nervosa?
2. What does anorexia cause?
3. Extreme weight loss is defined as what, according to the NIH?
4. What things do people with anorexia become obsessed with?
5. Under what conditions can compulsiveness cause refusal to eat?
6. What types of routines may people with anorexia adhere to in order to keep off weight?
7. What is a side effect of anorexia in women?
8. What is a side effect of anorexia in men?
9. What does NIH stand for?
10. What might a person with anorexia do when having friends over for dinner?

C. Free Recall

Topic 2
Homeopathy

Level 1

Homeopathic medicine is based on the use of natural substances, regulated by the U.S. Food and Drug Administration (FDA).

Level 1 Questions

A. Multiple-Choice Questions

1. Treatment based on the use of natural substances is known as:
   a. Aromatherapy
   b. Homeopathy
   c. Environmentalism
   d. Osteopathy

2. Substances used in homeopathic medicine are regulated by:
   a. The NIH
   b. The DEA
   c. The FDA
   d. The CIA

B. Open-Ended Questions

1. Treatment based on the use of natural substances is known as what?
2. Substances used in homeopathic medicine are regulated by what agency?

C. Free Recall

Level 2

Homeopathic medicine is based on the use of natural substances, regulated by the U.S. Food and Drug Administration (FDA), to treat acute and chronic illnesses. Homeopathic medicine also is used to prevent diseases.

Level 2 Questions

A. Multiple-Choice Questions

1. Treatment based on the use of natural substances is known as:
   a. Aromatherapy
   b. Homeopathy
   c. Environmentalism
   d. Osteopathy

2. Substances used in homeopathic medicine are regulated by:
   a. The NIH
   b. The DEA
   c. The FDA
   d. The CIA

3. Homeopathic medicine is used to:
   a. Treat chronic illness
   b. Treat acute illness
   c. Prevent disease
   d. All of the above

B. Open-Ended Questions

1. Treatment based on the use of natural substances is known as what?
2. Substances used in homeopathic medicine are regulated by what agency?
3. Homeopathic medicine is used to treat what?

C. Free Recall

Level 3

Homeopathic medicine is based on the use of natural substances, regulated by the U.S. Food and Drug Administration (FDA), to treat acute and chronic illnesses. Homeopathic medicine also is used to prevent diseases. Homeopathic drugs are made of plant, animal or mineral substances. This therapy treats ailments with very small amounts of the same substance that causes the patient's symptoms. The idea behind homeopathy is that if a large dosage of a certain substance produces certain symptoms, a small dosage of the same substance may cause the opposite effect.

Level 3 Questions

A. Multiple-Choice Questions

1. Treatment based on the use of natural substances is known as:
   a. Aromatherapy
   b. Homeopathy
   c. Environmentalism
   d. Osteopathy
2. Substances used in homeopathic medicine are regulated by:
   a. The NIH
   b. The DEA
   c. The FDA
   d. The CIA
3. Homeopathic medicine is used to:
   a. Treat chronic illness
   b. Treat acute illness
   c. Prevent disease
   d. All of the above
4. Homeopathic drugs are made of all of the following except:
   a. Plant substances
   b. Animal substances
   c. Synthetic substances
   d. Mineral substances

5. Homeopathy treats ailments with _____ amounts of the same substance that causes the patient's symptoms.
   a. Very small
   b. Very large
   c. Equivalent
   d. None of the above

6. The idea behind homeopathy is that if a large dosage of a certain substance produces certain symptoms, a small dosage of the same substance may cause:
   a. The opposite effect
   b. The same effect
   c. No effect
   d. A paradoxical effect

B. Open-Ended Questions

1. Treatment based on the use of natural substances is known as what?
2. Substances used in homeopathic medicine are regulated by what agency?
3. Homeopathic medicine is used to treat what?
4. What are homeopathic drugs made of?
5. Homeopathic drugs use small amounts of the same substances as what?
6. What is the idea behind homeopathy?

C. Free Recall

Level 4

Homeopathic medicine is based on the use of natural substances, regulated by the U.S. Food and Drug Administration (FDA), to treat acute and chronic illnesses. Homeopathic medicine also is used to prevent diseases. Homeopathic drugs are made of plant, animal or mineral substances. This therapy treats ailments with very small amounts of the same substance that causes the patient's symptoms. The idea behind homeopathy is that if a large dosage of a certain substance produces certain symptoms, a small dosage of the same substance may cause the opposite effect. Explanations for why homeopathy works range from the idea that homeopathic medicine stimulates the body's own natural defenses to the idea that homeopathic medicine retains a "memory" of the original substance. However, there is no factual explanation for why homeopathy works, and more research is needed. Homeopathic medicine is most often used to treat arthritis, asthma and allergies.

Level 4 Questions

A. Multiple-Choice Questions

1. Treatment based on the use of natural substances is known as:
   a. Aromatherapy
   b. Homeopathy
   c. Environmentalism
   d. Osteopathy

2. Substances used in homeopathic medicine are regulated by:
   a. The NIH
   b. The DEA
   c. The FDA
   d. The CIA

3. Homeopathic medicine is used to:
   a. Treat chronic illness
   b. Treat acute illness
   c. Prevent disease
   d. All of the above

4. Homeopathic drugs are made of all of the following except:
   a. Plant substances
   b. Animal substances
   c. Synthetic substances
   d. Mineral substances

5. Homeopathy treats ailments with _____ amounts of the same substance that causes the patient's symptoms.
   a. Very small
   b. Very large
   c. Equivalent
   d. None of the above

6. The idea behind homeopathy is that if a large dosage of a certain substance produces certain symptoms, a small dosage of the same substance may cause:
   a. The opposite effect
   b. The same effect
   c. No effect
   d. A paradoxical effect

7. Explanations of why homeopathy works include:
   a. Stimulating growth hormones
   b. Creating adverse reactions
   c. Stimulating the body's own natural defenses
   d. None of the above

8. What is the factual explanation of why homeopathy works?
   a. It boosts the body's immune system
   b. It creates antibodies to certain diseases
   c. Homeopathy does not work
   d. There is no factual explanation of why homeopathy works

9. Homeopathic medicines are often used to treat all of the following except:
   a. Allergies
   b. Asthma
   c. Arthritis
   d. Autism

10. What is needed to determine factually why homeopathy works?
    a. More research
    b. More drug development
    c. More serious diseases to treat
    d. All of the above

B. Open-Ended Questions

1. Treatment based on the use of natural substances is known as what?
2. Substances used in homeopathic medicine are regulated by what agency?
3. Homeopathic medicine is used to treat what?
4. What are homeopathic drugs made of?
5. Homeopathic drugs use small amounts of the same substances as what?
6. What is the idea behind homeopathy?
7. What are some explanations of why homeopathy works?
8. What is the factual explanation of why homeopathy works?
9. What is homeopathy most often used to treat?
10. What is needed to determine factually why homeopathy works?

C. Free Recall

Topic 3
Skin Cancer

Level 1

Skin cancer is the most common cancer in the United States and occurs most often in fair-skinned individuals who have been exposed to the sun for prolonged periods.

Level 1 Questions

A. Multiple-Choice Questions

1. What is the most common cancer in the U.S.?
   a. Lung cancer
   b. Skin cancer
   c. Breast cancer
   d. Prostate cancer

2. Skin cancer occurs most often in:
   a. Fair-skinned people with little sun exposure
   b. Dark-skinned people with a lot of sun exposure
   c. Fair-skinned people with a lot of sun exposure
   d. Dark-skinned people with little sun exposure

B. Open-Ended Questions

1. What is the most common cancer in the U.S.?
2. In what type of individuals does skin cancer occur most often?

C. Free Recall

Level 2

Skin cancer is the most common cancer in the United States and usually occurs in fair-skinned individuals who have been exposed to the sun for prolonged periods. Every year, skin cancers affect approximately 600,000 Caucasians, the highest risk group.

Level 2 Questions

A. Multiple-Choice Questions

1. What is the most common cancer in the U.S.?
   a. Lung cancer
   b. Skin cancer
   c. Breast cancer
   d. Prostate cancer

2. Skin cancer occurs most often in:
   a. Fair-skinned people with little sun exposure
   b. Dark-skinned people with a lot of sun exposure
   c. Fair-skinned people with a lot of sun exposure
   d. Dark-skinned people with little sun exposure

3. Approximately how many Caucasians does skin cancer affect each year?
   a. 100,000
   b. 350,000
   c. 600,000
   d. 850,000

B. Open-Ended Questions

1. What is the most common cancer in the U.S.?
2. In what type of individuals does skin cancer occur most often?
3. How many Caucasians does skin cancer affect each year?

C. Free Recall

Level 3

Skin cancer is the most common cancer in the United States and occurs most often in fair-skinned individuals who have been exposed to the sun for prolonged periods. Every year, skin cancers affect approximately 600,000 Caucasians, the highest risk group. The principal cause of skin cancer almost universally accepted by medical experts is overexposure to sunlight, especially when it results in sunburn and blistering.

Level 3 Questions

A. Multiple-Choice Questions

1. What is the most common cancer in the U.S?
   a. Lung cancer
   b. Skin cancer
   c. Breast cancer
   d. Prostate cancer
2. Skin cancer occurs most often in:
   a. Fair-skinned people
   b. Dark-skinned people
   c. Olive-skinned people
   d. People with little body hair
3. What type of prolonged exposure poses a risk for skin cancer?
   a. Sun
   b. X-rays
   c. Ultraviolet light
   d. All of the above
4. Approximately how many Caucasians does skin cancer affect each year?
   a. 100,000
   b. 350,000
   c. 600,000
   d. 850,000
5. What is the principal cause of skin cancer?
   a. Overexposure to heat
   b. Overexposure to sunlight
   c. Lack of proper hydration
   d. Lack of vitamin D
6. Overexposure to sunlight is particularly dangerous when it results in:
   a. Sunburn
   b. Blistering
   c. Neither a nor b
   d. Both a and b

B. Open-Ended Questions

1. What is the most common cancer in the U.S.?
2. In what type of individuals does skin cancer occur most often?
3. What type of exposure poses a risk for skin cancer?
4. How many Caucasians does skin cancer affect each year?
5. What is the principal cause of skin cancer?
6. When is overexposure to sunlight particularly dangerous?

C. Free Recall

Level 4

Skin cancer is the most common cancer in the United States and occurs most often in fair-skinned individuals who have been exposed to the sun, X rays or ultraviolet light for prolonged periods. Every year, skin cancers affect approximately 600,000 Caucasians, the highest risk group. The principal cause of skin cancer almost universally accepted by medical experts is overexposure to sunlight, especially when it results in sunburn and blistering. Avoiding sun overexposure is the best defense against skin cancer, and catching problems early provides a better chance for successful treatment.

Level 4 Questions

A. Multiple-Choice Questions

1. What is the most common cancer in the U.S.?
   a. Lung cancer
   b. Skin cancer
   c. Breast cancer
   d. Prostate cancer
2. Skin cancer occurs most often in:
   a. Fair-skinned people
   b. Dark-skinned people
   c. Olive-skinned people
   d. People with little body hair
3. What type of prolonged exposure poses a risk for skin cancer?
   a. Sun
   b. X-rays
   c. Ultraviolet light
   d. All of the above
4. Approximately how many Caucasians does skin cancer affect each year?
   a. 100,000
   b. 350,000
   c. 600,000
   d. 850,000
5. What is the principal cause of skin cancer?
   a. Overexposure to heat
   b. Overexposure to sunlight
   c. Lack of proper hydration
   d. Lack of vitamin D
6. Overexposure to sunlight is particularly dangerous when it results in:
   a. Sunburn
   b. Blistering
   c. Neither a nor b
   d. Both a and b

7. What is the best defense against skin cancer?
   a. Avoiding overexposure to the sun
   b. Adequate moisturizing of the skin
   c. Vitamin D supplements
   d. None of the above

8. Which is the highest risk group for skin cancer?
   a. African-Americans
   b. Asians
   c. Caucasians
   d. Native Americans

9. Which of the following statements is not true?
   a. Prolonged sun exposure is a major risk factor for skin cancer
   b. There are no effective treatments for skin cancer
   c. Avoiding sun exposure is the best way to avoid skin cancer
   d. Successful treatment is possible with early detection

10. A better chance for successful treatment is provided when:
    a. Proper medication is taken
    b. Problems are caught early
    c. Continued sun exposure is obtained
    d. All of the above

B. Open-Ended Questions

1. What is the most common cancer in the U.S.?
2. In what type of individuals does skin cancer occur most often?
3. What type of exposure poses a risk for skin cancer?
4. What group is at greatest risk for skin cancer?
5. How many Caucasians does skin cancer affect each year?
6. What is the principal cause of skin cancer?
7. What is the best defense against skin cancer?
8. When is overexposure to sunlight particularly dangerous?
9. What provides a better chance for successful treatment?
10. Name three dangerous sources of exposure that are linked to skin cancer.

C. Free Recall

Topic 4
Pathology

Level 1

Pathology is the study of disease. Pathologists are medical doctors.

Level 1 Questions

A. Multiple-Choice Questions

1. What is the study of disease called?
   a. Anatomy
   b. Physiology
   c. Pathology
   d. Microbiology

2. Doctors who study disease are known as:
   a. Physicians
   b. Physiologists
   c. Pathognomists
   d. Pathologists

B. Open-Ended Questions

1. What is the study of disease called?
2. What is the name for a doctor who studies pathology?

C. Free Recall

Level 2

Pathology is the study of disease. A pathologist, who is a medical doctor, looks at the causes of disease, how disease progresses and how disease affects the body.

Level 2 Questions

A. Multiple-Choice Questions

1. What is the study of disease called?
   a. Anatomy
   b. Physiology
   c. Pathology
   d. Microbiology

2. Doctors who study disease are known as:
   a. Pathologists
   b. Psychiatrists
   c. Endocrinologists
   d. Radiologists

3. What do pathologists study?
   a. Causes of disease
   b. How a disease progresses
   c. How a disease affects the body
   d. All of the above

B. Open-Ended Questions

1. What is the study of disease called?
2. What type of doctor studies disease?
3. What aspects of disease do pathologists study?

C. Free Recall

Level 3

Pathology is the study of disease. A pathologist, who is a medical doctor, looks at the causes of disease, how disease progresses and how disease affects the body. However, instead of examining the patient physically, a pathologist examines body fluids and tissue samples from that patient to help the primary physician make a diagnosis.

Level 3 Questions

A. Multiple-Choice Questions

1. What is the study of disease called?
   a. Anatomy
   b. Physiology
   c. Pathology
   d. Microbiology
2. Doctors who study disease are known as:
   a. Pathologists
   b. Physiatrists
   c. Endocrinologists
   d. Radiologists
3. What do pathologists study?
   a. Causes of disease
   b. How a disease progresses
   c. How a disease affects the body
   d. All of the above
4. Which of the following do pathologists not examine?
   a. The patient
   b. Bodily fluids
   c. Tissue samples
   d. Any of the above
5. Do pathologists perform physical exams on patients?
   a. Yes
   b. No
   c. Sometimes
   d. Pathologists are not licensed to perform physical exams
6. In what ways do pathologists help primary physicians?
   a. During surgery
   b. Making diagnoses
   c. Establishing a treatment plan
   d. None of the above

B. Open-Ended Questions

1. What is the study of disease called?
2. What type of doctor studies disease?
3. What aspects of disease do pathologists study?
4. What does the pathologist examine?
5. Do pathologists perform physical exams on patients?
6. In what way do pathologists help primary physicians?

C. Free Recall

Level 4

Pathology is the study of disease. A pathologist, who is a medical doctor, looks at the causes of disease, how disease progresses and how disease affects the body. However, instead of examining the patient physically, a pathologist examines body fluids and tissue samples from that patient to help the primary physician make a diagnosis. Most people have had some blood and urine tests done during their lifetime. Pathologists analyze these tests to help determine the next step in a patient's treatment plan.

Level 4 Questions

A. Multiple-Choice Questions

1. What is the study of disease called?
   a. Anatomy
   b. Physiology
   c. Pathology
   d. Microbiology

2. Doctors who study disease are known as:
   a. Pathologists
   b. Physiatrists
   c. Endocrinologists
   d. Radiologists

3. What do pathologists study?
   a. Causes of disease
   b. How a disease progresses
   c. How a disease affects the body
   d. All of the above

4. Which of the following do pathologists not examine?
   a. The patient
   b. Bodily fluids
   c. Tissue samples
   d. Any of the above

5. Do pathologists perform physical exams on patients?
   a. Yes
   b. No
   c. Sometimes
   d. Pathologists are not licensed to perform physical exams

6. In what way do pathologists help primary physicians?
   a. During surgery
   b. Making diagnoses
   c. Establishing a treatment plan
   d. None of the above

7. What type of doctors are pathologists?
   a. Homeopathic doctors
   b. Medical doctors
   c. Researchers
   d. Ph.D.s

8. Which of the following is true of blood and urine tests?
   a. Most people will never have them done
   b. They are only done in the hospital setting
   c. Most people have them done during their lifetime
   d. None of the above

9. Which of the following tests do pathologists commonly analyze?
   a. X-rays and EKGs
   b. X-rays and blood
   c. Urine and blood
   d. Urine and EKGs

10. What do tests analyzed by pathologists help to determine?
   a. The causes of diseases
   b. The cures for diseases
   c. The patient's genetic makeup
   d. The next step in the patient's treatment plan

B. Open-Ended Questions

1. What is the study of disease called?
2. What type of doctor studies disease?
3. What aspects of disease do pathologists study?
4. What does the pathologist examine?
5. Do pathologists perform physical exams on patients?
6. In what way do pathologists help primary physicians?
7. What kinds of tests do pathologists commonly analyze?
8. Is it common for most people to have these tests done during their lifetime?
9. What do these analyses help determine?
10. Are pathologists medical doctors?

C. Free Recall

Topic 5
Oral Health

Level 1

According to the Center for Disease Control (CDC), approximately 500 million dental visits occur annually in the United States.

Level 1 Questions

A. Multiple-Choice Questions

1. What does CDC stand for?
   a. Center for Disorders of the Colon
   b. Central Disease Coordination
   c. Committee for Disease Control
   d. Center for Disease Control

2. According to the CDC, how many dental visits occur per year in the U.S.?
   a. 100,000
   b. 1 million
   c. 50 million
   d. 500 million

B. Open-Ended Questions

1. What is the CDC?
2. According to the CDC, how many dental visits occur annually in the U.S.?

C. Free Recall

Level 2

According to the Center for Disease Control (CDC), approximately 500 million dental visits occur annually in the United States, with an estimated 50 billion dollars currently being spent on dental services. Yet, many children and adults needlessly suffer from oral diseases that could be prevented.

Level 2 Questions

A. Multiple-Choice Questions

1. What does CDC stand for?
   a. Center for Disorders of the Colon
   b. Central Disease Coordination
   c. Committee for Disease Control
   d. Center for Disease Control

2. According to the CDC, how many dental visits occur per year in the U.S.?
   a. 100,000
   b. 1 million
   c. 50 million
   d. 500 million

3. How much money is currently being spent on dental services in the U.S.?
   a. 10 million dollars
   b. 50 million dollars
   c. 50 billion dollars
   d. 500 billion dollars

B. Open-Ended Questions

1. What is the CDC?
2. According to the CDC, how many dental visits occur annually in the U.S.?
3. How much money is currently being spent on dental services in the U.S.?

C. Free Recall

Level 3

According to the Center for Disease Control (CDC), approximately 500 million dental visits occur annually in the United States, with an estimated 50 billion dollars currently being spent on dental services. Yet, many children and adults needlessly suffer from oral diseases that could be prevented. In fact, 30,000 Americans will be diagnosed with oral and pharyngeal cancers this year, resulting in more than 8,000 deaths, many of which could have been prevented.

Level 3 Questions

A. Multiple-Choice Questions

1. What does CDC stand for?
   a. Center for Disorders of the Colon
   b. Central Disease Coordination
   c. Committee for Disease Control
   d. Center for Disease Control
2. According to the CDC, how many dental visits occur per year in the U.S.?
   a. 100,000
   b. 1 million
   c. 50 million
   d. 500 million
3. How much money is currently being spent on dental services in the U.S.?
   a. 10 million dollars
   b. 50 million dollars
   c. 50 billion dollars
   d. 500 billion dollars
4. How many Americans will be diagnosed with oral and pharyngeal cancers this year?
   a. 3,000
   b. 10,000
   c. 30,000
   d. 100,000

5. How many deaths will result from oral and pharyngeal cancers this year?
   a. 4,000
   b. 8,000
   c. 40,000
   d. 80,000

6. Which of the following statements is true?
   a. Most oral diseases cannot be prevented
   b. Many oral diseases could be prevented
   c. Oral disease is not a major health or economic issue
   d. None of the above

B. Open-Ended Questions

1. What is the CDC?
2. According to the CDC, how many dental visits occur annually in the U.S.?
3. How much money is currently being spent on dental services in the U.S.?
4. How many Americans will be diagnosed with oral and pharyngeal cancers this year?
5. How many deaths will result from oral/pharyngeal cancers this year?
6. Can oral disease be prevented?

C. Free Recall

Level 4

According to the Center for Disease Control (CDC), approximately 500 million dental visits occur annually in the United States, with an estimated 50 billion dollars currently being spent on dental services. Yet, many children and adults needlessly suffer from oral diseases that could be prevented. In fact, 30,000 Americans will be diagnosed with oral and pharyngeal cancers this year, resulting in more than 8,000 deaths, many of which could have been prevented. Close to 20 percent of preschoolers have tooth decay, with 50 percent developing tooth decay by the third grade and 86 percent by age 17. But with proper preventive care, such as regular checkups, brushing, flossing and fluoridation, the risk of dental disease can be greatly reduced.

Level 4 Questions

A. Multiple-Choice Questions

1. What does CDC stand for?
   a. Center for Disorders of the Colon
   b. Central Disease Coordination
   c. Committee for Disease Control
   d. Center for Disease Control

2. According to the CDC, how many dental visits occur per year in the U.S.?
   a. 100,000
   b. 1 million
   c. 50 million
   d. 500 million

3. How much money is currently being spent on dental services in the U.S.?
   a. 10 million dollars
   b. 50 million dollars
   c. 50 billion dollars
   d. 500 billion dollars

4. How many Americans will be diagnosed with oral and pharyngeal cancers this year?
   a. 3,000
   b. 10,000
   c. 30,000
   d. 100,000

5. How many deaths will result from oral and pharyngeal cancers this year?
   a. 4,000
   b. 8,000
   c. 40,000
   d. 80,000

6. Which of the following statements is true?
   a. Most oral diseases cannot be prevented
   b. Many oral diseases could be prevented
   c. Oral disease is not a major health or economic issue
   d. None of the above

7. About what percentage of preschoolers has tooth decay?
   a. 20%
   b. 25%
   c. 30%
   d. 35%

8. What percentage of third graders has tooth decay?
   a. 10%
   b. 25%
   c. 50%
   d. 75%

9. What percentage of children develops tooth decay by age 17?
   a. 26%
   b. 48%
   c. 78%
   d. 86%

10. The risk of dental disease can be greatly reduced by all of the following except:
    a. Regular rinsing
    b. Regular checkups
    c. Flossing
    d. Brushing

B. Open-Ended Questions

1. What is the CDC?
2. According to the CDC, how many dental visits occur annually in the U.S.?
3. How much money is currently being spent on dental services in the U.S.?
4. How many Americans will be diagnosed with oral and pharyngeal cancers this year?
5. How many deaths will result from oral and pharyngeal cancers this year?
6. Can oral disease be prevented?
7. What percentage of preschoolers has tooth decay?
8. What percentage of third graders has tooth decay?
9. What percentage of children develops tooth decay by age 17?
10. How can the risk of dental disease be greatly reduced?

C. Free Recall

Topic 6
Cardiovascular Disease

Level 1

The cardiovascular system is made up of the heart and blood vessels.

Level 1 Questions

A. Multiple-Choice Questions.

1. Which of the following does not make up a part of the cardiovascular system?
   a. Lungs
   b. Heart
   c. Blood vessels
   d. All of the above are part of the cardiovascular system

2. The heart and blood vessels comprise what bodily system?
   a. Pulmonary
   b. Cardiac
   c. Gastrointestinal
   d. Cardiovascular

B. Open-Ended Questions

1. What makes up the cardiovascular system?
2. The heart and blood vessels comprise what bodily system?

C. Free Recall

Level 2

The cardiovascular system is made up of the heart and blood vessels. Cardiovascular diseases, as defined by the American Heart Association (AHA), include coronary heart disease, stroke, high blood pressure and rheumatic heart disease.

Level 2 Questions

A. Multiple-Choice Questions

1. Which of the following does not make up a part of the cardiovascular system?
   a. Lungs
   b. Heart
   c. Blood vessels
   d. All of the above are part of the cardiovascular system

2. What does AHA stand for?
   a. Association for Heart Attacks
   b. American Heart Association
   c. American Health Association
   d. Association of Health Administrators

3. Which of the following is not a type of cardiovascular disease?
   a. Stroke
   b. Hypertension
   c. Rheumatic heart disease
   d. Emphysema

B. Open-Ended Questions

1. What makes up the cardiovascular system?
2. What does AHA stand for?
3. Name four types of cardiovascular diseases.

C. Free Recall

Level 3

The cardiovascular system is made up of the heart and blood vessels. Cardiovascular diseases, as defined by the American Heart Association (AHA), include coronary heart disease, stroke, high blood pressure and rheumatic heart disease. Approximately 58,800,000 Americans have one or more forms of cardiovascular disease. Each year, cardiovascular diseases top the list of the country's most serious health problems. Coronary heart disease is the number one killer and stroke is the number three killer.

Level 3 Questions

A. Multiple-Choice Questions

1. Which of the following does not make up a part of the cardiovascular system?
   a. Lungs
   b. Heart
   c. Blood vessels
   d. All of the above are part of the cardiovascular system
2. What does AHA stand for?
   a. Association for Heart Attacks
   b. American Heart Association
   c. American Health Association
   d. Association of Health Administrators
3. Which of the following is not a type of cardiovascular disease?
   a. Stroke
   b. Hypertension
   c. Rheumatic heart disease
   d. Emphysema
4. Approximately how many Americans have cardiovascular disease?
   a. 280 thousand
   b. 12 million
   c. 58 million
   d. 360 million

5. What is the nation's number one killer?
   a. Stroke
   b. Coronary heart disease
   c. Rheumatic heart disease
   d. Cancer

6. What is the nation's number three killer?
   a. Lung cancer
   b. Heart attack
   c. Stroke
   d. Pneumonia

B. Open-Ended Questions

1. What makes up the cardiovascular system?
2. What does AHA stand for?
3. Name four types of cardiovascular diseases.
4. How many Americans have cardiovascular disease?
5. What is the nation's number one killer?
6. What is the nation's number three killer?

C. Free Recall

Level 4

The cardiovascular system is made up of the heart and blood vessels. Cardiovascular diseases, as defined by the American Heart Association (AHA), include coronary heart disease, stroke, high blood pressure and rheumatic heart disease. Approximately 58,800,000 Americans have one or more forms of cardiovascular disease. Each year, cardiovascular diseases top the list of the country's most serious health problems. Coronary heart disease is the number one killer and stroke is the number three killer. Stroke also is the number one cause of serious, long-term disability. Yet, studies show that nearly everyone can become "heart healthy" by following a proper diet, following an appropriate exercise program, following a routine health care plan and eliminating tobacco products.

Level 4 Questions

A. Multiple-Choice Questions

1. Which of the following does not make up a part of the cardiovascular system?
   a. Lungs
   b. Heart
   c. Blood vessels
   d. All of the above are part of the cardiovascular system

2. What does AHA stand for?
   a. Association for Heart Attacks
   b. American Heart Association
   c. American Health Association
   d. Association of Health Administrators

3. Which of the following is not a type of cardiovascular disease?
   a. Stroke
   b. Hypertension
   c. Rheumatic heart disease
   d. Emphysema
4. Approximately how many Americans have cardiovascular disease?
   a. 280 thousand
   b. 12 million
   c. 58 million
   d. 360 million
5. What is the nation's #1 killer?
   a. Stroke
   b. Coronary heart disease
   c. Rheumatic heart disease
   d. Cancer
6. What is the nation's #3 killer?
   a. Lung cancer
   b. Heart attack
   c. Stroke
   d. Pneumonia
7. What is the #1 cause of serious, long-term disability?
   a. Kidney disease
   b. Stroke
   c. Alzheimer's disease
   d. Hypertension
8. Which of the following statements is true?
   a. It is impossible to lower your risk of cardiovascular disease
   b. There is no such thing as being "heart healthy"
   c. Nearly everyone can become "heart healthy"
   d. None of the above
9. Individuals can become "heart healthy" by which of the following:
   a. Proper diet
   b. Regular exercise
   c. Eliminating tobacco
   d. All of the above
10. Which of the following is not a factor in cardiovascular disease?
   a. Smoking
   b. Following a routine health care plan
   c. Drinking plenty of fluids daily
   d. There are no risk factors for cardiovascular disease

B. Open-Ended Questions

1. What makes up the cardiovascular system?
2. What does AHA stand for?
3. Name four types of cardiovascular diseases.
4. How many Americans have cardiovascular disease?
5. What is the nation's number one killer?
6. What is the nation's number three killer?
7. What is the number one cause of serious, long-term disability?
8. Is it possible to lower one's risk of cardiovascular disease?
9. Is a proper diet a factor in preventing cardiovascular disease?
10. Name four ways in which individuals can become "heart healthy."

C. Free Recall

Topic 7
Digestive Disorders

Level 1

Each year 62 million Americans are diagnosed with digestive disorders.

Level 1 Questions

A. Multiple-Choice Questions

1. What topic is this sentence about?
   a. Disabilities
   b. Diabetes
   c. Digestive disorders
   d. Gallbladder disease

2. How many Americans are diagnosed with digestive disorders each year?
   a. 37 million
   b. 55 million
   c. 12 million
   d. 62 million

B. Open-Ended Questions

1. What topic is this sentence about?
2. How many Americans are diagnosed with digestive disorders each year?

C. Free Recall

Level 2

Each year 62 million Americans are diagnosed with digestive disorders, ranging from occasional upset stomach to the more life-threatening colon cancer.

Level 2 Questions

A. Multiple-Choice Questions

1. What topic is this sentence about?
   a. Disabilities
   b. Diabetes
   c. Digestive disorders
   d. Gallbladder disease

2. How many Americans are diagnosed with digestive disorders each year?
   a. 37 million
   b. 55 million
   c. 12 million
   d. 62 million

3. Digestive disorders may include:
   a. Upset stomach
   b. Hiccups
   c. Colon cancer
   d. Both a and c above

B. Open-Ended Questions

1. What topic is this passage about?
2. How many Americans are diagnosed with digestive disorders each year?
3. What range of digestive disorders was mentioned in this passage?

C. Free Recall

Level 3

Each year 62 million Americans are diagnosed with digestive disorders, ranging from occasional upset stomach to the more life-threatening colon cancer. They encompass disorders of the gastrointestinal tract as well as the liver, gallbladder and pancreas. They may be inherited or caused by multiple factors.

Level 3 Questions

A. Multiple-Choice Questions

1. What is this passage about?
   a. Disabilities
   b. Diabetes
   c. Digestive disorders
   d. Gallbladder disease
2. How many Americans are diagnosed with digestive disorders each year?
   a. 37 million
   b. 55 million
   c. 12 million
   d. 62 million
3. Digestive disorders may include:
   a. Upset stomach
   b. Hiccups
   c. Colon cancer
   d. Both a and c above
4. Digestive disorders encompass disorders of the:
   a. Liver
   b. Gallbladder
   c. Heart
   d. Both a and b
5. Digestive disorders are:
   a. Inherited
   b. Due to multiple factors
   c. Neither a nor b
   d. Both a and b
6. What disorders were labeled as "occasional" and "life-threatening" in this passage?
   a. Lung disease and pancreatic disease
   b. Upset stomach and headache
   c. Liver disease and colon cancer
   d. Upset stomach and colon cancer

B. Open-Ended Questions

1. What topic is this passage about?
2. How many Americans are diagnosed with digestive disorders each year?
3. What range of digestive disorders was mentioned in this passage?
4. What types of disorders are included in digestive system disorders?
5. What are the causes of digestive disorders?
6. What disorders were labeled as "occasional" and "life-threatening" in this piece?

C. Free Recall

Level 4

Each year 62 million Americans are diagnosed with digestive disorders, ranging from occasional upset stomach to the more life-threatening colon cancer. They encompass disorders of the gastrointestinal tract as well as the liver, gallbladder and pancreas. They may be inherited or caused by multiple factors such as stress, diet, smoking and abusing alcohol, which imposes the greatest risk. Reaching a diagnosis requires both a thorough medical history and physical examination.

Level 4 Questions

A. Multiple-Choice Questions

1. What topic is this passage about?
   a. Disabilities
   b. Diabetes
   c. Digestive disorders
   d. Gallbladder disease
2. How many Americans are diagnosed with digestive disorders each year?
   a. 37 million
   b. 55 million
   c. 12 million
   d. 62 million
3. Digestive disorders may include:
   a. Upset stomach
   b. Hiccups
   c. Colon cancer
   d. Both a and c
4. Digestive disorders encompass disorders of:
   a. Liver
   b. Gallbladder
   c. Heart
   d. Both a and b
5. What type of cancer was mentioned in this passage?
   a. Bone
   b. Brain
   c. Colon
   d. Breast
6. Digestive disorders are:
   a. Inherited
   b. Due to multiple factors
   c. Neither a nor b
   d. Both a and b

7. What disorders were labeled as "occasional" and "life-threatening" in this passage?
   a. Lung disease and pancreatic disease
   b. Upset stomach and headache
   c. Liver disease and colon cancer
   d. Upset stomach and colon cancer
8. Factors mentioned in the passage that may lead to digestive disorders may include:
   a. Smoking
   b. Heartburn
   c. Hiccupping
   d. Poor dental hygiene
9. Which of the following imposes the greatest risk for digestive disease?
   a. Fatigue
   b. Smoking
   c. Diet
   d. Alcohol
10. Obtaining a diagnosis involves:
   a. A thorough medical history
   b. A physical examination
   c. A special test
   d. Both a and b

B. Open-Ended Questions

1. What topic is this passage about?
2. How many Americans are diagnosed with digestive disorders each year?
3. What two primary factors lead to digestive disorders?
4. What is the greatest risk factor for digestive disease?
5. What disorder was labeled as "occasional" in this passage?
6. What disorder was labeled as "life-threatening" in this passage?
7. What type of cancer was mentioned in this passage?
8. How do you diagnose digestive disorders?
9. Name three types of digestive disorders mentioned.
10. What factors other than heredity may cause digestive disorders?

C. Free Recall

Topic 8
Physical Medicine and Rehabilitation

Level 1

Physical Medicine and Rehabilitation, also known as physiatry, involves the process of restoring lost abilities.

Level 1 Questions

A. Multiple-Choice Questions

1. Physical Medicine and Rehabilitation is also known as:
   a. Physical therapy
   b. Physiology
   c. Physiatry
   d. Psychiatry

2. Physiatry involves:
   a. Studying mental illness
   b. Restoring lost abilities
   c. Preventing disease
   d. Studying the heart and blood vessels

B. Open-Ended Questions

1. Physical Medicine and Rehabilitation is also known as what?
2. What is the function of physiatry?

C. Free Recall

Level 2

Physical Medicine and Rehabilitation, also known as physiatry, is a medical specialty that involves the process of restoring lost abilities. The musculoskeletal, pulmonary and central nervous systems are most often involved.

Level 2 Questions

A. Multiple-Choice Questions

1. Physical Medicine and Rehabilitation is also known as:
   a. Physical therapy
   b. Physiology
   c. Physiatry
   d. Psychiatry

2. Physiatry involves:
   a. Studying mental illness
   b. Restoring lost abilities
   c. Preventing disease
   d. Studying the heart and blood vessels

3. Which of the following systems are most often involved in physiatry?
   a. Central nervous system
   b. Pulmonary system
   c. Musculoskeletal system
   d. All of the above

B. Open-Ended Questions

1. Physical Medicine and Rehabilitation is also known as what?
2. What is the function of physiatry?
3. What systems are most often involved in physiatry?

C. Free Recall

Level 3

Physical Medicine and Rehabilitation (PM&R), also known as physiatry, is a medical specialty that involves the process of restoring lost abilities. The musculoskeletal, pulmonary and central nervous systems are most often involved. Using a multidisciplinary approach, PM&R covers everything from cardiac rehabilitation to pain management, recovering from a stroke to restoring cognitive function lost with Alzheimer's disease.

Level 3 Questions

A. Multiple-Choice Questions

1. Physical Medicine and Rehabilitation is also known as:
   a. Physical therapy
   b. Physiology
   c. Physiatry
   d. Psychiatry
2. Physiatry involves:
   a. Studying mental illness
   b. Restoring lost abilities
   c. Preventing disease
   d. Studying the heart and blood vessels
3. Which of the following systems are most often involved in physiatry?
   a. Central nervous system
   b. Pulmonary system
   c. Musculoskeletal system
   d. All of the above
4. What type of approach does PM&R utilize?
   a. Dogmatic
   b. Multisensory
   c. Multidisciplinary
   d. Transgenerational

5. Which of the following is not a common target of physiatry?
   a. Recovery from stroke
   b. Pain management
   c. Gastrointestinal disorders
   d. Cardiac rehabilitation

6. What type of function does PM&R restore in Alzheimer's disease?
   a. Motor
   b. Cognitive
   c. Emotional
   d. None of the above

B. Open-Ended Questions

1. Physical Medicine and Rehabilitation is also known as what?
2. What is the function of physiatry?
3. What systems are most often involved in physiatry?
4. What type of approach does PM&R utilize?
5. Name three areas that PM&R covers.
6. What type of function does PM&R restore in Alzheimer's disease?

C. Free Recall

Level 4

Physical Medicine and Rehabilitation (PM&R), also known as physiatry, is a medical specialty that involves the process of restoring lost abilities. The musculoskeletal, pulmonary and central nervous systems are most often involved. Using a multidisciplinary approach, PM&R covers everything from cardiac rehabilitation to pain management, recovering from a stroke to restoring cognitive function lost with Alzheimer's disease. PM&R can be used to retrain a person on the basics of daily living or may be used to help an elderly person recover from a fall. Regardless of what caused the disability, rehabilitation specialists work to restore maximum function and quality of life for the patient at home, in the workplace and in the community.

Level 4 Questions

A. Multiple-Choice Questions

1. Physical Medicine and Rehabilitation is also known as:
   a. Physical therapy
   b. Physiology
   c. Physiatry
   d. Psychiatry

2. Physiatry involves:
   a. Studying mental illness
   b. Restoring lost abilities
   c. Preventing disease
   d. Studying the heart and blood vessels

3. Which of the following systems are most often involved in physiatry?
   a. Central nervous system
   b. Pulmonary system
   c. Musculoskeletal system
   d. All of the above

4. What type of approach does PM&R utilize?
   a. Dogmatic
   b. Multisensory
   c. Multidisciplinary
   d. Transgenerational

5. Which of the following is not a common target of physiatry?
   a. Recovery from stroke
   b. Pain management
   c. Gastrointestinal disorders
   d. Cardiac rehabilitation

6. What type of function does PM&R restore in Alzheimer's disease?
   a. Motor
   b. Cognitive
   c. Emotional
   d. None of the above

7. PM&R can be used to:
   a. Retrain daily living skills
   b. Help recover from a fall
   c. Restore cognitive function
   d. All of the above

8. Depending on the cause of the disability:
   a. PM&R may not be appropriate
   b. PM&R can be helpful regardless of the cause of the disability
   c. Neither a nor b
   d. Both a and b

9. Rehabilitation specialists work to restore which of the following?
   a. Quality of life
   b. Maximum functioning
   c. Both a and b
   d. Neither a nor b

10. Each of the following settings is a target for physiatry except:
   a. Home
   b. Internal organs
   c. Community
   d. Workplace

B. Open-Ended Questions

1. Physical Medicine and Rehabilitation is also known as what?
2. What is the function of physiatry?
3. What systems are most often involved in physiatry?
4. What type of approach does PM&R utilize?
5. Name three areas that PM&R covers.
6. What type of function does PM&R restore in Alzheimer's disease?
7. What can PM&R be used for?
8. What do rehabilitation specialists work to restore?
9. In what settings do rehabilitation specialists focus on restoring function?
10. Does the cause of the disability determine whether or not rehabilitation specialists can help?

C. Free Recall

Auditory Recall Stories – Sports

Story 1
Baseball Clubs

Level 1

The oldest professional baseball club in North America is the Atlanta Braves.

Level 1 Questions

A. Multiple-Choice Questions

1. What baseball team is mentioned?
   a. New York Mets
   b. Oakland A's
   c. Atlanta Braves
   d. Chicago Cubs

2. What continent is mentioned?
   a. South America
   b. North America
   c. Europe
   d. Africa

B. Open-Ended Questions

1. What baseball team is mentioned?
2. What continent is mentioned?

C. Free Recall

Level 2

The oldest continuously operated professional baseball club in North America is the Atlanta Braves. When they first started in 1870, they were named the Boston Red Stockings.

Level 2 Questions

A. Multiple-Choice Questions

1. What baseball team is mentioned?
   a. New York Mets
   b. Oakland A's
   c. Atlanta Braves
   d. Chicago Cubs

2. What continent is mentioned?
   a. South America
   b. North America
   c. Europe
   d. Africa

3. What was the baseball team first called in 1870?
   a. Boston Red Sox
   b. Boston Red Coats
   c. Boston Red Shoes
   d. Boston Red Stockings

B. Open-Ended Questions

1. What baseball team is mentioned?
2. What continent is mentioned?
3. What was the baseball team first called in 1870?

C. Free Recall

Level 3

The oldest continuously operated professional baseball club in North America is the Atlanta Braves. When they first started in 1870, they were named the Boston Red Stockings. However, the oldest baseball club still in the same city, since 1874, is the Chicago Cubs.

Level 3 Questions

A. Multiple-Choice Questions

1. What is the name of the first baseball team mentioned?
   a. New York Mets
   b. Oakland A's
   c. Atlanta Braves
   d. Chicago Cubs
2. What continent is mentioned?
   a. South America
   b. North America
   c. Europe
   d. Africa
3. In what year was the baseball club started?
   a. 1870
   b. 1970
   c. 1770
   d. 1877
4. What where they first called?
   a. Boston Red Sox
   b. Boston Red Coats
   c. Boston Red Shoes
   d. Boston Red Stockings
5. What is the name of the oldest continuously operating baseball club that is still in the same city?
   a. New York Mets
   b. Oakland A's
   c. Atlanta Braves
   d. Chicago Cubs
6. In what year did that club begin?
   a. 1874
   b. 1870
   c. 1970
   d. 1876

B. Open-Ended Questions

1. What is the name of the first baseball team mentioned?
2. What continent is mentioned?
3. In what year was the oldest continuously operating baseball club started?
4. What was the oldest continuously operating baseball club first called?
5. What is the name of the oldest continuously operating baseball club that is still in the same city?
6. In what year did that club begin?

C. Free Recall

Level 4

The oldest continuously operated professional baseball club in North America is the Atlanta Braves. When they first started in 1870, they were named the Boston Red Stockings. However, the oldest baseball club that is still in the same city, since 1874, is the Chicago Cubs. They were first established in 1870 as the Chicago White Stockings and then took a two-year hiatus in 1872 and 1873.

Level 4 Questions

A. Multiple-Choice Questions

1. What is the name of the first baseball team mentioned?
   a. New York Mets
   b. Oakland A's
   c. Atlanta Braves
   d. Chicago Cubs
2. What continent is mentioned?
   a. South America
   b. North America
   c. Europe
   d. Africa
3. In what year was the baseball club started?
   a. 1870
   b. 1970
   c. 1770
   d. 1877
4. What were they first called?
   a. Boston Red Sox
   b. Boston Red Coats
   c. Boston Red Shoes
   d. Boston Red Stockings
5. What is the name of the oldest continuously operating baseball club that is still in the same city?
   a. New York Mets
   b. Oakland A's
   c. Atlanta Braves
   d. Chicago Cubs
6. In what year did that club begin?
   a. 1874
   b. 1870
   c. 1970
   d. 1876

7. What was the first name of the oldest continuously operating baseball club that is still in the same city?
   a. Chicago White Stockings
   b. Boston Red Stockings
   c. Chicago Red Stockings
   d. White Stockings

8. For how long did they take a hiatus?
   a. One year
   b. Two years
   c. Three years
   d. Four years

9. In what year did the hiatus begin?
   a. 1874
   b. 1872
   c. 1873
   d. 1875

10. In what year did the club resume operation?
    a. 1874
    b. 1872
    c. 1873
    d. 1875

B. Open-Ended Questions

1. What is the name of the first baseball team mentioned?
2. What continent is mentioned?
3. In what year was the oldest continuously operating baseball club started?
4. What was the oldest continuously operating baseball club first called?
5. What is the name of the oldest continuously operating baseball club that is still in the same city?
6. In what year did that club begin?
7. What was the first name of the oldest continuously operating baseball club that is still in the same city?
8. For how long did they take a hiatus?
9. In what year did the hiatus begin?
10. In what year did the club resume operation?

C. Free Recall

Story 2
Baseball Rules

Level 1

According to Major League Baseball rules, the minimal distance from home plate to the nearest fence is 325 feet.

Level 1 Questions

A. Multiple-Choice Questions

1. What sport is mentioned?
   a. Baseball
   b. Basketball
   c. Soccer
   d. Golf

2. How many feet away can a fence be?
   a. 355 ft.
   b. 375 ft.
   c. 325 ft.
   d. 315 ft.

B. Open-Ended Questions

1. What sport is mentioned?
2. How many feet away can a fence be?

C. Free Recall

Level 2

According to Major League Baseball rule 1.04a, as of June 1, 1958, the minimal distance from home plate to the nearest fence is 325 feet.

Level 2 Questions

A. Multiple-Choice Questions

1. What sport is mentioned?
   a. Baseball
   b. Basketball
   c. Soccer
   d. Golf

2. How many feet away can a fence be?
   a. 355 ft.
   b. 375 ft.
   c. 325 ft.
   d. 315 ft.

3. What rule number is mentioned?
   a. 1.03a
   b. 1.02a
   c. 1.04b
   d. 1.04a

B. Open-Ended Questions

1. What sport is mentioned?
2. How many feet away can a fence be?
3. What rule number is mentioned?

C. Free Recall

Level 3

According to Major League Baseball rule 1.04a, as of June 1, 1958, the minimal distance from home plate to the nearest fence, stand or other obstruction on the right and left field foul lines is 325 feet.

Level 3 Questions

A. Multiple-Choice Questions

1. What sport is mentioned?
   a. Baseball
   b. Basketball
   c. Soccer
   d. Golf
2. How many feet away can a fence be?
   a. 355 ft.
   b. 375 ft.
   c. 325 ft.
   d. 315 ft.
3. What rule number is mentioned?
   a. 1.03a
   b. 1.02a
   c. 1.04b
   e. 1.04a
4. What is the date of that rule?
   a. June 1, 1968
   b. June 1, 1958
   c. June 1, 1948
   d. June 1, 1978
5. Exactly what term was used to describe this distance?
   a. absolute distance
   b. maximum distance
   c. minimal distance
   d. measurable distance
6. What physical perimeters were defined in the paragraph?
   a. center field
   b. short stop
   c. behind home plate
   d. right and left field foul lines

B. Open-Ended Questions

1. What sport is mentioned?
2. How many feet away can a fence be?
3. What rule number is mentioned?
4. What is the date of that rule?
5. What exact term was used to describe the distance in rule 1.04a?
6. What physical perimeters were defined in the paragraph?

C. Free Recall

Level 4

According to Major League Baseball rule 1.04a, as of June 1, 1958, the minimal distance from home plate to the nearest fence, stand or other obstruction on the right and left field foul lines is 325 feet. However, Enron Field in Houston and Pac Bell Park in San Francisco were constructed in 1999 and did not follow this rule. They both have fences only 315 feet from home plate—10 feet closer than the rule allows.

Level 4 Questions

A. Multiple-Choice Questions

1. What sport is mentioned?
   a. Baseball
   b. Basketball
   c. Soccer
   d. Golf
2. How many feet away can a fence be?
   a. 355 ft.
   b. 375 ft.
   c. 325 ft.
   d. 315 ft.
3. What rule number is mentioned?
   a. 1.03a
   b. 1.02a
   c. 1.04b
   d. 1.04a
4. What is the date of the rule?
   a. June 1, 1968
   b. June 1, 1958
   c. June 1, 1948
   d. June 1, 1978
5. What are the names of the parks mentioned?
   a. Candlestick Park and Shea Stadium
   b. Fenway Park and Camden Yards
   c. Enron Field and Pac Bell Park
   d. Wrigley Field and Ebbets Field
6. In what year were the named parks constructed?
   a. 1999
   b. 1989
   c. 1979
   d. 1969
7. What two cities were named?
   a. Los Angeles and Dallas
   b. New York and Boston
   c. Chicago and Baltimore
   d. Houston and San Francisco
8. In the parks that did not follow the rule, how far are the fences from home plate?
   a. 325 ft.
   b. 315 ft.
   c. 305 ft.
   d. 320 ft.
9. According to the rules, can a stand be placed 305 feet away from home plate?
   a. Yes
   b. No
   c. Maybe
   d. I don't remember
10. By how many feet did the two parks violate the rule?
    a. 25 ft.
    b. 10 ft.
    c. 15 ft.
    d. 5 ft.

B. Open-Ended Questions

1. What sport is mentioned?
2. How many feet away can a fence be?
3. What rule number is mentioned?
4. What is the date of that rule?
5. What are the names of the parks mentioned?
6. In what year were the parks constructed?
7. What two cities were named?
8. In the parks that did not follow the rule, how far are the fences from home plate?
9. According to the rules, can a stand be placed 305 feet from home plate?
10. By how many feet did the two parks violate the rule?

C. Free Recall

Story 3
Women's National Basketball Association

Level 1

The NBA Board of Governors approved the Women's National Basketball Association to begin playing in June of 1997.

Level 1 Questions

A. Multiple-Choice Questions

1. What did the NBA Board of Governors approve?
   a. Women's National Basketball Association
   b. Women's National Baseball Association
   c. Women's National Baking Association
   d. Women's National Bowling Association

2. What month is mentioned in the story?
   a. August
   b. July
   c. January
   d. June

B. Open-Ended Questions

1. What did the NBA Board of Governors approve?
2. What month is mentioned in the story?

C. Free Recall

Level 2

On April 24, 1996, the NBA Board of Governors approved the Women's National Basketball Association to begin playing in June of 1997 as women's basketball announced "We Got Next."

Level 2 Questions

A. Multiple-Choice Questions

1. What did the NBA Board of Governors approve?
   a. Women's National Basketball Association
   b. Women's National Baseball Association
   c. Women's National Baking Association
   d. Women's National Bowling Association

2. In what month did the approval occur?
   a. August
   b. July
   c. April
   d. June

3. What slogan is quoted in the story?
   a. "We Got Game"
   b. "We Got It"
   c. "We Got Next"
   d. "We Got a Winner"

B. Open-Ended Questions

1. What did the NBA Board of Governors approve?
2. In what month did the approval occur?
3. What slogan is quoted in the story?

C. Free Recall

Level 3

On April 24, 1996, the NBA Board of Governors approved the Women's National Basketball Association to begin playing in June of 1997 as women's basketball announced "We Got Next." Eight teams were announced for the first season. On October 23, 1996, the first players signed on to join the league. They were Rebecca Lobo and Sheryl Swoops.

Level 3 Questions

A. Multiple-Choice Questions

1. What did the NBA Board of Governors approve?
   a. Women's National Basketball Association
   b. Women's National Baseball Association
   c. Women's National Baking Association
   d. Women's National Bowling Association
2. In what month did the approval occur?
   a. August
   b. July
   c. April
   d. June
3. On what date did the NBA give its approval?
   a. April 6, 1996
   b. April 14, 1996
   c. April 24, 1996
   d. April 24, 1997
4. What slogan is quoted in the story?
   a. "We Got Game"
   b. "We Got It"
   c. "We Got Next"
   d. "We Got a Winner"
5. How many teams played the first season?
   a. 8
   b. 10
   c. 18
   d. 5

6. What were the names of the first players to join the league?
   a. Rebecca Swoops and Sheryl Lobo
   b. Rebecca Lane and Sheryl Smith
   c. Rebecca Lobo and Sheryl Swoops
   d. Rebecca Locust and Sheryl Swift

B. Open-Ended Questions

1. What did the NBA Board of Governors approve?
2. In what month did the approval occur?
3. On what date did the NBA give its approval?
4. What slogan is quoted in the story?
5. How many teams played in the first season?
6. What were the names of the first players to join the league?

C. Free Recall

Level 4

On April 24, 1996, the NBA Board of Governors approved the Women's National Basketball Association to begin playing in June of 1997 as women's basketball announced "We Got Next." Eight teams were announced for the first season. On October 23, 1996, the first players signed on to join the league. They were Rebecca Lobo and Sheryl Swoops. Since then, eight more teams have joined the league. The 2000 season saw 176 players play 256 regular season games.

Level 4 Questions

A. Multiple-Choice Questions

1. What did the NBA Board of Governors approve?
   a. Women's National Basketball Association
   b. Women's National Baseball Association
   c. Women's National Baking Association
   d. Women's National Bowling Association

2. In what month did the approval occur?
   a. August
   b. July
   c. April
   d. June

3. On what date did the NBA give its approval?
   a. April 6, 1996
   b. April 14, 1996
   c. April 24, 1996
   d. April 24, 1997

4. What slogan is quoted in the story?
   a. "We Got Game"
   b. "We Got It"
   c. "We Got Next"
   d. "We Got a Winner"

5. How many teams played the first season?
   a. 8
   b. 10
   c. 18
   d. 5

6. What were the names of the first players to join the league?
   a. Rebecca Swoops and Sheryl Lobo
   b. Rebecca Lane and Sheryl Smith
   c. Rebecca Lobo and Sheryl Swoops
   d. Rebecca Locust and Sheryl Swift

7. How many teams now are in the league?
   a. 8
   b. 16
   c. 24
   d. 32

8. How many season games were played in the 2000 season?
   a. 265
   b. 252
   c. 256
   d. 245

9. In what month did the first players join the league?
   a. April
   b. June
   c. October
   d. August

10. How many players were there in the 2000 season?
    a. 175
    b. 176
    c. 174
    d. 177

B. Open-Ended Questions

1. What did the NBA Board of Governors approve?
2. In what month did the approval occur?
3. On what date did the NBA give its approval?
4. What slogan is quoted in the story?
5. How many teams played in the first season?
6. What were the names of the first players to join the league?
7. How many teams now are in the league?
8. How many season games were played in the 2000 season?
9. In what month did the first players join the league?
10. How many players were there in the 2000 season?

C. Free Recall

Story 4
Basketball

Level 1

The man who created basketball was Dr. James Naismeth of Springfield, Massachusetts.

Level 1 Questions

A. Multiple-Choice Questions

1. What was the man's name who created basketball?
   a. Dr. James Slantz
   b. Dr. James Naismeth
   c. Dr. James Ferro
   d. Dr. James Whalen

2. Where was he from?
   a. Springfield, NJ
   b. Springfield, CA
   c. Springfield, TX
   d. Springfield, MA

B. Open-Ended Questions

1. What was the man's name who created basketball?
2. Where was he from?

C. Free Recall

Level 2

The man who created basketball was Dr. James Naismeth of Springfield, Massachusetts. He began in a YMCA gymnasium with 18 men. It is now a game that is played by more than 300 million people worldwide.

Level 2 Questions

A. Multiple-Choice Questions

1. What was the man's name who created basketball?
   a. Dr. James Slantz
   b. Dr. James Naismeth
   c. Dr. James Ferro
   d. Dr. James Whalen

2. Where was he from?
   a. Springfield, NJ
   b. Springfield, CA
   c. Springfield, TX
   d. Springfield, MA

3. Where was the first game of basketball played?
   a. In a YMCA gymnasium
   b. In a school gymnasium
   c. In a park
   d. In a basement

B. Open-Ended Questions

1. What was the man's name who created basketball?
2. Where was he from?
3. Where was the first game of basketball played?

C. Free Recall

Level 3

The man who created basketball was Dr. James Naismeth of Springfield, Massachusetts. He began in a YMCA gymnasium with 18 men. It is now a game that is played by more than 300 million people worldwide. Dr. Luther Gulick asked Naismeth to create an indoor game that could help serve as an "athletic distraction" during the brutal New England winter.

Level 3 Questions

A. Multiple-Choice Questions

1. What was the man's name who created basketball?
   a. Dr. James Slantz
   b. Dr. James Naismeth
   c. Dr. James Ferro
   d. Dr. James Whalen
2. Where was he from?
   a. Springfield, NJ
   b. Springfield, CA
   c. Springfield, TX
   d. Springfield, MA
3. Where was the first game of basketball played?
   a. In a YMCA gymnasium
   b. In a school gymnasium
   c. In a park
   d. In a basement
4. How many people play basketball now?
   a. More than 100 million
   b. More than 200 million
   c. More than 300 million
   d. More than 400 million
5. Who asked the inventor to create a new game?
   a. Dr. Luther Gulick
   b. Dr. Luther Gibson
   c. Dr. Luther Glen
   d. Dr. Luther Glove
6. How many men played originally?
   a. 18
   b. 19
   c. 16
   d. 17

B. Open-Ended Questions

1. What was the man's name who created basketball?
2. Where was he from?
3. Where was the first game of basketball played?
4. How many people play basketball now?

5. Who asked the inventor to create a new game?
6. How many men played originally?

C. Free Recall

Level 4

The man who created basketball was Dr. James Naismeth of Springfield, Massachusetts. He began in a YMCA gymnasium with 18 men. It is now a game that is played by more than 300 million people worldwide. Dr. Luther Gulick asked Naismeth to create an indoor game that could help serve as an "athletic distraction" during the brutal New England winter. Dr. Naismeth was given only 14 days to complete this task. In that short amount of time, he developed the original 13 rules and the game of basketball. His biggest thrill came in 1936 when basketball became an Olympic sport.

Level 4 Questions

A. Multiple-Choice Questions

1. What was the man's name who created basketball?
   a. Dr. James Slantz
   b. Dr. James Naismeth
   c. Dr. James Ferro
   d. Dr. James Whalen
2. Where was he from?
   a. Springfield, NJ
   b. Springfield, CA
   c. Springfield, TX
   d. Springfield, MA
3. Where was the first game of basketball played?
   a. In a YMCA gymnasium
   b. In a school gymnasium
   c. In a park
   d. In a basement
4. How many people play basketball now?
   a. More than 100 million
   b. More than 200 million
   c. More than 300 million
   d. More than 400 million
5. Who asked the inventor to create a new game?
   a. Dr. Luther Gulick
   b. Dr. Luther Gibson
   c. Dr. Luther Glen
   d. Dr. Luther Glove
6. How long did he have to create this new game?
   a. 14 hours
   b. 14 days
   c. 14 months
   d. 14 weeks
7. How many original rules did he develop?
   a. 14
   b. 13
   c. 12
   d. 15
8. In what year did basketball become an Olympic sport?
   a. 1963
   b. 1935
   c. 1936
   d. 1953

9. How many men originally played the sport?
   a. 18
   b. 19
   c. 16
   d. 17

10. What region was mentioned?
    a. New London
    b. New Mexico
    c. New England
    d. New York

B. Open-Ended Questions

1. What was the man's name who created basketball?
2. Where was he from?
3. Where was the first game of basketball played?
4. How many people play basketball now?
5. Who asked the inventor to create a new game?
6. How long did he have to create this new game?
7. How many original rules did he develop?
8. In what year did basketball become an Olympic sport?
9. How many men originally played the sport?
10. What region was mentioned?

C. Free Recall

Story 5
Volleyball

Level 1

In 1895, William Morgan introduced the game of volleyball while he was teaching at a YMCA.

Level 1 Questions

A. Multiple-Choice Questions

1. In what year was volleyball introduced?
   a. 1895
   b. 1985
   c. 1785
   d. 1860

2. Who introduced this sport?
   a. William Miller
   b. William Morgan
   c. William Smith
   d. William Winter

B. Open-Ended Questions

1. In what year was volleyball introduced?
2. Who introduced this sport?

C. Free Recall

Level 2

In 1895, William Morgan introduced the game of volleyball while he was teaching at a YMCA in Holyoke, Massachusetts. He combined elements from three sports to create volleyball.

Level 2 Questions

A. Multiple-Choice Questions

1. In what year was volleyball introduced?
   a. 1895
   b. 1985
   c. 1785
   d. 1860

2. Who introduced this sport?
   a. William Miller
   b. William Morgan
   c. William Smith
   d. William Winter

3. From how many sports did he borrow elements to create volleyball?
   a. Four
   b. Three
   c. Six
   d. Seven

B. Open-Ended Questions

1. In what year was volleyball introduced?
2. Who introduced this sport?
3. From how many sports did he borrow elements to create volleyball?

C. Free Recall

Level 3

In 1895, William Morgan introduced the game of volleyball while he was teaching at a YMCA in Holyoke, Massachusetts. He combined elements from three sports to create volleyball. Morgan first called his new game "mintonette." However, following a demonstration of the game, it was suggested it be called "volleyball" because people were volleying the ball over the net. The first game of volleyball was played at Springfield College on July 7, 1896.

Level 3 Questions

A. Multiple-Choice Questions

1. In what year was volleyball introduced?
   a. 1895
   b. 1985
   c. 1785
   d. 1860
2. Who introduced this sport?
   a. William Miller
   b. William Morgan
   c. William Smith
   d. William Winter
3. From how many sports did he borrow elements to create volleyball?
   a. Four
   b. Three
   c. Six
   d. Seven
4. What was volleyball first called?
   a. Minutemen
   b. Mini-ball
   c. Mintonette
   d. Monster ball
5. On what date was the first game played?
   a. June 7, 1896
   b. July 6, 1896
   c. June 6, 1896
   d. July 7, 1896
6. Where was it played?
   a. Springfield College
   b. Smith College
   c. Molloy College
   d. Massachusetts College

B. Open-Ended Questions

1. In what year was volleyball introduced?
2. Who introduced this sport?
3. From how many sports did he borrow elements to create volleyball?

4. What was volleyball first called?
5. On what date was the first game played?
6. Where was it played?

C. Free Recall

Level 4

In 1895, William Morgan introduced the game of volleyball while he was teaching at a YMCA in Holyoke, Massachusetts. He combined elements from three sports to create a game for businessmen that required less physical contact than basketball. Morgan first called his new game "mintonette." However, following a demonstration of the game, it was suggested it be called "volleyball" because people were volleying the ball over the net. The first game of volleyball was played at Springfield College on July 7, 1896. In 1916, the National Collegiate Athletic Association formulated rules for this new game.

Level 4 Questions

A. Multiple-Choice Questions

1. In what year was volleyball introduced?
   a. 1895
   b. 1985
   c. 1785
   d. 1860
2. Who introduced this sport?
   a. William Miller
   b. William Morgan
   c. William Smith
   d. William Winter
3. In what city did Mr. Morgan teach?
   a. Boston, MA
   b. Holy Cross, MA
   c. Cambridge, MA
   d. Holyoke, MA
4. From how many sports did he borrow elements to create volleyball?
   a. Four
   b. Three
   c. Six
   d. Seven
5. What was volleyball first called?
   a. Minutemen
   b. Mini-ball
   c. Mintonette
   d. Monster ball
6. On what date was the first game played?
   a. June 7, 1896
   b. July 6, 1896
   c. June 6, 1896
   d. July 7, 1896
7. Where was it played?
   a. Springfield College
   b. Smith College
   c. Molloy College
   d. Massachusetts College
8. For what type of player was this new game created?
   a. Business partners
   b. Businesswomen
   c. Businessmen
   d. Business investors

9. In what year were the rules written?
   a. 1917
   b. 1947
   c. 1895
   d. 1916

10. What organization formed rules for volleyball?
    a. American Medical Association
    b. National Basketball Association
    c. National Collegiate Athletic Association
    d. International Volleyball Federation

B. Open-Ended Questions

1. In what year was volleyball introduced?
2. Who introduced this sport?
3. In what city did Mr. Morgan teach?
4. From how many sports did he borrow elements to create volleyball?
5. What was volleyball first called?
6. On what date was the first game played?
7. Where was it played?
8. For what type of player was this new game created?
9. In what year were the rules written?
10. What organization formed the rules for volleyball?

C. Free Recall

Story 6
The First African-American Baseball Players

Level 1

Jackie Robinson was the first African-American to play major league baseball.

Level 1 Questions

A. Multiple-Choice Questions

1. What was the man's name?
   a. Jackie Robinson
   b. Babe Ruth
   c. Lou Gehrig
   d. Mickey Mantle

2. What sport did he play?
   a. Basketball
   b. Baseball
   c. Golf
   d. Bowling

B. Open-Ended Questions

1. What was the man's name?
2. What sport did he play?

C. Free Recall

Level 2

Jackie Robinson was the first African-American to play major league baseball. On opening day of the 1947 season, he was part of the lineup for the Brooklyn Dodgers.

Level 2 Questions

A. Multiple-Choice Questions

1. What was the man's name?
   a. Jackie Robinson
   b. Babe Ruth
   c. Lou Gehrig
   d. Mickey Mantle

2. What sport did he play?
   a. Basketball
   b. Baseball
   c. Golf
   d. Bowling

3. On what major league team did he play?
   a. Boston Red Sox
   b. Cleveland Indians
   c. Brooklyn Dodgers
   d. New York Yankees

B. Open-Ended Questions

1. What was the man's name?
2. What sport did he play?
3. On what major league team did he play?

C. Free Recall

Level 3

Jackie Robinson was the first African-American to play major league baseball. Brookyn Dodgers president, Branch Ricky, had chosen Robinson for his athletic ability. On opening day of the 1947 season, he was part of the lineup for the Brooklyn Dodgers. Later that year, another African-American, Larry Doby, played for the Cleveland Indians.

Level 3 Questions

A. Multiple-Choice Questions

1. What was the first man's name?
   a. Jackie Robinson
   b. Babe Ruth
   c. Lou Gehrig
   d. Mickey Mantle
2. What sport did he play?
   a. Basketball
   b. Baseball
   c. Golf
   d. Bowling
3. On what major league team did he play?
   a. Boston Red Sox
   b. Cleveland Indians
   c. Brooklyn Dodgers
   d. New York Yankees
4. Who was the president of the Dodgers?
   a. Branch Ricky
   b. Ricky Branch
   c. Ranch Branch
   d. Mickey Branch
5. What year did Robinson begin playing for the Dodgers?
   a. 1946
   b. 1947
   c. 1948
   d. 1949
6. On what major league team did Larry Doby play?
   a. Boston Red Sox
   b. Cleveland Indians
   c. Brooklyn Dodgers
   d. New York Yankees

B. Open-Ended Questions

1. What was the first man's name?
2. What sport did he play?
3. On what major league team did he play?
4. Who was the president of the Dodgers?

5. What year did Robinson begin playing for the Dodgers?
6. On what major league team did Larry Doby play?

C. Free Recall

Level 4

Jackie Robinson was the first African-American to play major league baseball. Brooklyn Dodgers president, Branch Ricky, had chosen Robinson for his athletic ability. On opening day of the 1947 season, Robinson was part of the lineup for the Brooklyn Dodgers. Later that year, another African-American, Larry Doby, played for the Cleveland Indians. The Boston Red Sox were the last major league team to integrate their players in 1959. In 1957, Jackie Robinson was traded to the Dodgers' rival team, the New York Giants. Instead of playing for his longtime rival, Robinson chose to retire.

Level 4 Questions

A. Multiple-Choice Questions

1. What was the first man's name?
   a. Jackie Robinson
   b. Babe Ruth
   c. Lou Gehrig
   d. Mickey Mantle
2. What sport did he play?
   a. Basketball
   b. Baseball
   c. Golf
   d. Bowling
3. On what major league team did the first African-American play?
   a. Boston Red Sox
   b. Cleveland Indians
   c. Brooklyn Dodgers
   d. New York Yankees
4. Who was president of the Dodgers?
   a. Branch Ricky
   b. Ricky Branch
   c. Ranch Branch
   d. Mickey Branch
5. What year did Robinson begin playing for the Dodgers?
   a. 1946
   b. 1947
   c. 1948
   d. 1949
6. On what major league team did Larry Doby play?
   a. Boston Red Sox
   b. Cleveland Indians
   c. Brooklyn Dodgers
   d. New York Yankees
7. In what year did the first African-American to play major league baseball retire?
   a. 1947
   b. 1957
   c. 1967
   d. 1977
8. To what team was the first African-American to play major league baseball traded?
   a. New York Mets
   b. New York Yankees
   c. New York Giants
   d. New York Jets

9. In what year was the first African-American to play on a major league team traded?
   a. 1947
   b. 1948
   c. 1959
   d. 1957

10. In what year was the last major league team integrated?
   a. 1947
   b. 1948
   c. 1959
   d. 1957

B. Open-Ended Questions

1. What was the first man's name?
2. What sport did he play?
3. On what major league team did he play?
4. Who was president of the Dodgers?
5. What year did Robinson begin playing for the Dodgers?
6. On what major league team did Larry Doby play?
7. In what year did the first African-American to play baseball retire?
8. To what team was the first African-American to play baseball traded?
9. In what year was the first African-American major league baseball player traded?
10. In what year was the last major league team integrated?

C. Free Recall

Story 7
Bobby Orr

Level 1

Bobby Orr signed a junior contract with the Boston Bruins at age 13.

Level 1 Questions

A. Multiple-Choice Questions

1. With what team did Orr sign?
   a. New York Rangers
   b. Boston Bruins
   c. Boston Celtics
   d. New Jersey Devils

2. How old was he when he signed on?
   a. 13
   b. 14
   c. 15
   d. 16

B. Open-Ended Questions

1. With what team did Orr sign?
2. How old was he when he signed on?

C. Free Recall

Level 2

Bobby Orr of Parry Sound, Canada, signed a junior contract with the Boston Bruins at age 13.

Level 2 Questions

A. Multiple-Choice Questions

1. With what team did Orr sign?
   a. New York Rangers
   b. Boston Bruins
   c. Boston Celtics
   d. New Jersey Devils

2. How old was he when he signed on?
   a. 13
   b. 14
   c. 15
   d. 16

3. Where is he from?
   a. Russia
   b. United States
   c. England
   d. Canada

B. Open-Ended Questions

1. With what team did Orr sign?
2. How old was he when he signed on?
3. Where is he from?

C. Free Recall

Level 3

Bobby Orr of Parry Sound, Canada, signed a junior contract with the Boston Bruins at age 13. He won the Rookie of the Year award during the 1966-1967 season. One year later, he won his first Norris Trophy as best defenseman in the league.

Level 3 Questions

A. Multiple-Choice Questions

1. With what team did Orr sign?
   a. New York Rangers
   b. Boston Bruins
   c. Boston Celtics
   d. New Jersey Devils
2. How old was he when he signed on?
   a. 13
   b. 14
   c. 15
   d. 16
3. Where is he from?
   a. Russia
   b. United States
   c. England
   d. Canada
4. In what season did he win the Rookie of the Year award?
   a. 1965-1966
   b. 1966-1967
   c. 1967-1968
   d. 1968-1969
5. In what year did he win the Norris Trophy?
   a. 1967
   b. 1968
   c. 1969
   d. 1970
6. What was the Norris Trophy for?
   a. Best overall player
   b. Most improved player
   c. Best defenseman in the league
   d. Best offensive player in the league

B. Open-Ended Questions

1. With what team did Orr sign?
2. How old was he when he signed on?
3. Where is he from?
4. In what season did he win the Rookie of the Year award?

5. In what year did he win the Norris Trophy?
6. What was the Norris Trophy for?

C. Free Recall

Level 4

Bobby Orr of Parry Sound, Canada, signed a junior contract with the Boston Bruins at age 13. He won the Rookie of the Year award during the 1966-1967 season. One year later, he won his first Norris Trophy for best defenseman in the league. In the 1969-1970 Stanley Cup playoffs, the Boston Bruins played against the St. Louis Blues. Thirty seconds into overtime of game four, Orr scored the game-winning goal.

Level 4 Questions

A. Multiple-Choice Questions

1. With what team did Orr sign?
   a. New York Rangers
   b. Boston Bruins
   c. Boston Celtics
   d. New Jersey Devils
2. How old was he when he signed on?
   a. 13
   b. 14
   c. 15
   d. 16
3. Where is he from?
   a. Russia
   b. United States
   c. England
   d. Canada
4. In what season did he win the Rookie of the Year award?
   a. 1965-1966
   b. 1966-1967
   c. 1967-1968
   d. 1968-1969
5. In what year did he win the Norris Trophy?
   a. 1967
   b. 1968
   c. 1969
   d. 1970
6. What was the Norris Trophy for?
   a. Best overall player
   b. Most improved player
   c. Best defenseman in the league
   d. Best offensive player in the league
7. What is the name of the cup mentioned in the story?
   a. St. Louis Cup
   b. Sigmund Cup
   c. Stanford Cup
   d. Stanley Cup
8. In the 1969-1970 Stanley Cup playoffs, what team did the Boston Bruins play against?
   a. St. Louis Cardinals
   b. St. Louis Blues
   c. St. Louis Reds
   d. St. Louis Blue Jays
9. How many seconds into overtime did Orr score?
   a. 10
   b. 20
   c. 30
   d. 40

10. Who won the 1969-1970 Stanley Cup playoffs?
    a. Bruins
    b. Blues
    c. Rangers
    d. Devils

B. Open-Ended Questions

1. With what team did Orr sign?
2. How old was he when he signed on?
3. Where is he from?
4. In what season did he win the Rookie of the Year award?
5. In what year did he win the Norris Trophy?
6. What was the Norris Trophy for?
7. What is the name of the cup mentioned in this story?
8. In the 1969-1970 Stanley Cup playoffs, what team did the Boston Bruins play against?
9. How many seconds into overtime did Orr score?
10. Who won the 1969-1970 Stanley Cup playoffs?

C. Free Recall

Story 8
Kareem Abdul Jabbar

Level 1

Kareem Abdul Jabbar retired from basketball in 1989.

Level 1 Questions

A. Multiple-Choice Questions

1. Who is mentioned in this sentence?
   a. Wilt Chamberlain
   b. Mohammed Ali
   c. Kareem Abdul Jabbar
   d. Michael Jordan

2. In what year did he retire?
   a. 1989
   b. 1979
   c. 1965
   d. 1973

B. Open-Ended Questions

1. Who is this sentence about?
2. In what year did he retire?

C. Free Recall

Level 2

Kareem Abdul Jabbar played for the Los Angeles Lakers from 1975 until 1989, when he announced his retirement. In 1969, he was the number one draft pick by the Milwaukee Bucks.

Level 2 Questions

A. Multiple-Choice Questions

1. Who is this passage about?
   a. Wilt Chamberlain
   b. Mohammed Ali
   c. Kareem Abdul Jabbar
   d. Michael Jordan

2. In what year did he retire?
   a. 1989
   b. 1979
   c. 1965
   d. 1973

3. What team first drafted him?
   a. Bucks
   b. Jazz
   c. Lakers
   d. Knicks

B. Open-Ended Questions

1. Who is this passage about?
2. In what year did he retire?
3. What team first drafted him?

C. Free Recall

Level 3

Kareem Abdul Jabbar played for the Los Angeles Lakers from 1975 until 1989, when he announced his retirement. In 1969, he was the number one draft pick by the Milwaukee Bucks. In his first year with the Bucks, he averaged 28.8 points a game. In his second season, he won his first NBA title.

Level 3 Questions

A. Multiple-Choice Questions

1. Who is this passage about?
   a. Wilt Chamberlain
   b. Mohammed Ali
   c. Kareem Abdul Jabbar
   d. Michael Jordan
2. What team was Jabbar playing with when he retired?
   a. Celtics
   b. Lakers
   c. Jazz
   d. Knicks
3. In what year did he retire?
   a. 1989
   b. 1979
   c. 1965
   d. 1973
4. What team first drafted him?
   a. Bucks
   b. Jazz
   c. Lakers
   d. Knicks
5. In his first year of playing, how many points did Jabbar average per game?
   a. 29.8
   b. 28.8
   c. 27.8
   d. 26.8
6. What event took place during his second season playing basketball?
   a. His team lost the NBA title
   b. His team won the NBA title
   c. His team traded him
   d. His team came in fifth

B. Open-Ended Questions

1. Who is this passage about?
2. What team was Jabbar playing with when he retired?
3. In what year did he retire?
4. What team first drafted him?

5. In his first year of playing, how many points did Jabbar average per game?
6. What event took place during his second season playing basketball?

C. Free Recall

Level 4

Kareem Abdul Jabbar played for the Los Angeles Lakers from 1975 until 1989, when he announced his retirement. In 1969, he was the number one draft pick by the Milwaukee Bucks. In his first year with the Bucks, he averaged 28.8 points a game. In his second season, he won his first NBA title. During 1971, he embraced the Islamic faith and changed his name from Lew Alcindor to Kareem Abdul Jabbar. When he retired, he had accumulated 38,887 career points.

Level 4 Questions

A. Multiple-Choice Questions

1. Who is this passage about?
   a. Wilt Chamberlain
   b. Mohammed Ali
   c. Kareem Abdul Jabbar
   d. Michael Jordan
2. What team was Jabbar playing with when he retired?
   a. Celtics
   b. Lakers
   c. Jazz
   d. Knicks
3. In what year did he retire?
   a. 1989
   b. 1979
   c. 1965
   d. 1973
4. What team first drafted him?
   a. Bucks
   b. Jazz
   c. Lakers
   d. Knicks
5. In his first year of playing, how many points did Jabbar average per game?
   a. 29.8
   b. 28.8
   c. 27.8
   d. 26.8
6. What event took place during his second season playing basketball?
   a. His team lost the NBA title
   b. His team won the NBA title
   c. His team traded him
   d. His team came in fifth
7. What was his birth name?
   a. Lew Alcindor
   b. Lou Alexander
   c. Louis Adams
   d. Lou Andretti
8. What religion prompted him to change his name?
   a. Judaism
   b. Christianity
   c. Buddhism
   d. Islam

9. In what year did he change his name?
   a. 1975
   b. 1971
   c. 1973
   d. 1970

10. How many career scoring points did he have when he retired?
   a. 31,421
   b. 21,421
   c. 38,887
   d. 28,887

B. Open-Ended Questions

1. Who is this passage about?
2. What team was Jabbar playing with when he retired?
3. In what year did he retire?
4. What team first drafted him?
5. In his first year of playing, how many points did Jabbar average per game?
6. What event took place during his second season playing basketball?
7. What was his birth name?
8. What religion prompted him to change his name?
9. In what year did he change his name?
10. How many career scoring points did he have when he retired?

C. Free Recall

Chapter 5

Visual Recall Exercises

These exercises provide practice in strategy use to facilitate recall of visually presented information of increasing levels of difficulty.

Contents

Calendar Exercises

Strategies

Instruct the client to use several strategies, such as *visualizing* the location of the event on the calendar and *associating* the event with the date on the calendar; or to personalize by *association* with an event in their lives (for example, the doctor's appointment is on the same day as Valentine's Day).

During the learning phase of the exercise, encourage the client to *write* the information on a separate sheet of paper as a means of processing the information more actively and having a record to refer to and *rehearse* the important dates and events to be recalled.

Instructions

1. Determine the appropriate exercise level for the client, based on clinical judgment and the following guidelines:

Skill Level	Exercise
Level 1—Severe impairment	1 and 2
Level 2—Moderate impairment	3 and 4
Level 3—Mild impairment	5 and 6
Level 4—Advanced skill level	7

2. Provide a copy of the calendar at the appropriate level.
3. Have the client study the calendar for five minutes. (You may want to modify this time based on the client's need.)
4. While the client is studying the material, provide a reminder to boost recall by using the strategies discussed above.
5. Have the client place the calendar out of sight (for example, turned over or placed under the chair).
6. Using clinical judgment, select one of the following recall formats:

   a. Multiple-Choice Questions (the easiest way to recall the presented information)

   There are two ways to present multiple-choice questions:

   - Give the client a copy of the multiple-choice questions that correspond to the calendar you have selected. Instruct the client to read the questions and circle the correct answers.

Have the client work independently for a set amount of time. Then review the answers with the client.

- Read the questions aloud, and have the client respond verbally. Then review the answers with the client.

b. Open-Ended Questions (a moderately difficult way to recall the presented information)

   There are two ways to present open-ended questions:

   - Give the client a copy of the open-ended questions that correspond to the calendar you have selected. Instruct the client to read the questions and write the answers. Have the client work independently for a set amount of time. Then review the answers with the client.

   - Read the questions aloud, and have the client respond verbally. Then review the answers with the client.

c. Free Recall (the most difficult way to recall the presented information)

   Provide a blank calendar (page 187). Have the client fill in all the information that can be recalled.

7. While the client is completing the worksheet, provide a reminder to use strategies to enhance recall.

Please note: When you use the open-ended questions with a client, you will need to cover up other parts of the worksheet that appear on the same page when you photocopy it so the answers are not available.

Calendar 1

SUNDAY	MONDAY	TUESDAY	WEDNESDAY	THURSDAY	FRIDAY	SATURDAY
			1	2	3	4
5	6	7	8	9	10 Gram's Birthday	11
12	13	14	15	16	17	18
19	20 Doctor's Appointment	21	22	23	24	25
26	27	28	29	30	31	

Name________________________________ Date______________________

Calendar Exercise 1

A. Multiple-Choice Questions

1. Whose birthday is on the 10th?
   a. George
   b. Gram
   c. Lisa
   d. Dad
2. On what date is your doctor's appointment?
   a. 2
   b. 14
   c. 20
   d. 30

B. Open-Ended Questions

1. Whose birthday is on the 10th? ____________________
2. On what date is your doctor's appointment? ____________________

Calendar 2

SUNDAY	MONDAY	TUESDAY	WEDNESDAY	THURSDAY	FRIDAY	SATURDAY
			1	2	3	4
5	6	7	8	9	10 Gram Dot's 90th Birthday	11
12	13	14	15	16	17	18
19	20 10:30 Dr. Paul Appointment	21	22	23	24	25
26	27	28	29	30	31	

Name________________________________ Date______________________

Calendar Exercise 2

A. Multiple-Choice Questions

1. Whose birthday is on the 10th?
   a. Gram Ann
   b. Gram Lisa
   c. Gram Dot
   d. Gram Denise
2. How old will she be on her birthday?
   a. 90
   b. 80
   c. 60
   d. 70
3. On what date is your doctor's appointment?
   a. 2
   b. 14
   c. 20
   d. 30
4. What time is your doctor's appointment?
   a. 9:30
   b. 12:30
   c. 11:30
   d. 10:30
5. What is your doctor's name?
   a. Peter
   b. Michael
   c. Paul
   d. Steven

B. Open-Ended Questions

1. Whose birthday is on the 10th?____________________
2. How old will she be on her birthday? ____________________
3. On what date is your doctor's appointment? ____________________
4. What time is your doctor's appointment? ____________________
5. What is your doctor's name? ____________________

Calendar 3

SUNDAY	MONDAY	TUESDAY	WEDNESDAY	THURSDAY	FRIDAY	SATURDAY
			1 5:45 Soccer Game	2	3	4
5	6	7	8	9	10 Gram Dot's 90th Birthday	11
12	13	14	15	16	17	18
19	20 10:30 Dr. Paul Appointment	21	22	23	24	25
26	27	28	29	30	31	

Name________________________________ Date______________________

Calendar Exercise 3

A. Multiple-Choice Questions

1. Whose birthday is on the 10th?
   a. Gram Ann
   b. Gram Lisa
   c. Gram Dot
   d. Gram Denise
2. How old will she be on her birthday?
   a. 90
   b. 80
   c. 60
   d. 70
3. On what date is your doctor's appointment?
   a. 2
   b. 14
   c. 20
   d. 30
4. What time is your doctor's appointment?
   a. 9:30
   b. 12:30
   c. 11:30
   d. 10:30
5. What is your doctor's name?
   a. Peter
   b. Michael
   c. Paul
   d. Steven
6. What is the date of the soccer game?
   a. 10
   b. 1
   c. 12
   d. 4
7. What time is the soccer game?
   a. 4:45
   b. 2:45
   c. 6:45
   d. 5:45

B. Open-Ended Questions

1. Whose birthday is on the 10th? ____________________
2. How old will she be on her birthday? ____________________
3. On what date is your doctor's appointment? ____________________
4. What time is your doctor's appointment? ____________________
5. What is your doctor's name? ____________________
6. What is the date of the soccer game? ____________________
7. What time is the soccer game? ____________________

Calendar 4

SUNDAY	MONDAY	TUESDAY	WEDNESDAY	THURSDAY	FRIDAY	SATURDAY
			1 5:45 Soccer Game	2	3	4
5	6	7	8	9	10 Gram Dot's 90th Birthday	11
12	13	14	15	16	17	18
19	20 10:30 Dr. Paul Appointment	21	22	23	24 Holiday	25
26	27	28	29	30	31	

Name______________________________ Date____________________

Calendar Exercise 4

A. Multiple-Choice Questions

1. Whose birthday is on the 10th?
   a. Gram Ann
   b. Gram Lisa
   c. Gram Dot
   d. Gram Denise
2. How old will she be on her birthday?
   a. 90
   b. 80
   c. 60
   d. 70
3. On what date is your doctor's appointment?
   a. 2
   b. 14
   c. 20
   d. 30
4. What time is your doctor's appointment?
   a. 9:30
   b. 12:30
   c. 11:30
   d. 10:30
5. What is your doctor's name?
   a. Peter
   b. Michael
   c. Paul
   d. Steven
6. What is the date of the soccer game?
   a. 10
   b. 1
   c. 12
   d. 4
7. What time is the soccer game?
   a. 4:45
   b. 2:45
   c. 6:45
   d. 5:45
8. What is the date of the holiday?
   a. 24
   b. 29
   c. 26
   d. 21

B. Open-Ended Questions

1. Whose birthday is on the 10th? __________________
2. How old will she be on her birthday? __________________
3. On what date is your doctor's appointment? __________________
4. What time is your doctor's appointment? __________________
5. What is your doctor's name? __________________
6. What is the date of the soccer game? __________________
7. What time is the soccer game? __________________
8. What is the date of the holiday? __________________

Calendar 5

SUNDAY	MONDAY	TUESDAY	WEDNESDAY	THURSDAY	FRIDAY	SATURDAY
			1 5:45 Soccer Game	2	3	4
5	6	7	8	9	10 Gram Dot's 90th Birthday	11
12	13	14	15	16	17	18 Mom & Dad's 35th Anniversary
19	20 10:30 Dr. Paul Appointment	21	22	23	24 Holiday	25
26	27	28	29	30	31	

Name______________________________ Date____________________

Calendar Exercise 5

A. Multiple-Choice Questions

1. Whose birthday is on the 10th?
   a. Gram Ann
   b. Gram Lisa
   c. Gram Dot
   d. Gram Denise

2. How old will she be on her birthday?
   a. 90
   b. 80
   c. 60
   d. 70

3. On what date is your doctor's appointment?
   a. 2
   b. 14
   c. 20
   d. 30

4. What time is your doctor's appointment?
   a. 9:30
   b. 12:30
   c. 11:30
   d. 10:30

5. What is your doctor's name?
   a. Peter
   b. Michael
   c. Paul
   d. Steven

6. What is the date of the soccer game?
   a. 10
   b. 1
   c. 12
   d. 4

7. What time is the soccer game?
   a. 4:45
   b. 2:45
   c. 6:45
   d. 5:45

8. What is the date of the holiday?
   a. 24
   b. 29
   c. 26
   d. 21

9. When is Mom and Dad's anniversary?
   a. 12
   b. 18
   c. 17
   d. 19

10. What number anniversary is it?
    a. 35
    b. 30
    c. 33
    d. 37

Name________________________________ Date______________________

Calendar Exercise 5

B. Open-Ended Questions

1. Whose birthday is on the 10th? ____________________
2. How old will she be on her birthday? ____________________
3. On what date is your doctor's appointment? ____________________
4. What time is your doctor's appointment? ____________________
5. What is your doctor's name? ____________________
6. What is the date of the soccer game? ____________________
7. What time is the soccer game? ____________________
8. What is the date of the holiday? ____________________
9. When is Mom and Dad's anniversary? ____________________
10. What number anniversary is it? ____________________

Calendar 6

SUNDAY	MONDAY	TUESDAY	WEDNESDAY	THURSDAY	FRIDAY	SATURDAY
			1 5:45 Soccer Game	2	3	4
5	6	7	8	9	10 Gram Dot's 90th Birthday	11
12 Dan & Lisa's Wedding	13	14	15	16	17	18 Mom & Dad's 35th Anniversary
19	20 10:30 Dr. Paul Appointment	21	22	23	24 Holiday	25
26	27	28	29	30	31	

Name________________________________ Date______________________

Calendar Exercise 6

A. Multiple-Choice Questions

1. Whose birthday is on the 10th?
   a. Gram Ann
   b. Gram Lisa
   c. Gram Dot
   d. Gram Denise
2. How old will she be on her birthday?
   a. 90
   b. 80
   c. 60
   d. 70
3. On what date is your doctor's appointment?
   a. 2
   b. 14
   c. 20
   d. 30
4. What time is your doctor's appointment?
   a. 9:30
   b. 12:30
   c. 11:30
   d. 10:30
5. What is your doctor's name?
   a. Peter
   b. Michael
   c. Paul
   d. Steven
6. What is the date of the soccer game?
   a. 10
   b. 1
   c. 12
   d. 4
7. What time is the soccer game?
   a. 4:45
   b. 2:45
   c. 6:45
   d. 5:45
8. What is the date of the holiday?
   a. 24
   b. 29
   c. 26
   d. 21
9. When is Mom and Dad's anniversary?
   a. 12
   b. 18
   c. 17
   d. 19
10. What number anniversary is it?
    a. 35
    b. 30
    c. 33
    d. 37
11. Who is getting married on the 12th?
    a. Dan and Linda
    b. Dave and Lelia
    c. Dan and Lisa
    d. Doug and Lisa

Name________________________________ Date______________________

Calendar Exercise 6

B. Open-Ended Questions

1. Whose birthday is on the 10th? ____________________
2. How old will she be on her birthday? ____________________
3. On what date is your doctor's appointment? ____________________
4. What time is your doctor's appointment? ____________________
5. What is your doctor's name? ____________________
6. What is the date of the soccer game? ____________________
7. What time is the soccer game? ____________________
8. What is the date of the holiday? ____________________
9. When is Mom and Dad's anniversary? ____________________
10. What number anniversary is it? ____________________
11. Who is getting married on the 12th? ____________________

Calendar 7

SUNDAY	MONDAY	TUESDAY	WEDNESDAY	THURSDAY	FRIDAY	SATURDAY
			1 5:45 Soccer Game	2	3	4
5	6	7	8	9	10 Gram Dot's 90th Birthday	11
12 Dan & Lisa's Wedding	13	14	15	16	17	18 Mom & Dad's 35th Anniversary
19	20 10:30 Dr. Paul Appointment	21	22	23	24 Holiday	25
26	27	28 2:15 Shamus to the Vet	29	30	31	

Name______________________________ Date____________________

Calendar Exercise 7

A. Multiple-Choice Questions

1. Whose birthday is on the 10th?
   a. Gram Ann
   b. Gram Lisa
   c. Gram Dot
   d. Gram Denise
2. How old will she be on her birthday?
   a. 90
   b. 80
   c. 60
   d. 70
3. On what date is your doctor's appointment?
   a. 2
   b. 14
   c. 20
   d. 30
4. What time is your doctor's appointment?
   a. 9:30
   b. 12:30
   c. 11:30
   d. 10:30
5. What is your doctor's name?
   a. Peter
   b. Michael
   c. Paul
   d. Steven
6. What is the date of the soccer game?
   a. 10
   b. 1
   c. 12
   d. 4
7. What time is the soccer game?
   a. 4:45
   b. 2:45
   c. 6:45
   d. 5:45
8. What is the date of the holiday?
   a. 24
   b. 29
   c. 26
   d. 21
9. When is Mom and Dad's anniversary?
   a. 12
   b. 18
   c. 17
   d. 19
10. What number anniversary is it?
    a. 35
    b. 30
    c. 33
    d. 37
11. Who is getting married on the 12th?
    a. Dan and Linda
    b. Dave and Lelia
    c. Dan and Lisa
    d. Doug and Lisa
12. Who has a doctor's appointment on the 28th?
    a. Shane
    b. Shamus
    c. Snoopy
    d. Sam

Name________________________________ Date______________________

Calendar Exercise 7

A. Multiple-Choice Questions continued

13. What time is his appointment on the 28th?
    a. 4:15
    b. 2:15
    c. 5:15
    d. 1:15

B. Open-Ended Questions

1. Whose birthday is on the tenth? ____________________
2. How old will she be on her birthday? ____________________
3. On what date is your doctor's appointment? ____________________
4. What time is your doctor's appointment? ____________________
5. What is your doctor's name? ____________________
6. What is the date of the soccer game? ____________________
7. What time is the soccer game? ____________________
8. What is the date of the holiday? ____________________
9. When is Mom and Dad's anniversary? ____________________
10. What number anniversary is it? ____________________
11. Who is getting married on the 12th? ____________________
12. Who has a doctor's appointment on the 28th? ____________________
13. What time is his appointment on the 28th? ____________________

Calendar 8

SUNDAY	MONDAY	TUESDAY	WEDNESDAY	THURSDAY	FRIDAY	SATURDAY
			1	2	3	4
5	6	7	8	9	10	11
12	13	14	15	16	17	18
19	20	21	22	23	24	25
26	27	28	29	30	31	

To Do Lists

Strategies

Instruct the client to use several strategies, such as *visualizing* the location of the event on the list and *associating* the event with the time on the list; or use *first-letter mnemonics* to recall sequences of events (for example, MD to remember **m**edications and **d**ental appointment).

During the learning phase of the exercise, encourage clients to *write* the information on a separate sheet of paper as a means of processing the information more accurately and having a record to refer to and *rehearse* the important times and events to be recalled.

Instructions

1. Determine the appropriate exercise level for the client, based on clinical judgment and the following guidelines:

Skill Level	Exercise
Level 1—Severe impairment	1 and 2
Level 2—Moderate impairment	3 and 4
Level 3—Mild impairment	5 and 6
Level 4—Advanced skill level	7

2. Provide a copy of the To Do List at the appropriate level.
3. Have the client study the list for five minutes. (You may want to modify this time based on the client's needs.)
4. While the client is studying the material, provide a reminder to boost recall by using the strategies discussed above.
5. Have the client place the list out of sight (for example, turned over or placed under the chair).
6. Using clinical judgment, select one of the following recall formats:

   a. Multiple-Choice Questions (the easiest way to recall the presented information)

   There are two ways to present multiple-choice questions:

   - Give the client a copy of the multiple-choice questions that correspond to the list you have selected. Instruct the client to read the questions and circle the correct answers. Have the client work independently for a set amount of time. Then review the answers with the client.

- Read the questions aloud, and have the client respond verbally. Then review the answers with the client.

b. Open-Ended Questions (a moderately difficult way to recall the presented information)

There are two ways to present open-ended questions:

- Give the client a copy of the open-ended questions that correspond to the list you have selected. Instruct the client to read the questions and write the answers. Have the client work independently for a set amount of time. Then review the answers with the client.
- Read the questions aloud, and have the client respond verbally. Then review the answers with the client.

c. Free Recall (the most difficult way to recall the presented information)

Provide a blank To Do List (page 209). Have the client fill in all the information that can be recalled.

7. While the client is completing the worksheet, provide a reminder to use strategies to enhance recall.

Please note: When you use the open-ended questions with a client, you will need to cover up other parts of the worksheet that appear on the same page when you photocopy it so the answers are not available.

To Do List 1

Things To Do Today

8:00	Take medications
9:00	
10:00	
11:00	
NOON	Lunch with Laura
1:00	
2:00	
3:00	
4:00	
5:00	
6:00	

Name______________________________ Date______________________

To Do List 1

A. Multiple-Choice Questions

1. What time do you have to take medications?
   a. 10:00
   b. 9:00
   c. 8:00
   d. 7:00

2. Who are you meeting for lunch?
   a. Laura
   b. Jennifer
   c. Stephanie
   d. Lisa

3. What time are you meeting her?
   a. 11:00
   b. 1:00
   c. 12:00
   d. 11:30

B. Open-Ended Questions

1. What time do you have to take medications? ______________
2. Who are you meeting for lunch? __________________
3. What time are you meeting her? ___________________

To Do List 2

Things To Do Today

8:00	Take medications
9:00	
10:00	
11:00	
NOON	Lunch with Laura at diner
1:00	
2:00	
3:00	Dentist appointment
4:00	
5:00	
6:00	

Name____________________________ Date____________________

To Do List 2

A. Multiple-Choice Questions

1. What time do you have to take medications?
   a. 10:00
   b. 9:00
   c. 8:00
   d. 7:00
2. Who are you meeting for lunch?
   a. Laura
   b. Jennifer
   c. Stephanie
   d. Lisa
3. What time are you meeting her?
   a. 11:00
   b. 1:00
   c. 12:00
   d. 11:30
4. Where are you meeting for lunch?
   a. Coffee shop
   b. Diner
   c. Deli
   d. Her house
5. Where do you have to go at 3:00?
   a. Dancing
   b. Drugstore
   c. Gym
   d. Dentist

B. Open-Ended Questions

1. What time do you have to take medications?______________
2. Who are you meeting for lunch?___________________
3. What time are you meeting her?____________________
4. Where are you meeting for lunch?____________________
5. Where do you have to go at 3:00?_____________________

To Do List 3

Things To Do Today

8:00	Take medications after breakfast
9:00	
10:00	
11:00	
NOON	Lunch with Laura at diner
1:00	
2:00	
3:00	Dentist appointment for cleaning
4:00	
5:00	
6:00	

Name______________________________ Date____________________

To Do List 3

A. Multiple-Choice Questions

1. What time do you have to take medications?
   a. 10:00
   b. 9:00
   c. 8:00
   d. 7:00

2. Who are you meeting for lunch?
   a. Laura
   b. Jennifer
   c. Stephanie
   d. Lisa

3. What time are you meeting her?
   a. 11:00
   b. 1:00
   c. 12:00
   d. 11:30

4. Where are you meeting for lunch?
   a. Coffee shop
   b. Diner
   c. Deli
   d. Her house

5. Where do you have to go at 3:00?
   a. Dancing
   b. Drugstore
   c. Gym
   d. Dentist

6. What are you having done at 3:00?
   a. Cleaning
   b. Fitting
   c. Adjustment
   d. Polishing

7. Medications are taken after what?
   a. Lunch
   b. Snack
   c. Breakfast
   d. Dinner

B. Open-Ended Questions

1. What time do you have to take medications?______________
2. Who are you meeting for lunch?__________________
3. What time are you meeting her?__________________
4. Where are you meeting for lunch?__________________
5. Where do you have to go at 3:00?__________________
6. What are you having done at 3:00?________________
7. Medications are taken after what? __________________

To Do List 4

Things To Do Today

8:00	Take medications after breakfast
9:00	
10:00	Withdraw $40.00 at ATM from savings
11:00	
NOON	Lunch with Laura at diner
1:00	
2:00	
3:00	Dentist appointment for cleaning
4:00	
5:00	
6:00	

Name________________________________ Date______________________

To Do List 4

A. Multiple-Choice Questions

1. What time do you have to take medications?
   a. 10:00
   b. 9:00
   c. 8:00
   d. 7:00
2. Who are you meeting for lunch?
   a. Laura
   b. Jennifer
   c. Stephanie
   d. Lisa
3. What time are you meeting her?
   a. 11:00
   b. 1:00
   c. 12:00
   d. 11:30
4. Where are you meeting for lunch?
   a. Coffee shop
   b. Diner
   c. Deli
   d. Her house
5. Where do you have to go at 3:00?
   a. Dancing
   b. Drugstore
   c. Gym
   d. Dentist
6. What are you having done at 3:00?
   a. Cleaning
   b. Fitting
   c. Adjustment
   d. Polishing
7. Medications are taken after what?
   a. Lunch
   b. Snack
   c. Breakfast
   d. Dinner
8. How much money are you withdrawing at the ATM?
   a. $40.00
   b. $50.00
   c. $30.00
   d. $60.00
9. From which account are you withdrawing money?
   a. Checking
   b. Credit card
   c. Savings

Name______________________________ Date____________________

To Do List 4

B. Open-Ended Questions

1. What time do you have to take medications?_____________
2. Who are you meeting for lunch?__________________
3. What time are you meeting her?__________________
4. Where are you meeting for lunch?__________________
5. Where do you have to go at 3:00?____________________
6. What are you having done at 3:00?_________________
7. Medications are taken after what? __________________
8. How much money are you withdrawing at the ATM? _____________
9. From which account are you withdrawing money?_____________

To Do List 5

Things To Do Today

8:00	Take medications after breakfast
9:00	Call Dr. Pine's office for a physical
10:00	Withdraw $40.00 at ATM from savings
11:00	
NOON	Lunch with Laura at diner on Main Street
1:00	
2:00	
3:00	Dentist appointment for cleaning
4:00	
5:00	
6:00	

Name______________________________ Date______________________

To Do List 5

A. Multiple-Choice Questions

1. What time do you have to take medications?
   a. 10:00
   b. 9:00
   c. 8:00
   d. 7:00
2. Who are you meeting for lunch?
   a. Laura
   b. Jennifer
   c. Stephanie
   d. Lisa
3. What time are you meeting her?
   a. 11:00
   b. 1:00
   c. 12:00
   d. 11:30
4. Where are you meeting for lunch?
   a. Coffee shop
   b. Diner
   c. Deli
   d. Her house
5. Where is the food establishment located?
   a. Mountain St.
   b. Main St.
   c. South St.
   d. Locust St.
6. Where do you have to go at 3:00?
   a. Dancing
   b. Drugstore
   c. Gym
   d. Dentist
7. What are you having done at 3:00?
   a. Cleaning
   b. Fitting
   c. Adjustment
   d. Polishing
8. Medications are taken after what?
   a. Lunch
   b. Snack
   c. Breakfast
   d. Dinner
9. How much money are you withdrawing at the ATM?
   a. $40.00
   b. $50.00
   c. $30.00
   d. $60.00
10. From which account are you withdrawing money?
    a. Checking
    b. Credit card
    c. Savings
11. Who are you calling at 9:00?
    a. Dr. Peter
    b. Dr. Oak
    c. Dr. Pine
    d. Dr. Maple
12. What do you have to schedule?
    a. Physical
    b. Shots
    c. Blood work
    d. X-rays

Name________________________________ Date______________________

To Do List 5

B. Open-Ended Questions

1. What time do you have to take medications?______________
2. Who are you meeting for lunch?____________________
3. What time are you meeting her?____________________
4. Where are you meeting for lunch?____________________
5. Where is the food establishment located? ____________________
6. Where do you have to go at 3:00?____________________
7. What are you having done at 3:00?__________________
8. Medications are taken after what? ___________________
9. How much money are you withdrawing at the ATM? _______________
10. From which account are you withdrawing money?______________
11. Who are you calling at 9:00? ______________
12. What do you have to schedule? ___________________

To Do List 6

Things To Do Today

8:00	Take medications after breakfast
9:00	Call Dr. Pine's office for a physical
10:00	Withdraw $40.00 at ATM from savings
11:00	
NOON	Lunch with Laura at diner on Main Street
1:00	
2:00	
3:00	Dentist appointment for cleaning
4:00	
5:00	Go to grocery store
6:00	

Name________________________________ Date______________________

To Do List 6

A. Multiple-Choice Questions

1. What time do you have to take medications?
   a. 10:00
   b. 9:00
   c. 8:00
   d. 7:00
2. Who are you meeting for lunch?
   a. Laura
   b. Jennifer
   c. Stephanie
   d. Lisa
3. What time are you meeting her?
   a. 11:00
   b. 1:00
   c. 12:00
   d. 11:30
4. Where are you meeting for lunch?
   a. Coffee shop
   b. Diner
   c. Deli
   d. Her house
5. Where is the food establishment located?
   a. Mountain St.
   b. Main St.
   c. South St.
   d. Locust St.
6. Where do you have to go at 3:00?
   a. Dancing
   b. Drugstore
   c. Gym
   d. Dentist
7. What are you having done at 3:00?
   a. Cleaning
   b. Fitting
   c. Adjustment
   d. Polishing
8. Medications are taken after what?
   a. Lunch
   b. Snack
   c. Breakfast
   d. Dinner
9. How much money are you withdrawing at the ATM?
   a. $40.00
   b. $50.00
   c. $30.00
   d. $60.00
10. From which account are you withdrawing money?
    a. Checking
    b. Credit card
    c. Savings

Name________________________________ Date____________________

11. Who are you calling at 9:00?
    a. Dr. Peter
    b. Dr. Oak
    c. Dr. Pine
    d. Dr. Maple

12. What do you have to schedule?
    a. Physical
    b. Shots
    c. Blood work
    d. X-rays

13. Where do you have to go at 5:00?
    a. Home
    b. Grocery store
    c. Bakery
    d. Gas station

B. Open-Ended Questions

1. What time do you have to take medications?______________
2. Who are you meeting for lunch?__________________
3. What time are you meeting her?__________________
4. Where are you meeting for lunch?__________________
5. Where is the food establishment located?__________________
6. Where do you have to go at 3:00?__________________
7. What are you having done at 3:00?_________________
8. Medications are taken after what?_________________
9. How much money are you withdrawing at the ATM? ______________
10. From which account are you withdrawing money?_____________
11. Who are you calling at 9:00? _____________
12. What do you have to schedule? _________________
13. Where do you have to go at 5:00?________________

To Do List 7

Things To Do Today

8:00	Take medications after breakfast
9:00	Call Dr. Pine's office for a physical
10:00	Withdraw $40.00 at ATM from savings
11:00	
NOON	Lunch with Laura at diner on Main Street
1:00	
2:00	Mail Mom's birthday present at the post office
3:00	Dentist appointment with Dr. Woods for cleaning
4:00	Pick up Suzie at dance class at 4:15
5:00	Go to grocery store
6:00	

Name________________________________ Date______________________

To Do List 7

A. Multiple-Choice Questions

1. What time do you have to take medications?
   a. 10:00
   b. 9:00
   c. 8:00
   d. 7:00

2. Who are you meeting for lunch?
   a. Laura
   b. Jennifer
   c. Stephanie
   d. Lisa

3. What time are you meeting her?
   a. 11:00
   b. 1:00
   c. 12:00
   d. 11:30

4. Where are you meeting for lunch?
   a. Coffee shop
   b. Diner
   c. Deli
   d. Her house

5. Where is the food establishment located?
   a. Mountain St.
   b. Main St.
   c. South St.
   d. Locust St.

6. Where do you have to go at 3:00?
   a. Dancing
   b. Drugstore
   c. Gym
   d. Dentist

7. What are you having done at 3:00?
   a. Cleaning
   b. Fitting
   c. Adjustment
   d. Polishing

8. Medications are taken after what?
   a. Lunch
   b. Snack
   c. Breakfast
   d. Dinner

9. How much money are you withdrawing at the ATM?
   a. $40.00
   b. $50.00
   c. $30.00
   d. $60.00

10. From which account are you withdrawing money?
    a. Checking
    b. Credit card
    c. Savings

11. Who are you calling at 9:00?
    a. Dr. Peter
    b. Dr. Oak
    c. Dr. Pine
    d. Dr. Maple

12. What do you have to schedule?
    a. Physical
    b. Shots
    c. Blood work
    d. X-rays

Name______________________________ Date____________________

13. Where do you have to go at 5:00?
    a. Home
    b. Grocery store
    c. Bakery
    d. Gas station

14. Who are you mailing a present to?
    a. Mother-in-law
    b. Father
    c. Sister
    d. Mother

15. What time do you have to pick up Suzie?
    a. 5:15
    b. 4:15
    c. 3:15
    d. 6:15

16. Where do you have to pick up Suzie?
    a. Dance
    b. Diner
    c. Friend's house
    d. School

B. Open-Ended Questions

1. What time do you have to take medications?_____________
2. Who are you meeting for lunch?_________________
3. What time are you meeting her?__________________
4. Where are you meeting for lunch?__________________
5. Where is the food establishment located?__________________
6. Where do you have to go at 3:00?__________________
7. What are you having done at 3:00?_________________
8. Medications are taken after what? _________________
9. How much money are you withdrawing at the ATM? ______________
10. From which account are you withdrawing money?_____________
11. Who are you calling at 9:00? _____________
12. What do you have to schedule? ________________
13. Where do you have to go at 5:00?________________
14. Who are you mailing a present to?________________
15. What time do you have to pick up Suzie?__________
16. Where do you have to pick up Suzie?____________

Name________________________________ Date______________________

To Do List

Things To Do Today

8:00

9:00

10:00

11:00

NOON

1:00

2:00

3:00

4:00

5:00

6:00

Catalog Exercises

Strategies

Instruct the client to use several strategies, such as *visualizing* the price of each item on the page and *associating* the price with the item.

During the learning phase of the exercise, encourage clients to *write* the information on a separate sheet of paper as a means of processing the information more accurately and having a record to refer to and *rehearse* the prices and items to be recalled.

Instructions

1. Determine the appropriate exercise level for the client, based on clinical judgment and the following guidelines:

Skill Level	Exercise
Level 1—Severe impairment	1 and 2
Level 2—Moderate impairment	3 and 4
Level 3—Mild impairment	5 and 6
Level 4—Advanced skill level	7

2. Provide a copy of the catalog page at the appropriate level.
3. Have the client study the catalog page for five minutes. (You may want to modify this time based on the client's needs.)
4. While the client is studying the material, provide a reminder to boost recall by using the strategies discussed above.
5. Have the client place the catalog page out of sight (for example, turned over or placed under the chair).
6. Using clinical judgment, select one of the following recall formats:

   a. Multiple-Choice Questions (the easiest way to recall the presented information)

   There are two ways to present multiple-choice questions:

   - Give the client a copy of the multiple-choice questions that correspond to the catalog page you have selected. Instruct the client to read the questions and circle the correct answers. Have the client work independently for a set amount of time. Then review the answers with the client.
   - Read the questions aloud, and have the client respond verbally. Then review the answers with the client.

b. Open-Ended Questions (a moderately difficult way to recall the presented information)

There are two ways to present open-ended questions:

- Give the client a copy of the open-ended questions that correspond to the catalog page you have selected. Instruct the client to read the questions and write the answers. Have the client work independently for a set amount of time. Then review the answers with the client.
- Read the questions aloud, and have the client respond verbally. Then review the answers with the client.

c. Free Recall (the most difficult way to recall the presented information)

Provide a copy of the "What Are the Prices?" page that corresponds to the catalog page you have selected. Have the client fill in all the prices that can be recalled.

7. While the client is completing the worksheet, provide a reminder to use strategies to enhance recall.

Please note: When you use the open-ended questions or the free recall section with a client, you will need to cover up other parts of the worksheet that appear on the same page when you photocopy it so the answers are not available.

Catalog Exercise 1

Pens

$6.99 per box of 50

Pencils

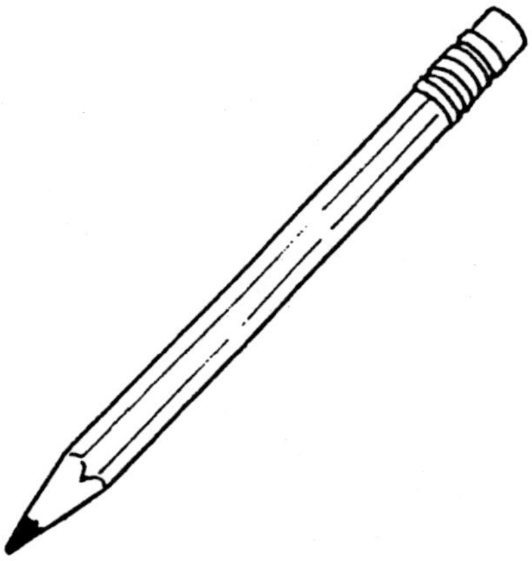

$1.29 per box of 100

Name______________________________ Date____________________

Catalog Exercise 1

A. Multiple-Choice Questions

1. Name one item shown on the catalog page.
   a. Pens
   b. Shirts
   c. Spoons
   d. Animals

2. How much does a box of pencils cost?
   a. $2.59
   b. $3.89
   c. $1.29
   d. $4.39

B. Open-Ended Questions

1. Name one item shown on the catalog page.____________________

2. How much does a box of pencils cost?________________________

C. Free Recall

What Are the Prices?

Pens

______ **per box of 50**

Pencils

______ **per box of 100**

Catalog Exercise 2

Pencils

$1.29 per box of 100

Pens

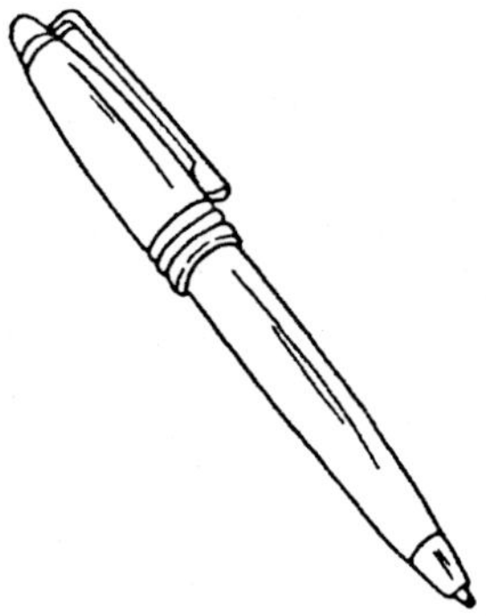

$6.99 per box of 50

Highlighters

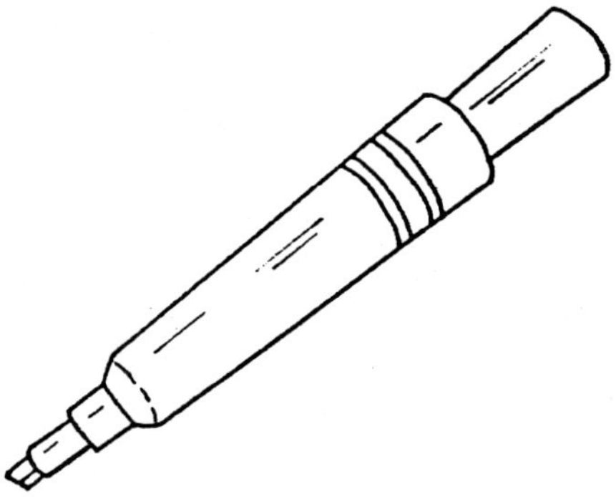

$1.69 each

Name________________________________ Date______________________

Catalog Exercise 2

A. Multiple-Choice Questions

1. Name one item shown on the catalog page.
   a. Pens
   b. Shirts
   c. Spoons
   d. Animals
2. How much does each highlighter cost?
   a. \$2.59
   b. \$3.89
   c. \$1.69
   d. \$4.39
3. Which item comes in a box of 50?
   a. Matches
   b. Pens
   c. Toothpicks
   d. Crayons

B. Open-Ended Questions

1. Name one item shown on the catalog page.

   ____

2. How much does each highlighter cost?____________________________
3. Which item comes in a box of 50?________________________________

Name______________________________ Date____________________

Catalog Exercise 2

C. Free Recall

What Are the Prices?

Pencils

________ per box of 100

Highlighters

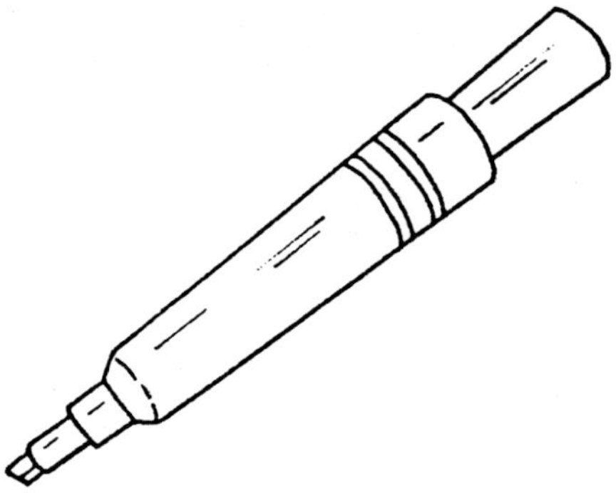

________ each

Pens

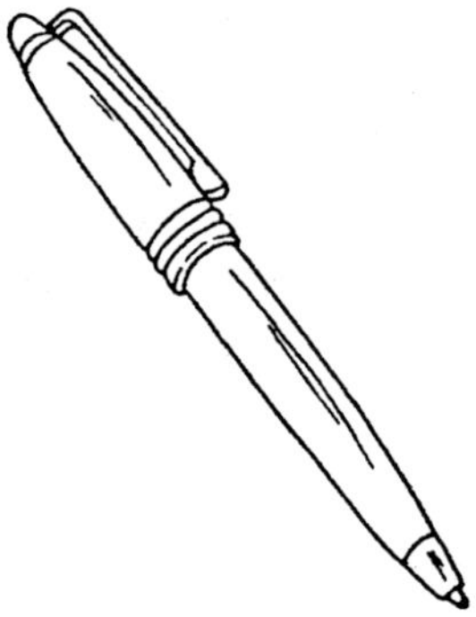

________ per box of 50

Catalog Exercise 3

Glue

$.99 each

Pencils

$1.29 per box of 100

Pens

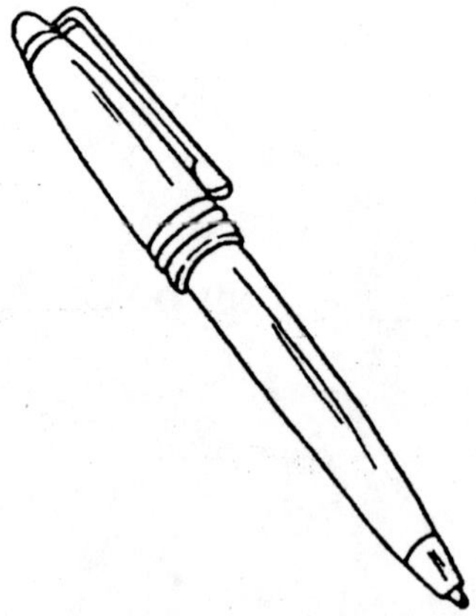

$6.99 per box of 50

Highlighters

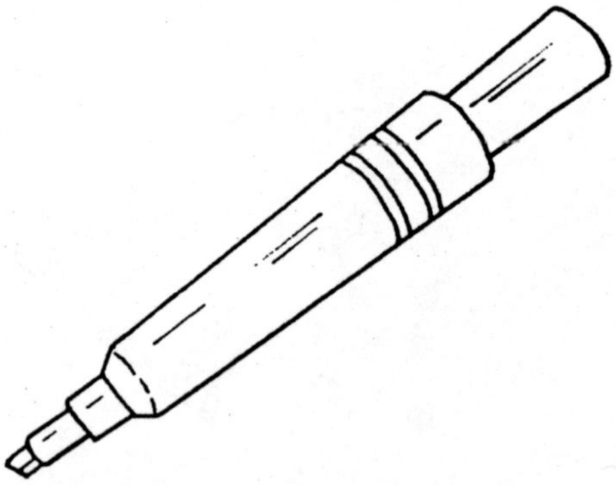

$1.69 each

Name______________________________ Date____________________

Catalog Exercise 3

A. Multiple-Choice Questions

1. Which item is not shown in the catalog?
   a. Tape
   b. Glue
   c. Pens
   d. Pencils

2. How much does each highlighter cost?
   a. $2.59
   b. $3.89
   c. $1.69
   d. $4.39

3. Which item comes in a box of 50?
   a. Matches
   b. Pens
   c. Toothpicks
   d. Crayons

4. Which two items are sold individually?
   a. Glue and pens
   b. Pencils and pens
   c. Glue and highlighters
   d. Tape and glue

B. Open-Ended Questions

1. Name all of the items shown on the catalog page.

   ____

2. How much does each highlighter cost?________________________

3. Which item comes in a box of 50?____________________________

4. Name two items that are sold individually.

   ____

Name________________________________ Date______________________

Catalog Exercise 3

C. Free Recall

What Are the Prices?

Glue

________ each

Pencils

________ per box of 100

Pens

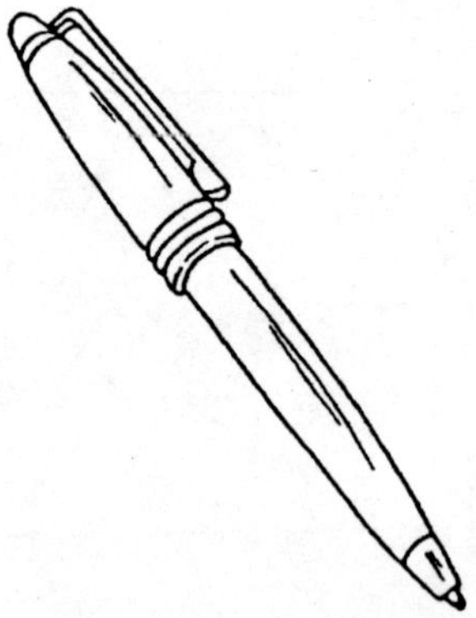

________ per box of 50

Highlighters

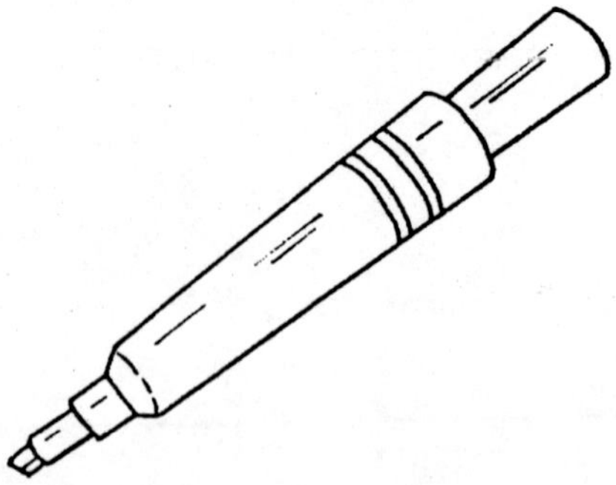

________ each

Catalog Exercise 4

Glue	Paper clips
	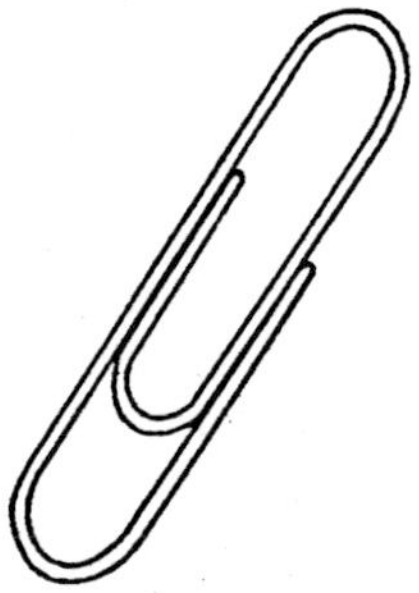
$.99 each	**$1.79 per box of 200**

Pencils

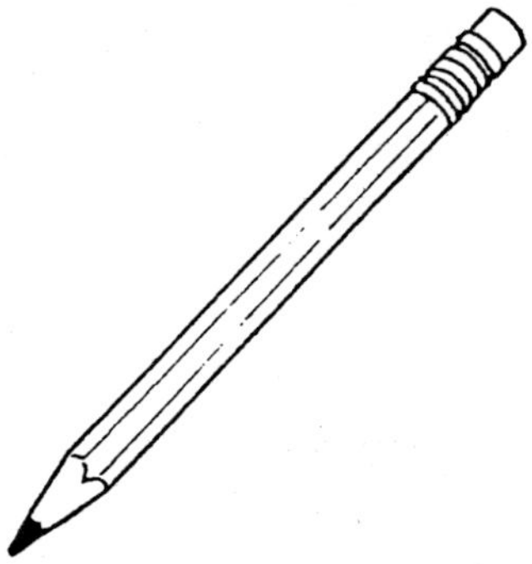

$1.29 per box of 100

Pens	Highlighters
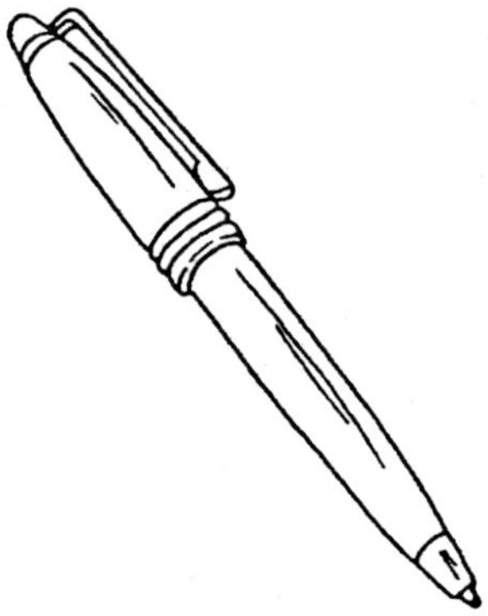	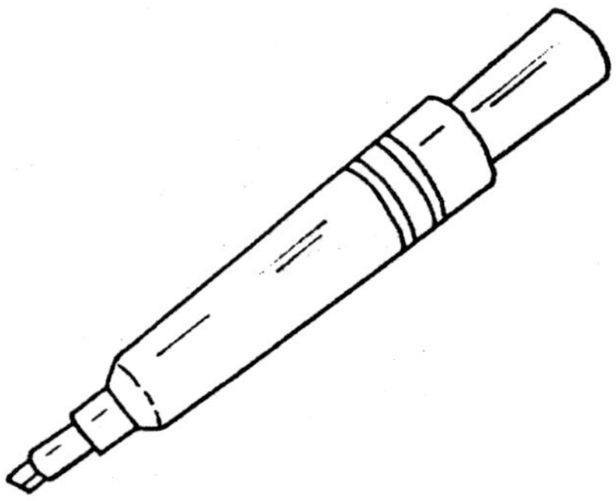
$6.99 per box of 50	**$1.69 each**

Name________________________________ Date______________________

Catalog Exercise 4

A. Multiple-Choice Questions

1. Which item is not shown in the catalog?
   a. Tape
   b. Glue
   c. Pens
   d. Pencils
2. How much does each highlighter cost?
   a. $2.59
   b. $3.89
   c. $1.69
   d. $4.39
3. Which item comes in a box of 50?
   a. Matches
   b. Pens
   c. Toothpicks
   d. Crayons
4. Which two items are sold individually?
   a. Glue and pens
   b. Pencils and pens
   c. Glue and highlighters
   d. Tape and glue
5. Which item is sold in a box of 100?
   a. Pens
   b. Paper clips
   c. Pencils
   d. Highlighters
6. How much does each box of paper clips cost?
   a. $1.69
   b. $1.49
   c. $1.59
   d. $1.79

B. Open-Ended Questions

1. Name all of the items shown on the catalog page.
   ____
2. How much does each highlighter cost?______________________
3. Which item comes in a box of 50?__________________________
4. Name two items that are sold individually.
   ____
5. Which item is sold in a box of 100?________________________
6. How much does each box of paper clips cost?________________

Name________________________________ Date______________________

Catalog Exercise 4

C. Free Recall

What Are the Prices?

Glue

__________ **each**

Paper clips

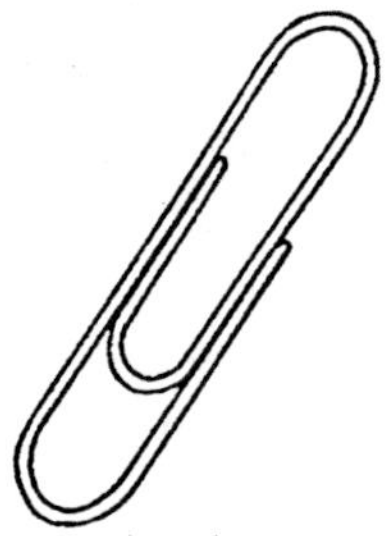

__________ **per box of 200**

Pencils

__________ **per box of 100**

Pens

__________ **per box of 50**

Highlighters

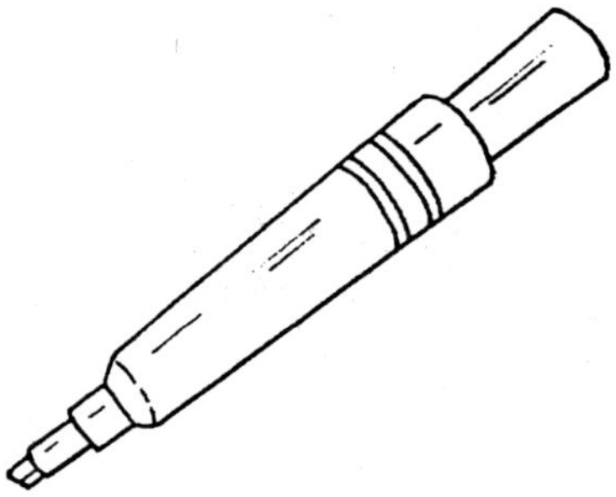

__________ **each**

Catalog Exercise 5

Glue

$.99 each

Paper clips

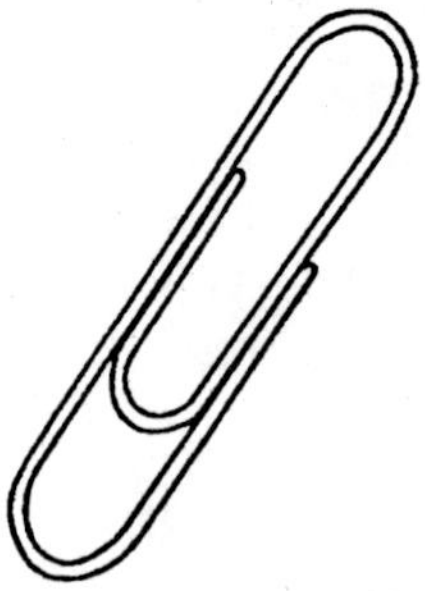

$1.79
per box of 200

Scissors

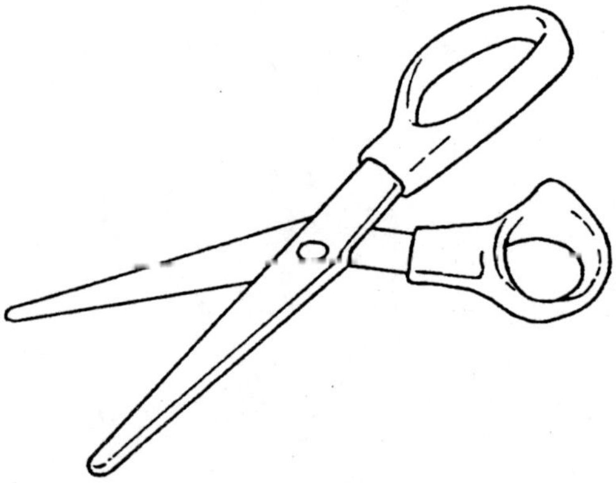

$8.99 each

Pencils

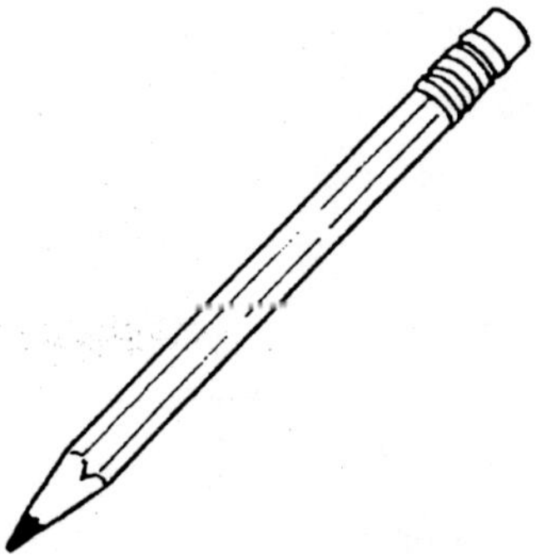

$1.29 per box of 100

Pens

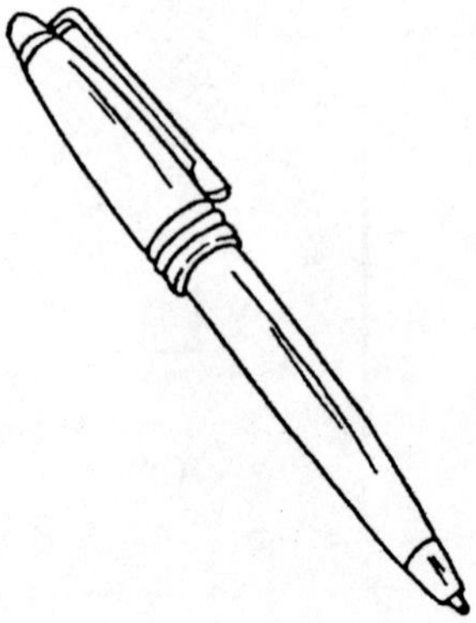

$6.99 per box of 50

Highlighters

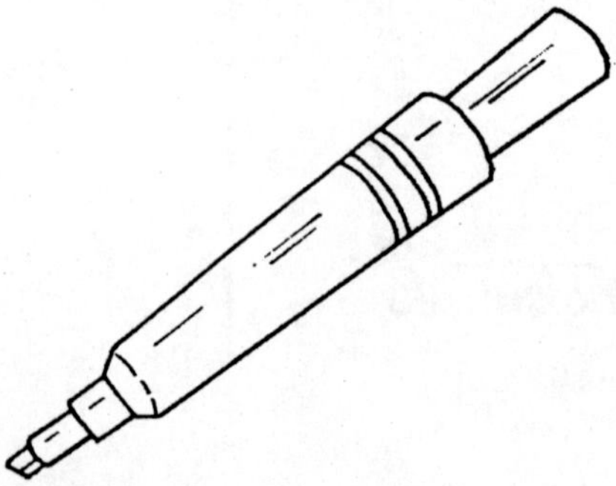

$1.69 each

Name________________________________ Date______________________

Catalog Exercise 5

A. Multiple-Choice Questions

1. Which item is not shown on the catalog page?
   a. Tape
   b. Glue
   c. Pens
   d. Pencils

2. How much does each highlighter cost?
   a. $2.59
   b. $3.89
   c. $1.69
   d. $4.39

3. Which item comes in a box of 50?
   a. Matches
   b. Pens
   c. Toothpicks
   d. Crayons

4. Which two items are sold individually?
   a. Glue and pens
   b. Pencils and pens
   c. Glue and highlighters
   d. Tape and glue

5. Which item is sold in a box of 100?
   a. Pens
   b. Paper clips
   c. Pencils
   d. Highlighters

6. How much does each box of paper clips cost?
   a. $1.69
   b. $1.49
   c. $1.59
   d. $1.79

7. Which item costs $8.99 each?
   a. Scissors
   b. Pens
   c. Glue
   d. Highlighter

8. Which item is not sold individually?
   a. Pens
   b. Highlighter
   c. Glue
   d. Scissors

B. Open-Ended Questions

1. Name all of the items shown on the catalog page.
   ____
2. How much does each highlighter cost?______________________
3. Which item comes in a box of 50? ______________________
4. Which item is sold in a box of 100? ______________________
5. How much does each box of paper clips cost?
   ____
6. Which item costs $8.99 each? ______________________
7. Name all the items that are sold individually.
   ____

Name________________________________ Date______________________

Catalog Exercise 5

C. Free Recall

What Are the Prices?

Glue

________ each

Paper clips

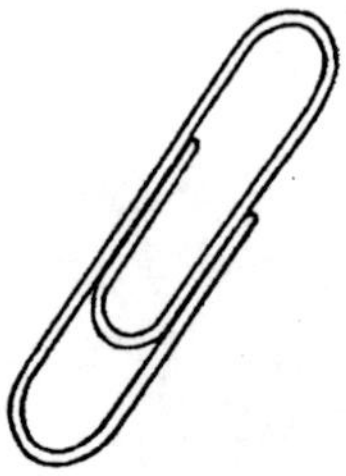

________ per box of 200

Scissors

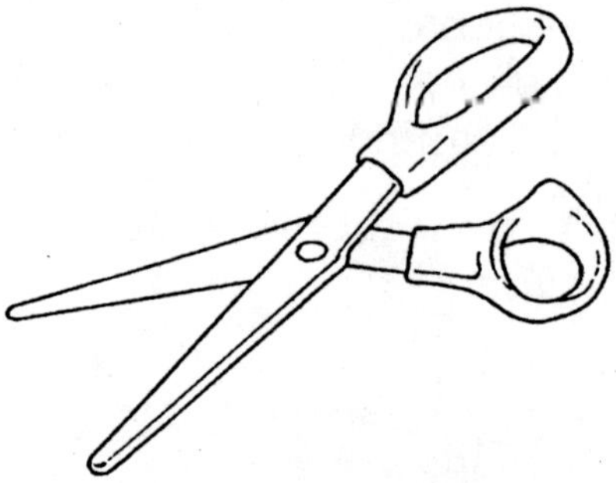

________ each

Pencils

________ per box of 100

Pens

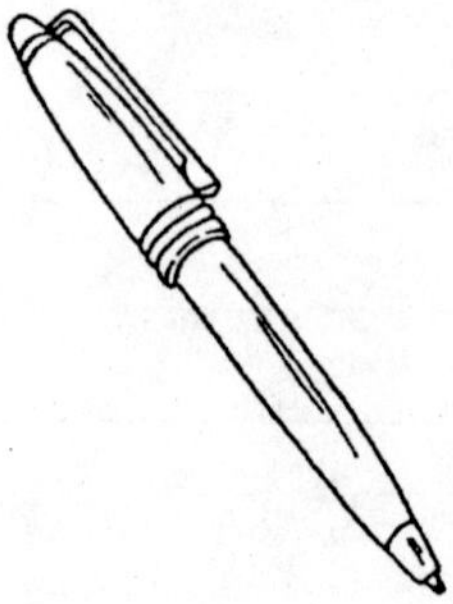

________ per box of 50

Highlighters

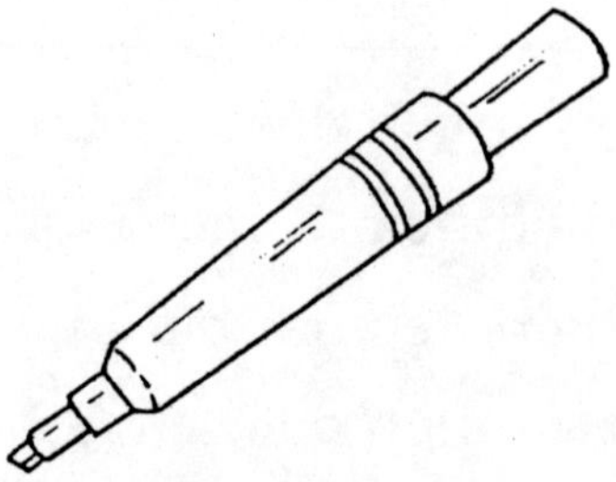

________ each

Catalog Exercise 6

Stapler

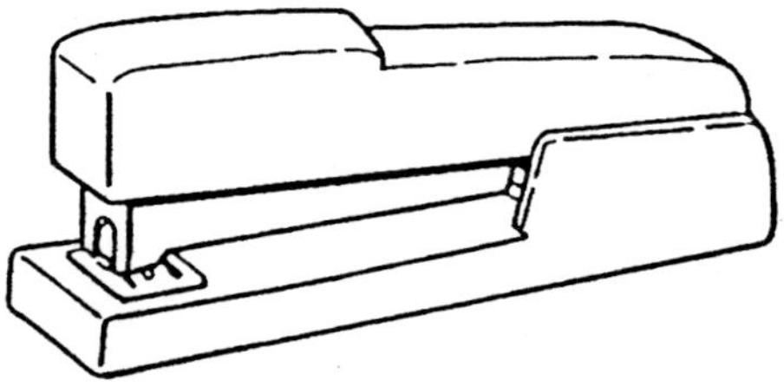

$5.99 each

Paper clips

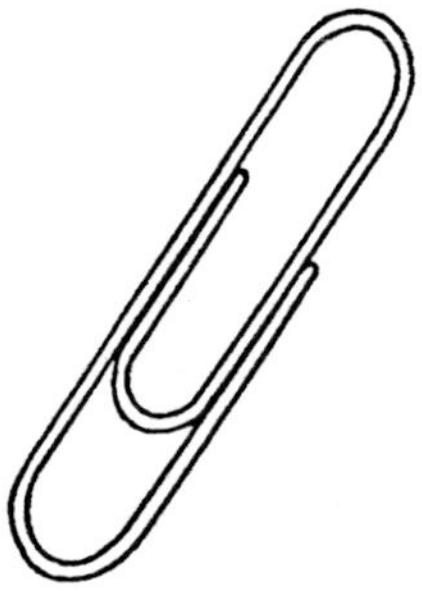

$1.79 per box of 200

Glue

$.99 each

Scissors

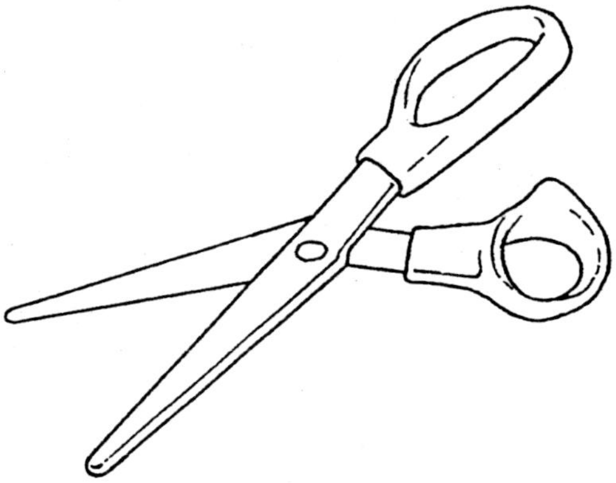

$8.99 each

Highlighters

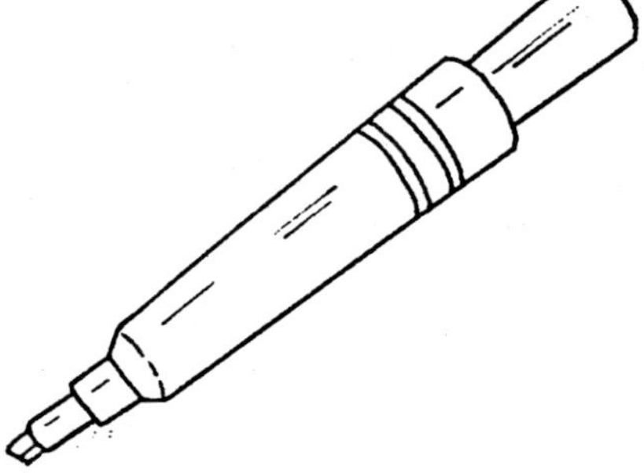

$1.69 each

Pens

$6.99 per box of 50

Pencils

$1.29 per box of 100

Name______________________________ Date____________________

Catalog Exercise 6

A. Multiple-Choice Questions

1. Which item is not shown on the catalog page?
   a. Tape
   b. Scissors
   c. Pens
   d. Paper clips

2. How much does each high-lighter cost?
   a. $2.59
   b. $3.89
   c. $1.69
   d. $4.39

3. Which item comes in a box of 50?
   a. Matches
   b. Pens
   c. Toothpicks
   d. Crayons

4. Which two items are sold individually?
   a. Glue and pens
   b. Pencils and pens
   c. Glue and highlighters
   d. Tape and glue

5. Which item is sold in a box of 100?
   a. Pens
   b. Paper clips
   c. Pencils
   d. Highlighters

6. How much does each box of paper clips cost?
   a. $1.69
   b. $1.49
   c. $1.59
   d. $1.79

7. Which item costs $8.99 each?
   a. Scissors
   b. Pens
   c. Glue
   d. Highlighter

8. Which item is not sold individually?
   a. Pens
   b. Highlighter
   c. Glue
   d. Scissors

9. How much does the stapler cost?
   a. $4.99
   b. $5.99
   c. $6.99
   d. $3.99

Name______________________________ Date____________________

Catalog Exercise 6

B. Open-Ended Questions

1. Name all of the items shown on the catalog page.

____

____

2. How much does each highlighter cost?____________________
3. Which item comes in a box of 50?______________________
4. Which item is sold in a box of 100?____________________
5. How much does each box of paper clips cost?

____

6. Which item costs $8.99 each?__________________________
7. Name all the items that are sold individually.

____

____

8. How much does each stapler cost?__________________

Name______________________________ Date____________________

Catalog Exercise 6

C. Free Recall

What Are the Prices?

Stapler

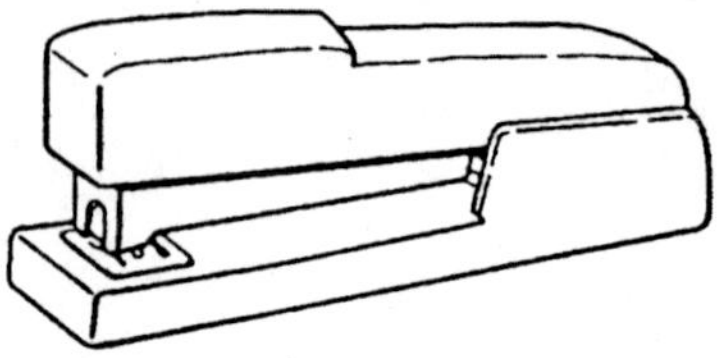

__________ **each**

Paper clips

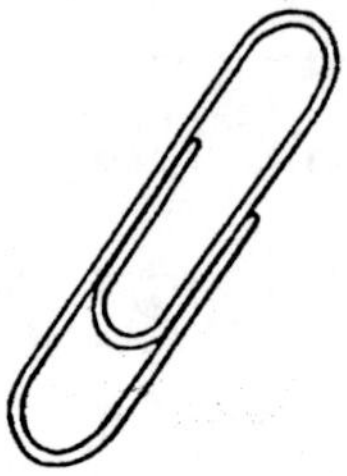

__________ **per box of 200**

Glue

__________ **each**

Scissors

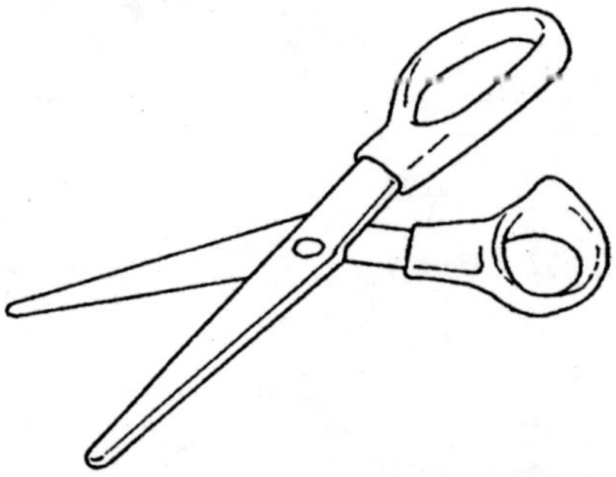

__________ **each**

Highlighters

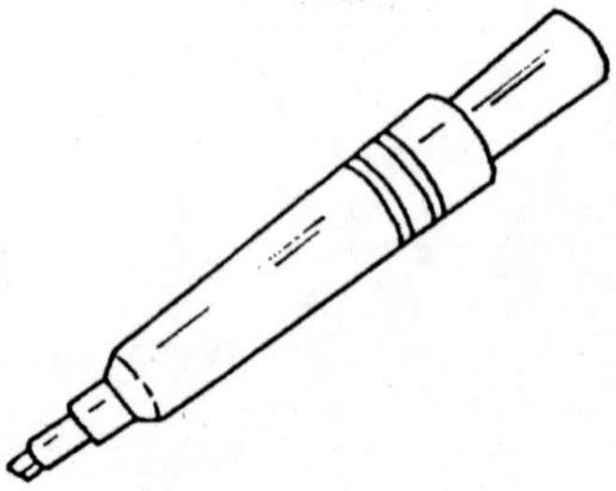

__________ **each**

Pens

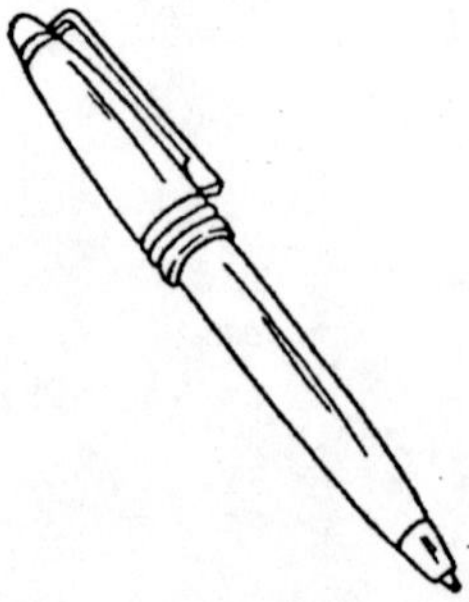

________ **per box of 50**

Pencils

_______ **per box of 100**

Catalog Exercise 7

Stapler

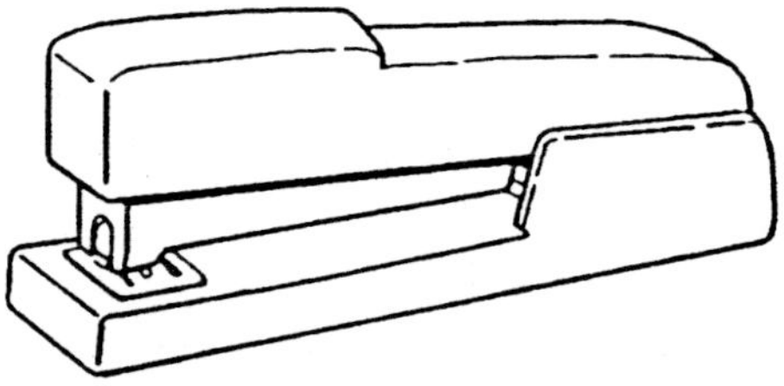

$5.99 each

Push pins

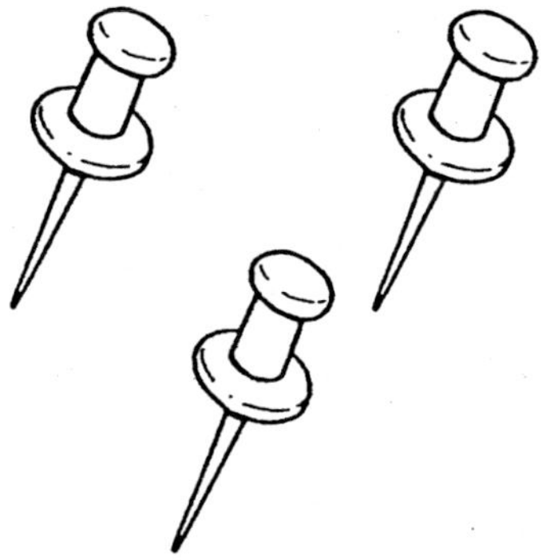

$1.99 per box of 100

Paper clips

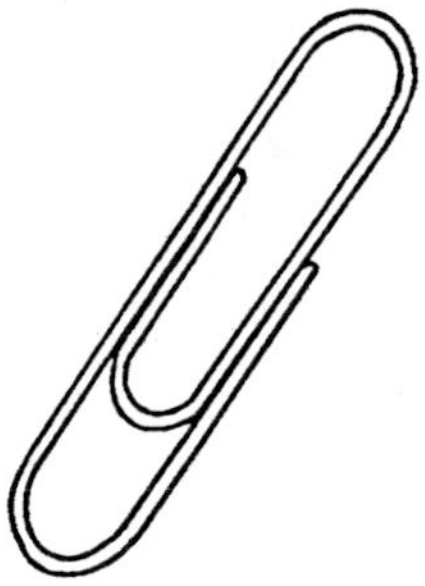

$1.79 per box of 200

Glue

$.99 each

Pens

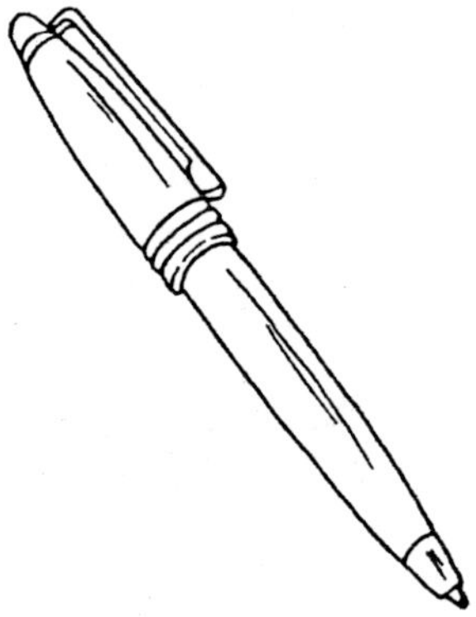

$6.99 per box of 50

Scissors

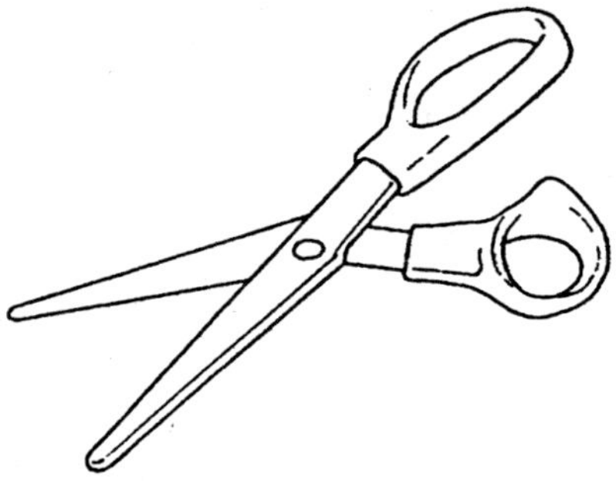

$8.99 each

Pencils

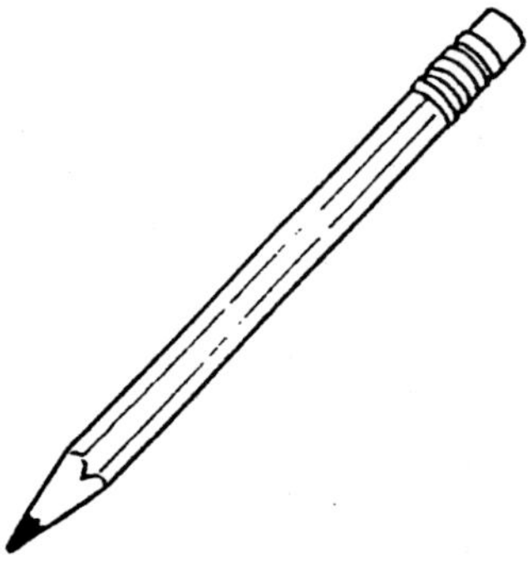

$1.29 per box of 100

Highlighters

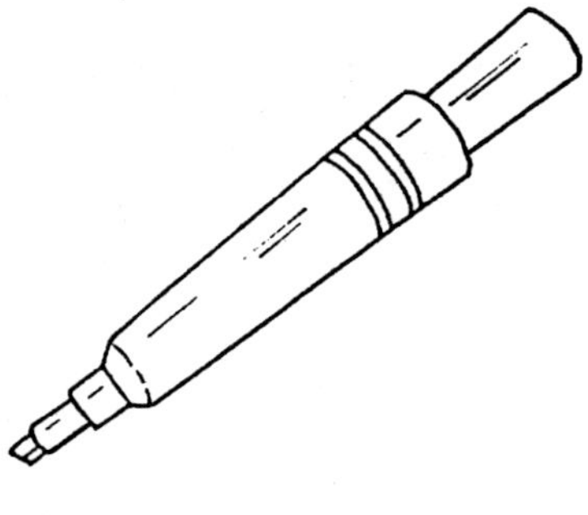

$1.69 each

Name________________________________ Date______________________

Catalog Exercise 7

A. Multiple-Choice Questions

1. Which item is not shown on the catalog page?
   a. Tape
   b. Scissors
   c. Pens
   d. Paper clips

2. How much does each highlighter cost?
   a. $2.59
   b. $3.89
   c. $1.69
   d. $4.39

3. Which item comes in a box of 50?
   a. Matches
   b. Pens
   c. Toothpicks
   d. Crayons

4. Which two items are sold individually?
   a. Glue and pens
   b. Pencils and pens
   c. Glue and highlighters
   d. Tape and glue

5. Which item is sold in a box of 200?
   a. Pens
   b. Paper clips
   c. Pencils
   d. Highlighters

6. How much does each box of paper clips cost?
   a. $1.69
   b. $1.49
   c. $1.59
   d. $1.79

7. Which item costs $8.99 each?
   a. Scissors
   b. Pens
   c. Glue
   d. Highlighter

8. Which item is not sold individually?
   a. Pens
   b. Highlighter
   c. Glue
   d. Scissors

9. How much does the stapler cost?
   a. $4.99
   b. $5.99
   c. $6.99
   d. $3.99

10. Which two items are sold in boxes of 100?
    a. Pens and paper clips
    b. Pencils and push pins
    c. Pens and push pins
    d. Paper clips and push pins

Name______________________________ Date____________________

Catalog Exercise 7

B. Open-Ended Questions

1. Name all of the items shown on the catalog page.

   ____

   ____

   ____

2. How much does each highlighter cost?____________________
3. Which item comes in a box of 50?____________________
4. Which item is sold in a box of 200?____________________
5. How much does each box of paper clips cost? ____________________
6. Which item costs $8.99 each? ____________________
7. Name all the items that are sold individually.

   ____

   ____

8. How much does the stapler cost?____________________
9. Which two items are sold in boxes of 100?____________________

   ____

Name______________________________ Date_____________________

Catalog Exercise 7

C. Free Recall

What Are the Prices?

Stapler

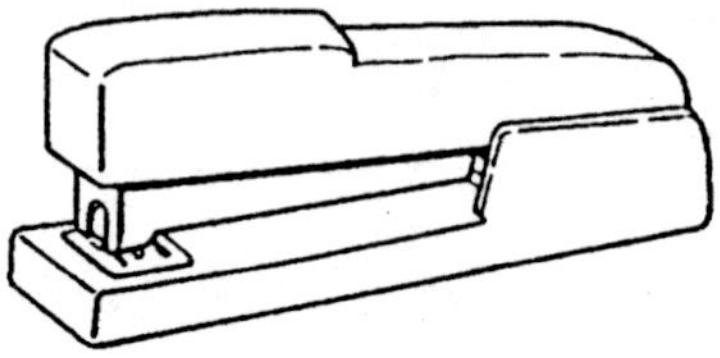

_________ each

Push pins

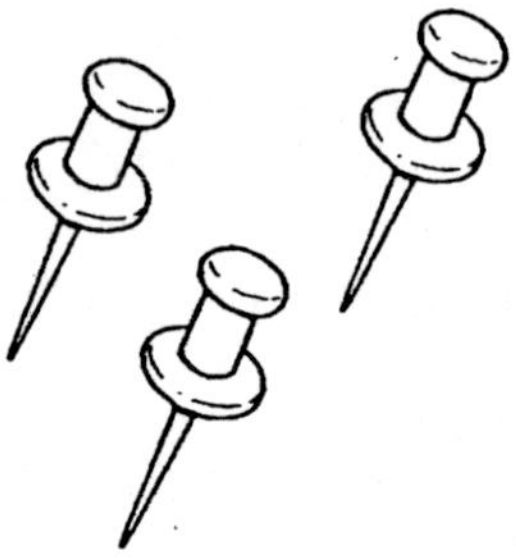

_______ per box of 100

Paper clips

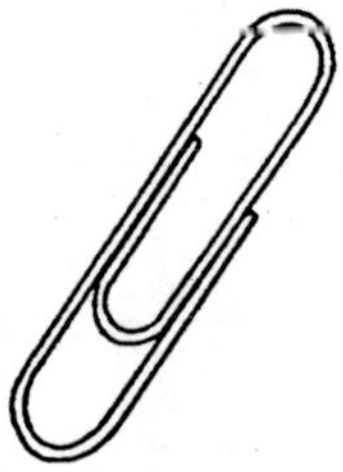

_______ per box of 200

Glue

_________ each

Pens

_______ per box of 50

Scissors

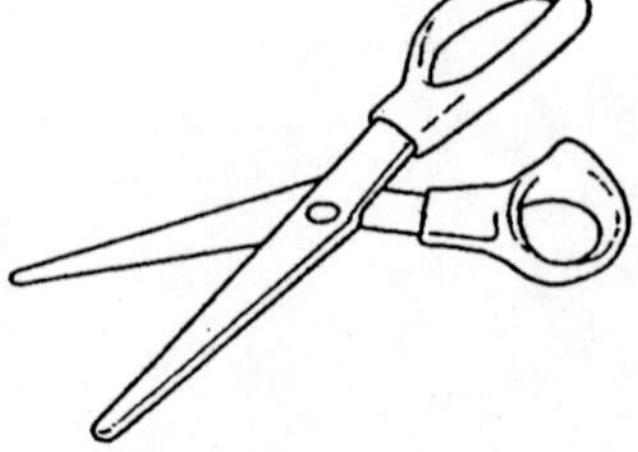

_________ each

Pencils

_______ per box of 100

Highlighters

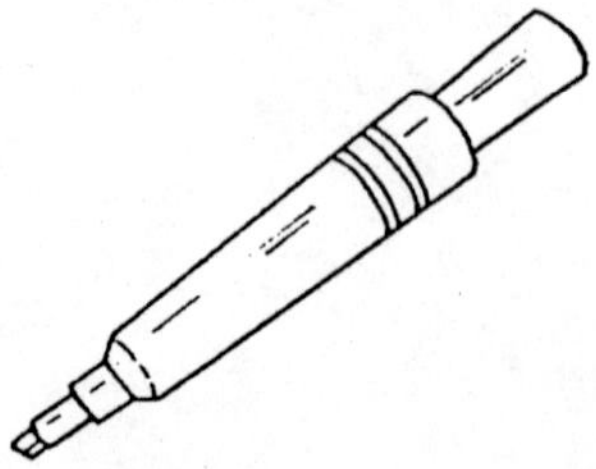

_________ each

Map Exercises

Strategies

Instruct the client to use strategies, such as *semantic elaboration,* in which the client makes up a story connecting buildings, landmarks and street names.

During the learning phase of the exercise, encourage the client to *write* the information on a separate sheet of paper as a means of processing the information more actively and having a record to refer to and *rehearse* the location of buildings, landmarks and street names to be recalled.

Other helpful strategies include *chunking* the features on various sections of the map and *visualization* of a particular street feature.

Instructions

1. Determine the appropriate exercise level for the client, based on clinical judgment and the following guidelines:

Skill Level	Exercise
Level 1—Severe impairment	1 and 2
Level 2—Moderate impairment	3 and 4
Level 3—Mild impairment	5 and 6
Level 4—Advanced skill level	7

2. Provide a copy of the map at the appropriate level.
3. Have the client study the map for five minutes. (You may want to modify this time based on the client's need.)
4. While the client is studying the map, provide a reminder to boost recall by using the strategies discussed above.
5. Have the client place the map out of sight (for example, turned over or placed under the chair).
6. Using clinical judgment, select one of the following recall formats:
   a. Multiple-Choice Questions (the easiest way to recall the presented information)

      There are two ways to present multiple-choice questions:

      - Give the client a copy of the multiple-choice questions that correspond to the map you have selected. Instruct the client to read the questions and circle the correct answers. Have the client work independently for a set amount of time. Then review the answers with the client.

- Read the questions aloud, and have the client respond verbally. Then review the answers with the client.

b. Open-Ended Questions (a moderately difficult way to recall the presented information)

There are two ways to present open-ended questions:

- Give the client a copy of the open-ended questions that correspond to the map you have selected. Instruct the client to read the questions and write the answers. Have the client work independently for a set amount of time. Then review the answers with the client.
- Read the questions aloud, and have the client respond verbally. Then review the answers with the client.

c. Free Recall (the most difficult way to recall the presented information)

Provide a blank map (page 247). Have the client fill in the names of the streets and draw in the buildings.

7. While the client is completing the worksheet, provide a reminder to use strategies to enhance recall.

Please note: When you use the open-ended questions with a client, you will need to cover up other parts of the worksheet that appear on the same page when you photocopy it so the answers are not available.

Map Exercise 1

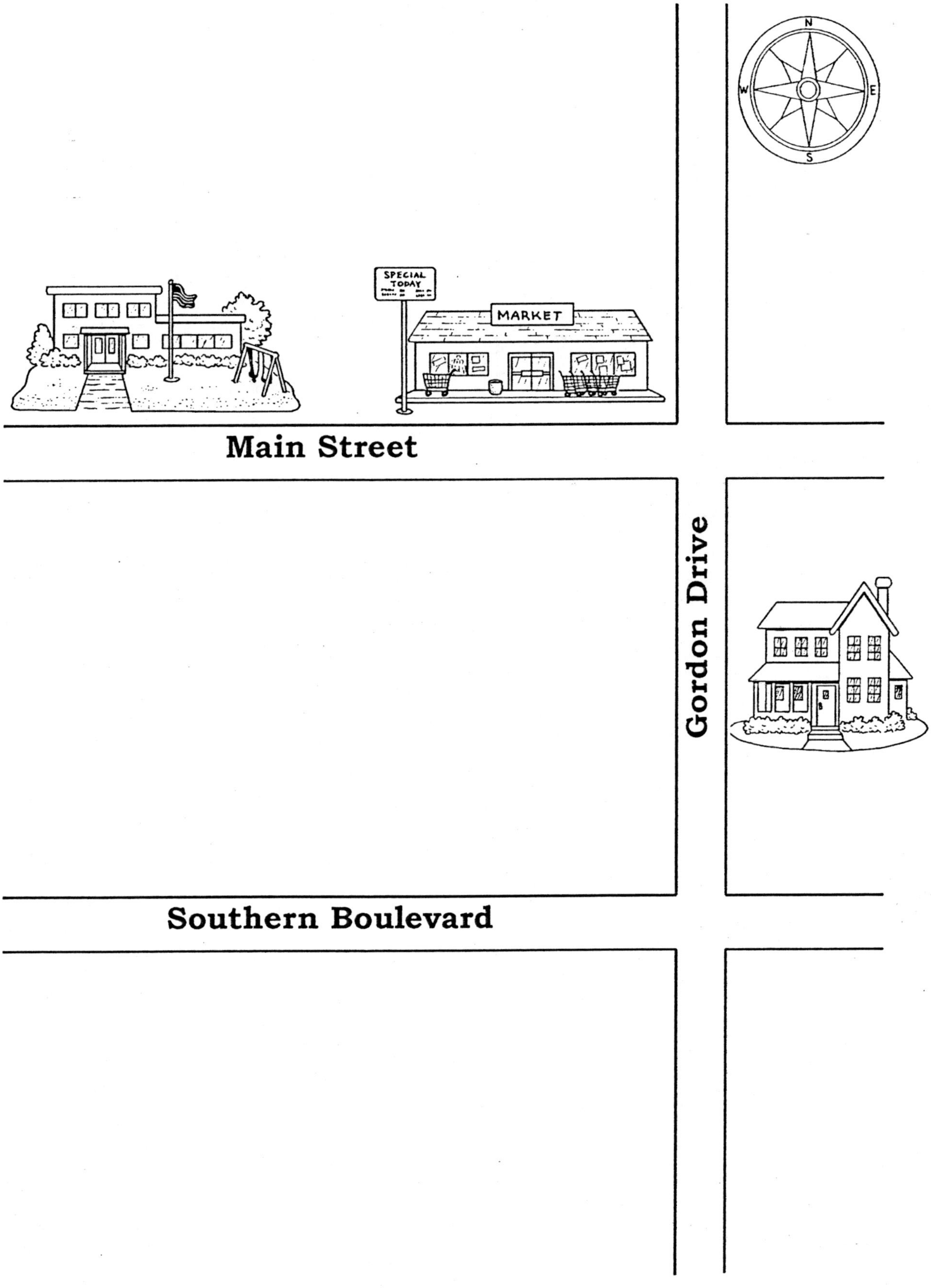

Name______________________________ Date____________________

Map Exercise 1

A. Multiple-Choice Questions

1. What is a street name on the map?
   a. Locust Street
   b. Gordon Drive
   c. Elm Way
   d. Center Lane

2. Is there a school pictured on the map?
   a. Yes
   b. No
   c. I don't remember

3. What is the name of the street where the food store is located?
   a. Main Street
   b. Gordon Drive
   c. Southern Boulevard
   d. Center Lane

B. Open-Ended Questions

1. Name one of the streets on the map. ____________________

2. Is there a school pictured on the map? ____________________

3. Name the street where the food store is located.

   ____

Map Exercise 2

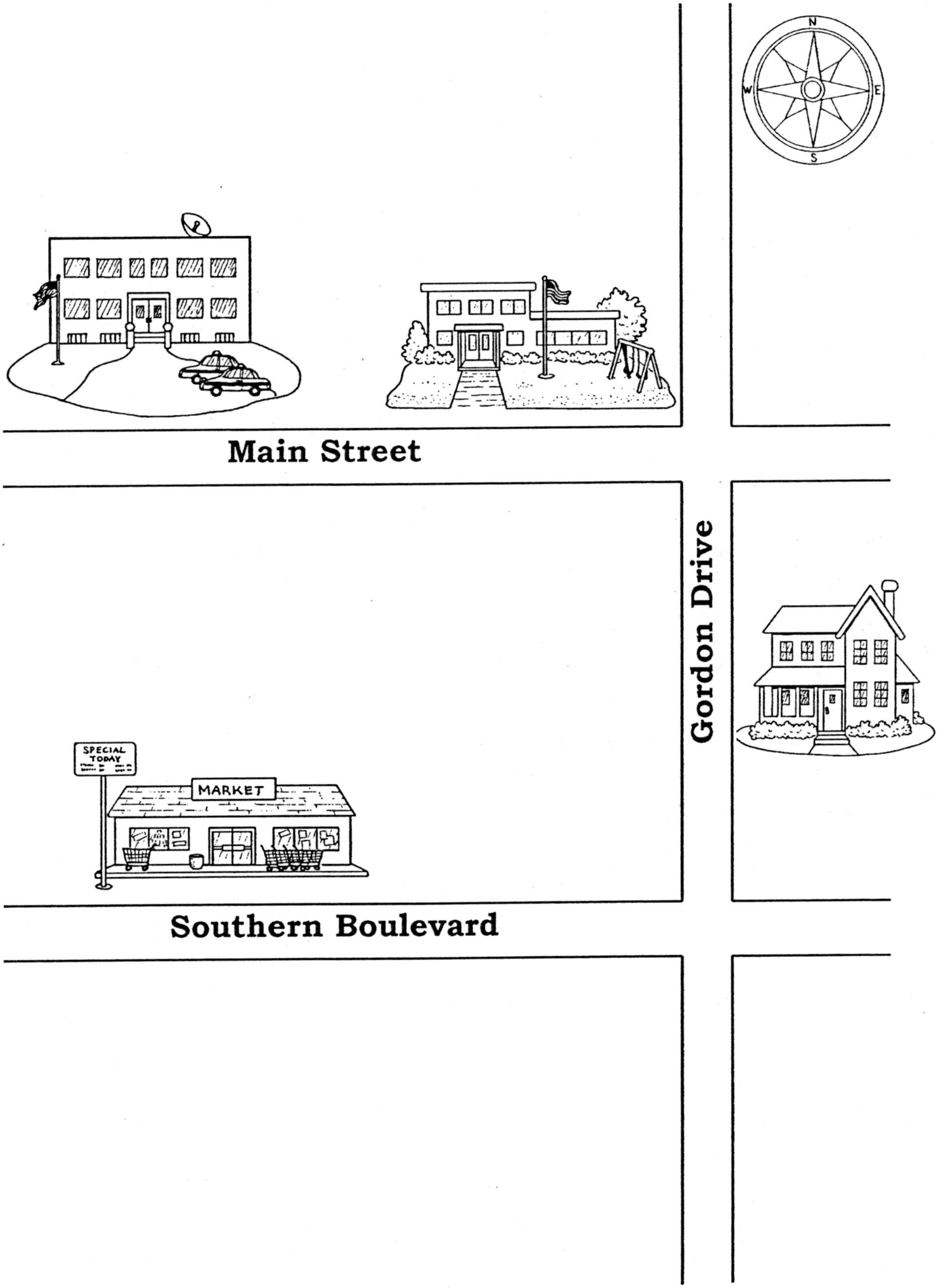

Name________________________________ Date______________________

Map Exercise 2

A. Multiple-Choice Questions

1. What is a street shown on the map?
   a. Locust Street
   b. Gordon Drive
   c. Elm Way
   d. Center Lane
2. Is there a school pictured on the map?
   a. Yes
   b. No
   c. I don't remember
3. What is the name of the street where the food store is located?
   a. Main Street
   b. Gordon Drive
   c. Southern Boulevard
   d. Center Lane
4. Which two buildings are located on Main Street?
   a. House and school
   b. Food store and police station
   c. House and police station
   d. Police station and school
5. Which building is located east of the food store?
   a. Police station
   b. School
   c. House
   d. Gas station

B. Open-Ended Questions

1. Name two of the streets on the map. ____________________________
2. Is there a school pictured on the map? ____________________________
3. Name the street where the food store is located.
   ____
4. Name the two buildings located on Main Street.
   ____
5. What building is located east of the food store?
   ____

Map Exercise 3

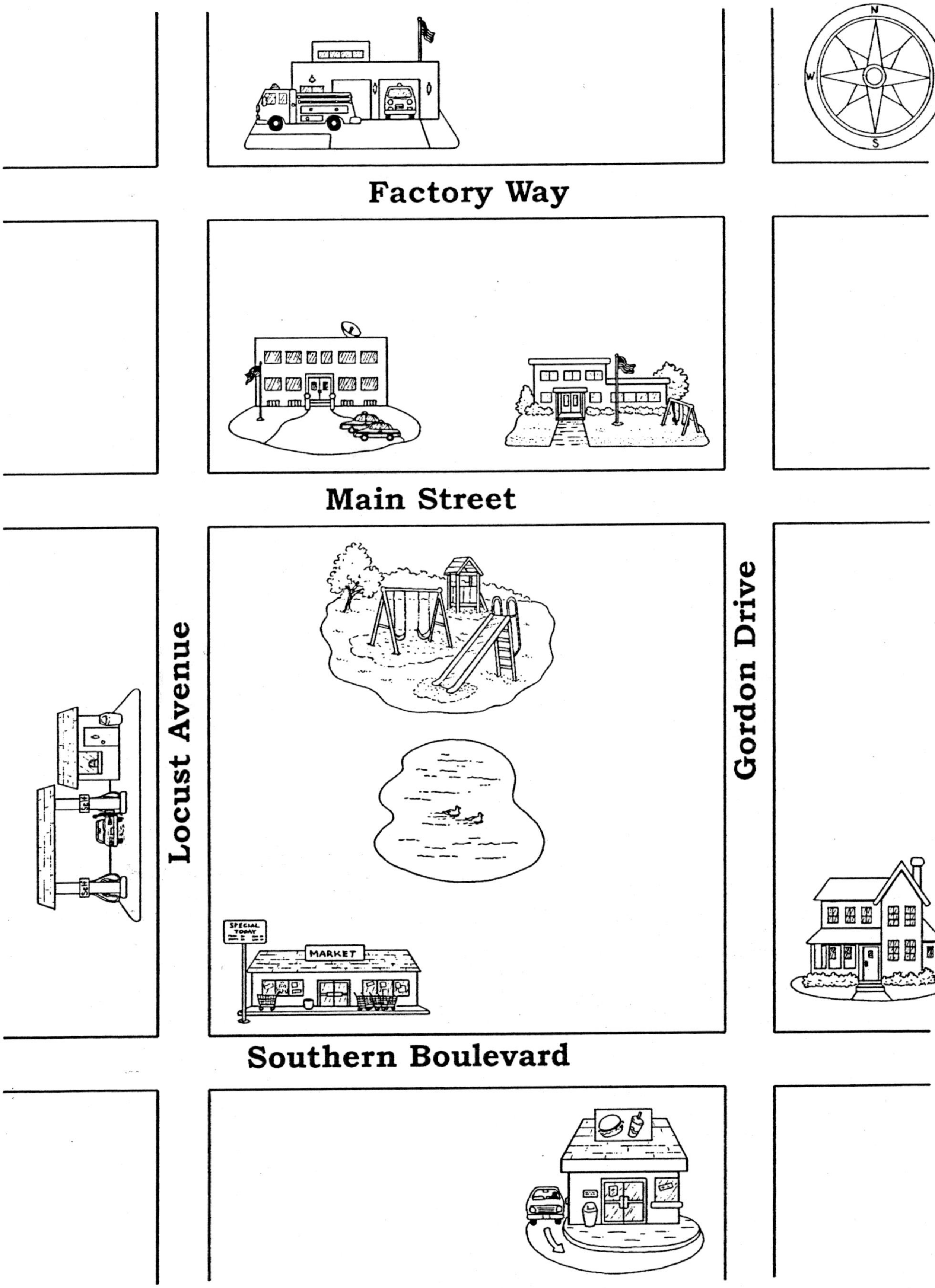

Name________________________________ Date______________________

Map Exercise 3

A. Multiple-Choice Questions

1. Which street name is shown on the map?
   a. Locust Street
   b. Gordon Drive
   c. Elm Way
   d. Factory Lane
2. Is there a school pictured on the map?
   a. Yes
   b. No
   c. I don't remember
3. What is the name of the street where the food store is located?
   a. Main Street
   b. Gordon Drive
   c. Southern Boulevard
   d. Center Lane
4. Which two buildings are located on Main Street?
   a. House and school
   b. Food store and police station
   c. House and police station
   d. Police station and school
5. Which building is located east of the food store?
   a. Police station
   b. School
   c. House
   d. Gas station
6. Which building is located the farthest north on the map?
   a. Factory
   b. Police station
   c. Fire station
   d. Fast-food restaurant
7. Which of the following are located between Main Street and Southern Boulevard?
   a. Police station and school
   b. Lake and gas station
   c. Playground and lake
   d. Fast-food restaurant and food store

Name________________________________ Date______________________

Map Exercise 3

B. Open-Ended Questions

1. Name three of the streets that are on the map.

   ____

2. Is there a school pictured on the map?

   ____

3. Name the street where the food store is located.

   ____

4. Name the two buildings located on Main Street.

   ____

5. What building is located east of the food store?

   ____

6. What building is located the farthest north on the map?

   ____

7. Name two landmarks that are located between Main Street and Southern Boulevard.

   ____

Map Exercise 4

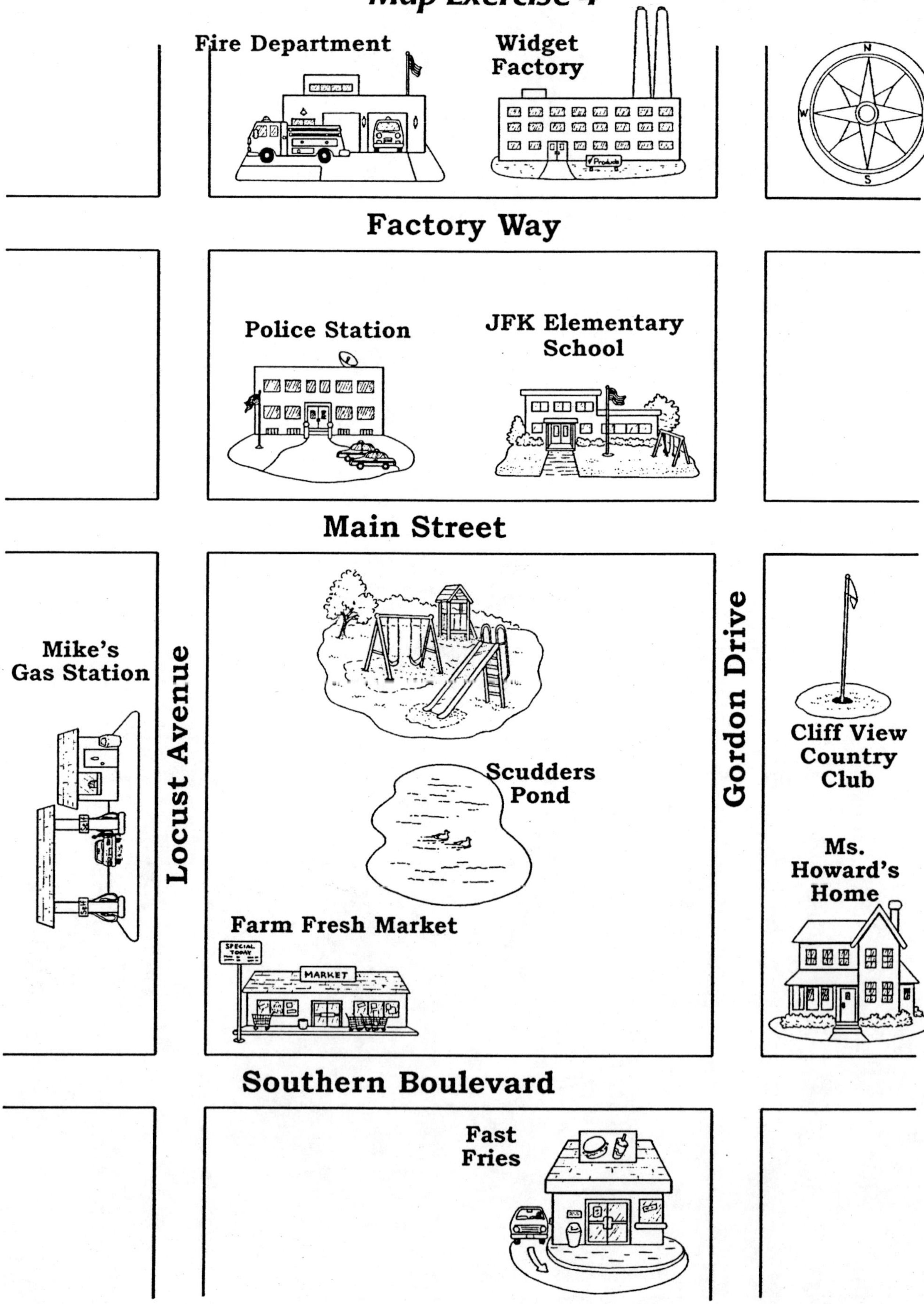

Name______________________ Date______________________

Map Exercise 4

A. Multiple-Choice Questions

1. What is the name of the street located farthest east on the map?
   a. Locust Avenue
   b. Gordon Drive
   c. Main Street
   d. Factory Way
2. Which is not on the map?
   a. Pond
   b. Country club
   c. Airport
   d. Factory
3. On which street is the gas station located?
   a. Southern Boulevard
   b. Main Street
   c. Locust Avenue
   d. Gordon Drive
4. What is the name of the country club?
   a. Cliff Walk
   b. Cliff View
   c. Cliff Side
   d. Ocean Cliff
5. What building is located at the intersection of Southern Boulevard and Gordon Drive?
   a. Farm Fresh Market
   b. Mike's Gas Station
   c. Fast Fries
   d. Value Shopping Center
6. What is the name of the factory?
   a. Widget
   b. Fidget
   c. Digit
   d. Smidget
7. What is located directly north of the pond?
   a. Playground
   b. Farm Fresh Market
   c. Ms. Howard's house
   d. Value Shopping Center
8. What is the name of the pond?
   a. Shutters
   b. Scudders
   c. Shuttles
   d. Swishing
9. What is located west of the factory?
   a. JFK Elementary School
   b. Police station
   c. Fire station
   d. Gas station
10. What building is located farthest east and south of the fire station?
    a. Ms. Howard's house
    b. Fast Fries
    c. Farm Fresh Market
    d. Mike's Gas Station

Name______________________________ Date____________________

Map Exercise 4

B. Open-Ended Questions

1. Name all of the streets on the map.

____

____

2. What is the name of the school? ______________________________

3. On what street is the gas station located?

____

4. What is the name of the country club?

____

5. What building is located at the intersection of Southern Boulevard and Gordon Drive?

____

6. What is the name of the factory? ______________________________

7. What is located directly north of the pond?

____

8. What is the name of the pond?

____

9. What is located west of the factory? ___________________________

10. What building is located farthest east and south of the fire station?

____

Blank Map

Chapter 6

Sequential Recall Exercises

Sequential recall exercises present a double challenge for clients. They require both recall of information and retrieval of a specific sequence. The exercises provide practice in attention to detail, delayed recall and attention to the order in which information is presented.

Contents

Sequential Recall Stories

Strategies

Instruct the client to pay attention to the details while listening to the verbally presented story, and then *visualize* the specific details as the story unfolds. Also remind the client to *associate* the new information with personal memories. *First-letter mnemonics* also are useful in recalling a sequence. Encourage the client to *write* the relevant details as a means of processing the information more actively and having a record to refer to and use for *rehearsing* the presented points.

Instructions

Select appropriate exercises and task presentation, based on clinical judgment and the following guidelines:

Skill Level and Task Presentation

Level 1—Severe impairment. Verbally present the introductory statement only. Ask the client to recall the five or six facts from the introduction.

Level 2—Moderate impairment. Verbally present the introductory statement and the first three sentences in the sequence of six sentences. Ask the client to recall both the introductory statement and the first three sentences.

Level 3—Mild impairment. Verbally present the introductory statement followed by the first three sentences in the sequence of six sentences. Then test the client's retention of the introduction and first three sentences by asking the client (or different clients) to retrieve the facts of the story. Once recall is mastered, present the last three sentences and test on the introduction and the six sentences that follow.

To increase speed of information processing, ability to shift attention and delayed sequential recall, call on different clients to recall a specific event by number in the sequence (for example, "What was the fourth sentence about?").

Sequential Recall Story 1

Lucille Brown, a 32-year-old teacher, lives in Scarsdale, New York. This story begins early on a Saturday in April.

1. Mrs. Brown takes her eldest child, Carl, to her mother's home in East Meadow.
2. Mrs. Brown takes her youngest child, George, to her sister's home in Glen Oaks.
3. Lucille and her husband, Frank, board an American Airlines flight to Boston.
4. The Browns' closest friends, Tom and Tammy, who are getting married that evening, meet them at Logan Airport.
5. The Browns have some spare time after checking into their hotel, and they take a walk along the Charles River in Cambridge for 45 minutes.
6. The wedding begins at 7:00 p.m. with 350 attendees.

Sequential Recall Story 2

Pierre LaRue is a 51-year-old male metals trader who lives in New Orleans. His story takes place on a Wednesday in August.

1. Pierre stops at the coffee shop for a hazelnut-flavored latte on his way to the streetcar.
2. He meets two of his traveling buddies, Charles and Marion, on the streetcar.
3. He reads three articles in *Fortune* magazine during the ride to his office.
4. He meets with three partners to review the past quarter's earnings, which were above original projections.
5. He makes travel arrangements for his forthcoming business trip to Australia, which will be in September.
6. After dinner, he meets his closest friend, Jeff, and they hit golf balls at the driving range at their country club.

Sequential Recall Story 3

Ed Kramer is a 55-year-old male who loves to kayak. His story takes place in August.

1. On Sunday, Ed has his wife, Peggy, drive him to the north fork on Long Island.
2. He brings along his kayak and camping gear and food for a week.
3. He camps overnight on a deserted beach.
4. In the morning, at sunrise, he has breakfast, cleans up the camping equipment and sets off heading westward along the shore of Long Island.
5. After two days, he is at the halfway point, where he meets his wife for dinner at a lovely seaside restaurant.
6. She warns him of impending bad weather heading his way, so the next day he completes the trip, paddling for more than 10 hours.

Sequential Recall Story 4

Josh Carver is a 26-year-old computer engineer working in Denver. His story takes place in October.

1. Josh takes the bus to work on Monday. There, he learns that he is to leave for San Francisco the following day.
2. When he gets to the airport, he learns that his plane will depart two hours late due to the weather.
3. He must call his business associates to explain the delay and reschedule his meeting, originally set for immediately after his 10:00 a.m. arrival.
4. At the meeting, he learns that his company will be receiving a contract for $1 million for a project he has been working on.
5. He phones his associates in Denver on Tuesday afternoon with the great news, and he talks for 45 minutes about the business plan.
6. He flies home on Wednesday, is picked up at the airport by his girlfriend, Amy, and they go to Sam's Seafood to celebrate the new contract.

Sequential Recall Story 5

Eartha is a 42-year-old editor who lives in Boulder, Colorado. Her story takes place on a Friday evening in May.

1. She takes her 9-year-old son, Kyle, to a piano lesson at 6:00 p.m.
2. She goes to a jewelry store to buy earrings for her mother-in-law for her birthday.
3. She picks up Kyle and takes him and his closest friend, Nicholas, to Big Show Video.
4. At home, she does the laundry while the boys watch the video.
5. She bakes brownies with walnuts and raisins.
6. Once Kyle is asleep, she talks for 40 minutes with her husband, Paul, who is in Hong Kong on business.

Sequential Recall Story 6

Tammy is a 32-year-old law school student living in New Haven. Her story begins on Friday afternoon in May.

1. She and her friend, William, meet Hilda and Rachel at the Yale Law Library for a study session beginning at 4:00 p.m. and lasting for two hours.
2. She walks six blocks to her apartment and phones her brother, Everett, who lives in California, and they talk about her plan to visit him this summer.
3. She makes dinner consisting of eggplant, zucchini, peppers and mushrooms over linguini and asks her roommate, Karen, to join her.
4. She arranges to go to California in four weeks for six days, leaving on a Saturday from Kennedy Airport in New York City.
5. She goes to a bookstore on Saturday and chooses a bestseller to get her mind off all legal matters while she is in California.
6. She works on her budget for the trip after she pays her rent, Visa, American Express and phone bills for the month of June.

Sequential Recall Story 7

Max David is a 7-year-old who lives in Great Neck. The story takes place on a Tuesday in July.

1. Max's mother, Gloria, drops him off at 251st Street at 7:45 a.m. to board Andrea's bus to Camp Sunshine.
2. Max's first activity at camp is tennis.
3. His second and third activities are cooking and basketball.
4. For lunch, Max has three hot dogs but no sauerkraut.
5. After lunch, Max passes the deep-water swimming test and is presented with a blue bracelet.
6. On a scavenger hunt at 2:30, Max and his friend, Ian, find yellow swimming goggles, a new shiny quarter and three red crayons.

Sequential Recall Story 8

Candy is a 41-year-old single college professor who teaches psychology at UCLA. Her story takes place in May on a Sunday afternoon.

1. Candy meets her friend, Vickie, at the Black Forest Café for lunch at 1:30.
2. Vickie tells Candy about Keith, a man she met the previous evening at a fund-raising event for cancer care, who she feels may be a suitable match for Candy.
3. Candy agrees to meet Keith that evening after speaking on the phone with him for more than two hours.
4. Candy and Keith have coffee at a local diner, talking about their families and careers and their mutual interest in biking.
5. Candy returns home to grade 23 term papers on child development.
6. Candy then begins preparing a course outline for a new course she will be teaching over the summer in psychological statistics.

Sequential Recall Story 9

Harry Fields is a 20-year-old truck driver from Kansas City. His story takes place on a Thursday in January.

1. Harry is driving his 18-wheel truck full of couches to Independence, Missouri.
2. Harry likes country-western music and listens to station WCTY.
3. Harry hears, "Your Cheating Heart," which reminds him of his recent breakup with Jane, his girlfriend for 3 years.
4. Harry has been working 10-hour days, 6 days a week, for the last 7 months.
5. He decides he must cut back his hours and wants to limit work to 8 hours a day, 5 days a week.
6. When he arrives home, he phones Jane, who agrees to meet him for dinner at a Mexican restaurant.

Sequential Recall Story 10

Inez Ramirez is a 74-year-old retired secretary. Her story takes place in June on a Tuesday.

1. After eating waffles for breakfast, Inez walks three miles with her neighbor, Sophie.
2. She then goes shopping at Granny's Toy Shop and buys her grandson, Juan, a scooter and a blue helmet.
3. She also buys her daughter-in-law, Bonita, a red and gold scarf at Sam's Department Store for her 46th birthday.
4. She then goes food shopping with her twin sister, Elena, at Western Supermarket.
5. Because she slept only 4½ hours the night before due to a headache, Inez takes a nap from 4:00 in the afternoon until 5:30.
6. She makes dinner of broiled fish, rice and salad and invites her neighbor, Ethel, to join her.

Sequential Recall Story 11

Dolores is a 52-year-old dancer who had a stroke in June. Her story takes place on a Monday in November.

1. Her first day at a new rehabilitation facility begins at 9:00 a.m. in physical therapy (PT).
2. After PT, she meets with her case manager, Maria, who explains the program.
3. At 11:00 a.m., she has a speech-language evaluation by Peggy.
4. At lunch, she sits next to Carlos and Robert, who also are recovering from strokes.
5. After lunch, she has an occupational therapy (OT) evaluation by John in the OT suite on the third floor.
6. At 3:00 p.m., her brother, Lenny, picks her up to drive her home to East St. Louis.

Sequential Recall Story 12

Lin Chu is a 33-year-old mother of three who lives in Seattle. Her story takes place on a Sunday in December.

1. Lin gets up at 6:00 a.m. to feed her youngest child, Lon, who is 3 months old.
2. She gathers the laundry from her 3-year-old daughter Soo Lin's room and goes to the basement of their apartment building.
3. In the laundry room, she meets her neighbors, Mr. Lau and Mrs. Woo, who live on the fifth floor.
4. While the laundry is washing, Lin gets breakfast ready for Soo Lin and Mai Cho, who is 6 years old.
5. After breakfast, Lin, Soo and Mai return to the basement from their third-floor apartment to finish the laundry.
6. Lin and her three children go to the grocery store to buy food for the day's meal.

Sequential Recall Story 13

Mario is a 42-year-old butcher who lives in Chicago's suburb of Evanston. His story takes place on a Saturday in March.

1. He gets up at 4:00 a.m. to drive to the market section on Chicago's west side to select the meat for his store.
2. He gets a flat tire on his way to Chicago and is angry when he finds he has no air in his spare tire.
3. He walks ½ mile to a phone and calls his brother, Sal, at Parker Truck Repair.
4. Sal arrives in 45 minutes with an air compressor, and he pumps up the spare.
5. Mario's first customer, Mrs. Leone, is waiting for him as he arrives back at his store at 7:30 a.m.
6. Mario's day begins to improve when Mrs. Leone buys sausage, chopped meat, veal and steak to serve at a party she is having that evening.

Sequential Recall Story 14

Uncle Patrick is a 68-year-old man who owns a tavern on Boston's south side. His story takes place on a Wednesday evening in July.

1. The tavern closes at midnight during a thunderstorm.
2. Uncle Pat has difficulty starting his old Plymouth, which was parked two blocks away.
3. He phones his brother-in-law, Sean, and wakes him up.
4. Sean tells his son, Dennis, to get the jumper cables and meet him in the garage as soon as possible.
5. Their drive from Worcester takes only 25 minutes because there is no traffic on the Massachusetts Turnpike.
6. Uncle Pat eventually gets home at 2:30 a.m., where he finds his wife, Margaret Mary, asleep.

Sequential Recall Story 15

Dr. Kathleen Stone is a 54-year-old pediatrician who is attending a conference in Virginia. The story takes place in April.

1. Dr. Stone arrives in Virginia from Orlando on Friday evening and has dinner at the Hilton Hotel with three of her colleagues.
2. She attends an address at 8:45 Saturday morning on an HIV camp funded by a celebrity.
3. At 11:15 a.m., she presents a lecture on infant pain management in Conference Room L-3.
4. At noontime, she has lunch with her former supervisor, Dr. Godfried.
5. On Sunday evening, she takes a 7:15 p.m. flight home to Orlando.
6. Returning home by 9:30, she completes a conference report that is due on Monday morning.

Sequential Recall Story 16

Mr. and Mrs. Takamori are celebrating their 50th wedding anniversary on Saturday, May 7.

1. Their oldest son, Suki, brings a bouquet of long-stem roses in shades of red and white at 10:30 a.m.
2. Nancy, their daughter, arrives at noon and drives her parents to lunch at their other daughter Helen's home in San Francisco.
3. While at Helen's home, a telegram arrives from the president of the United States acknowledging their anniversary.
4. When lunch is almost over, they receive a phone call from Mrs. Takamori's cousin, Lin, from Tokyo.
5. When they return home from Helen's, they open their gifts, which include a lovely photo album assembled by all of their grandchildren.
6. When they arrive for dinner with their youngest son, Jimmy, they are surprised to find 70 other friends and relatives joining the celebration.

Sequential Recall Story 17

Marty and Sylvia live in the suburbs of New York. Their story takes place on a summer weekend.

1. At 5:30 a.m., Marty and Sylvia pack their van and drive to Bennington, Vermont, a 7-hour drive.
2. They bring their oboes, sheet music and reservation information for the conference they are attending.
3. While they register, they meet their fellow orchestra members, Jonathan, Lillian and Augustus.
4. They meet at 2:30 for a 2-hour practice session, beginning with Mozart and finishing with Vivaldi.
5. At 5:00 p.m., they have an early dinner and then take a half-hour walk around town.
6. At 7:10 p.m., the orchestra, in formal attire, assembles backstage before their performance at 7:30 p.m.

Sequential Recall Story 18

Cathy and Warren Brill are neighbors of Roberta and Neil Cole. Their story takes place on a Wednesday evening in the spring.

1. Cathy and Roberta had met for lunch and decided to meet again for dinner with their spouses that evening at 7:00 p.m.
2. During dinner at the Brills' home, the conversation turns to vacation plans each couple is considering.
3. They all decide that a trip to Washington State would be enjoyable, and they begin planning a trip for late September or early October.
4. Using the Internet, they investigate kayaking in the San Juan Islands, hiking at Mount Rainier and a drive along the Olympic Peninsula.
5. They request information from the Office of Tourism in Seattle regarding lodging accommodations.
6. Before the evening has ended, the Brills and the Coles decide to begin their journey on September 15 and return on September 29.

Sequential Recall Story 19

Bill is a 57-year-old pilot from Palo Alto. His story takes place on a Saturday in August.

1. Bill gets a phone call from his boss, Jose, at 5:00 a.m. to get to San Jose Airport by 7:30 a.m.
2. Bill learns that his friend, Carla, also a pilot, is unable to fly that day.
3. Bill wakes his wife, Carol, and kids, Paul, 7, and Cindy, 9, to say goodbye.
4. He drives to the airport down Route 101 in 45 minutes.
5. Bill's flight takes him from San Jose to Phoenix, Dallas and St. Louis.
6. After spending the night in St. Louis, he boards another flight, returning directly to San Jose at 11:00 a.m. the next morning.

Sequential Recall Story 20

Dr. Luis Hernandez is a 32-year-old dentist from Santa Fe. His story takes place on a Tuesday in November.

1. Luis arrives at his office on El Camino Encanto at 7:30 a.m.
2. His first patient, Mrs. Younger, arrives promptly for her appointment at 8:00 a.m.
3. After seeing Mrs. Younger, Dr. Hernandez treats a 4-year-old boy, Brian, who is having his first dental checkup.
4. Dr. Hernandez' son, Michael, is 4, so he is accustomed to young children.
5. For the remainder of the day, Dr. Hernandez treats a 15-year-old boy, a 66-year-old male and a 3-year-old who has broken a tooth.
6. He reviews his appointments for the day and sees he'll be treating six adults and seven children.

Sequential Recall Story 21

Rosa Francisco is a 47-year-old restaurant owner from Boston's north side. Her story takes place on a Saturday in May.

1. Rosa's day begins at 5:30 a.m. as she departs for the fresh produce, meat and fish markets.
2. She buys sea bass and octopus, veal, chicken, eggplant and zucchini.
3. She arrives at her restaurant, Bella Luna, by 8 a.m., where she meets with the chef, Antonio, to plan the menu and specials for the day.
4. They decide upon osso bucco, eggplant parmesan and calamari with marinara sauce.
5. By 8:00 p.m., there is a line waiting to get into Bella Luna, where the waiters are busy tending to the 20 tables.
6. Rosa's day ends with dinner with the staff of eight, and they enjoy a sampling of the specials.

Sequential Recall Story 22

Henry is a 48-year-old clothing manufacturer from Memphis, Tennessee. His story takes place on board a flight from Nashville to Las Vegas, Nevada, on August 25.

1. Henry is traveling alone to Las Vegas to a men's wholesale clothing convention.
2. He expects to meet his partner, Mel, before boarding the plane that is scheduled to depart at 12:10 p.m.
3. He boards the plane alone, unable to find Mel in the crowded waiting area.
4. Although Henry has a coach ticket, the plane is overbooked and the last remaining seat is in first class.
5. He is delighted with the dinner of roast duck, pureed carrots and stuffed mushrooms.
6. Once in Las Vegas, he takes a taxi to The Gambler's Hotel, where he phones his wife to tell her of his good fortune in flying first class.

Sequential Recall Story 23

Margaret Watt is a 29-year-old mother of two who lives in Wichita, Kansas. Her story takes place on a Tuesday morning.

1. Margaret goes to the grocery market, Young's, after her children, Kenny and Carol Ann, leave for school.
2. She remembers to buy cupcake mix for Kenny's scout meeting on Thursday.
3. She stops at the drugstore to pick up shaving cream for Arthur, her husband.
4. From 12:00 noon to 2:30, she volunteers at Memorial Hospital in the pediatric unit, helping to feed the newborns.
5. At 3:00 p.m., Margaret is home when the children arrive on the bus from Oakwood Elementary School.
6. The children help Margaret make the cupcakes for the scout meeting, then start their homework before dinner at 6:00 p.m.

Sequential Recall Story 24

Diane is a 55-year-old president of the Orange County Garden Club. Her story takes place during the first week in May.

1. On Monday, Diane phones Elise, the organizer of this week's Garden Club meeting, to confirm arrangements for Friday's meeting.
2. Elise tells Diane that the speaker, Mr. Cooper, will be arriving on Thursday afternoon at 4:00 p.m.
3. Diane calls Sunshine Transport to have Mr. Cooper picked up at Los Angeles International Airport.
4. On Thursday, Diane calls Johanna to discuss the final plans for the meeting at her home on Friday.
5. Johanna phones Diane on Thursday night to report that all the flowers, speaker's materials and chairs for the tent have been assembled.
6. Friday dawns sunny and warm. The speaker delivers an interesting talk about ponds, fish and predators, and the meeting is judged a tremendous success.

Sequential Recall Story 25

Julia is a 17-year-old student who lives in Hamburg, Germany. Her story takes place in April.

1. She wakes up at 4:30 a.m. to finish packing for her trip to New York as an exchange student.
2. On Sunday, Julia's class arrives at John F. Kennedy International Airport at 5:30 p.m. and is greeted by Mr. Goldberg from Whitman High School. He takes the students to meet their sponsor families, who drive them to their homes on Manhasset, Long Island.
3. On Monday, the group travels by train to New York City, where they have lunch in Central Park, take a boat ride to the Statue of Liberty and have dinner at Tavern on the Green.
4. On Tuesday and Wednesday, Julia and her friend Lisa attend German and math classes at Whitman High School.
5. On Friday, the group from Hamburg boards the train in Cold Spring to journey to Washington D.C., where they visit the White House, Congress and the Smithsonian Institution.
6. After spending 9 days in the U.S., Julia returns to Hamburg, where she tells her parents and younger sister, Helga, about her experiences.

Sequential Recall Story 26

Ranjit is getting dressed for an important job interview at Blinking Cursor Computer Company.

1. He opens the top left-hand drawer of his dresser and takes out a pair of navy blue socks.
2. Next, he walks to the closet to get his navy blue pinstriped suit, white button-down shirt and yellow-and-red striped tie.
3. He sits on the edge of his queen-sized bed to put on his socks, right foot, then left. He stands up to put on his pants, left leg, then right leg, his shirt and tie.
4. He walks back to the closet to retrieve his black, wing-tipped shoes, black belt with gold buckle and briefcase.
5. He sits on the green chair and puts on his shoes. Standing up, he slides the belt through the six loopholes on his pants and slips his arms into the suit jacket.
6. With a final glance in his wife's full-length mirror, he quickly adjusts his tie and runs his hands through his hair before heading for the door.

Sequential Recall Story 27

Jillian wants to make Sunday morning breakfast for her husband, Robert.

1. She opens the refrigerator door and removes eggs, milk, butter, orange juice, Muenster cheese and pumpernickel bread.
2. After placing the ingredients on the counter, she opens the lower cabinet next to the stove and retrieves a 12-inch frying pan. Placing the pan on the stove, she sets the control to medium heat.
3. She places four slices of pumpernickel bread into the toaster, sets it on medium dark and presses START. She cracks four eggs into a bowl, adds two splashes of milk and whisks the egg mixture.
4. With the pan hot, Jillian adds two pats of butter. When they are melted, she adds the whisked eggs to the pan, stirring with a wooden spatula. When the toaster pops, she butters two slices for Robert and places the four slices of toast on a blue-flowered plate.
5. Jillian quickly removes the eggs from the heat and divides them between two blue-striped plates. She fills two juice glasses with orange juice and brings the eggs, toast and juice to the table.
6. Next to each plate on the left, she places a folded napkin that has a vegetable print on it. To the right of the plate, she places a knife and spoon, and on the left she places a fork. She calls to her husband, "Breakfast is ready!"

Sequential Recall Story 28

Denise is getting ready for her first day at her new job.

1. She opens the medicine cabinet and removes the Smile Brite toothpaste from the top shelf. To her left is a yellow cup, which holds her green toothbrush.
2. She turns on the water and passes her toothbrush three times underneath the ice-cold water. After unscrewing the toothpaste cap, she squeezes just enough mint-flavored toothpaste to cover the bristles on her toothbrush.
3. She places the toothbrush in her mouth and begins to brush the top left portion of her mouth, then the lower left, next the bottom right, upper right, and finishes by brushing her front top and bottom teeth.
4. She removes a paper cup with a daisy pattern on it from the dispenser underneath the sink. Filling it halfway with lukewarm water, she rinses her mouth, then rinses the brush and replaces it in the yellow cup.

5. Denise cups her hands underneath the running water and splashes her face twice with warm water. With a pink hand towel, she dries her face and hands.
6. She brushes her shoulder-length chestnut hair and places a red headband on her head. Finally, she applies red lipstick with four quick strokes, smiles and walks out of the bathroom.

Sequential Recall Story 29

It is the end of October and Saul must pay his credit card bill from the OK-To-Charge-It Company.

1. On the kitchen table he places a pencil, the bill, a book of stamps, his checkbook and a calculator.
2. Saul opens the envelope and tears the return coupon along the dotted line. His credit card balance is $831.56. He decides to pay $486.32.
3. Opening his checkbook, he fills out check number 719. He then turns to his transaction book and deducts the amount from his balance of $1,395.02.
4. He places the coupon and check inside the return envelope.
5. He places a stamp on the envelope and writes his address: 45 Western Way Lane, Albuquerque, NM 91021.
6. He walks to the corner of Lone Pine Lane and Cottonwood Drive, puts the envelope in the mailbox and notes that it will be picked up at 1:00 p.m. that afternoon.

Sequential Recall Story 30

It is Thursday, and Tyrone needs to do his laundry before he visits his sister.

1. Tyrone places a box of Get-It-Clean detergent and plastic bag of quarters on top of his purple laundry basket overflowing with clothes. He walks down three flights of steps to the laundry room.
2. In the laundry room, he separates the items into three piles, the largest consisting of towels and sheets, another pile containing white T-shirts and socks, and the last having jeans, sweatshirts and sweaters.
3. Tyrone decides to wash the largest pile first. He turns the water temperature dial to WARM/COLD and the load size dial to EXTRA LARGE. Then he turns the cycle dial to ON and the washer begins to fill with water.

4. He measures ¾ cup of detergent and pours it into the washer. After allowing the soap to dissolve for one minute, he begins to add his laundry. When the washer is full, he closes the lid and places the laundry basket on top of the machine.
5. Tyrone sits on an orange plastic chair and begins to read the newspaper. When he has read halfway through the paper, the washer has completed its cycle. He places the newspaper on the yellow counter, walks to the dryer and opens the washer door.
6. He begins to transfer the wet items to the dryer. When it is full, he places a sheet of Softy on top of the wet clothes, closes the door, turns the dial to HIGH HEAT and pushes START.

Four-Question Exercises

This is a group activity.

Four-question exercises require the client to selectively attend and to shift and sustain attention and concentration. The exercises provide practice in skills needed in everyday communication with groups of people. These skills include:

- Sustained and divided attention
- Processing, comprehension and recall of new information

Strategies

Instruct clients to use internal strategies, such as *visualizing* the answers presented by other group members, *associating* the answers with pre-existing memories and using *first-letter mnemonics* to encode the questions. Encourage clients to *write* key words to help them recall the sequence of questions that are presented.

Instructions

1. Determine the appropriate exercise level for the client, based on clinical judgment and the following guidelines:

Skill Level	**Exercise**
Level 1—Severe impairment	One or two questions
Level 2—Moderate impairment	Two or three questions
Level 3—Mild impairment	Four questions

2. Select questions from the lists presented below. Ask the question(s), and have individual clients answer concisely. Instruct clients to listen carefully to other group members' answers and boost recall by using the strategies discussed above. The clients have to perform two tasks:

   a. Answer questions posed by the clinician.

   b. Remember the answers (to the same questions) generated by the other group members in the sequence in which the questions were presented.

   You may select all questions from the same category, which facilitates recall because of the common association, or you may present a more difficult challenge by selecting questions from several categories. For example, ask the following four unrelated questions:

Who is the most athletic person you know?

What is your favorite magazine?

How have your peers in rehabilitation influenced you?

What was your favorite type of music when you were in high school?

In this example, the *first-letter mnemonic* AM, PM (Athletic, Magazine, Peers, Music) can help clients encode the sequence of unrelated items in a cohesive manner. Help the group members to identify the key words to form the mnemonic.

The five categories presented below are not all-inclusive. You may want to develop categories that are specific to individuals or to the group itself. Other categories might include sports, medicine, history, entertainment, travel and famous people.

Favorites

Begin with the carrier phrase, "What is your favorite ________?"

- restaurant
- magazine
- sport
- vacation
- subject in school
- season
- meal
- song
- car
- book
- movie
- dessert
- accomplishment
- hobby
- type of transportation
- time of the day
- pet
- work of art
- year of life up to now
- leisure activity

Attributes

Ask, "Who is the most _____ person you know?"

- athletic
- friendly
- irritable
- health-conscious
- adventurous
- talented
- private
- trustworthy
- logical
- hard-working
- humorous
- fun-loving
- compassionate
- admirable
- cooperative
- high-strung
- optimistic
- pessimistic
- glamorous
- generous

Rehabilitation-Related Experiences

What has been the hardest challenge since your injury?

What has been the most frustrating aspect of your injury?

What have you found most helpful in your rehabilitation program?

What do you consider is your greatest area of strength since your injury?

What do you value most since your injury?

What is your attitude toward rehabilitation?

How has your self-confidence changed since the injury?

What is your greatest source of anger since your injury?

Who has been most affected by your injury?

Has anything positive resulted from your injury?

In what month and year did your injury occur?

Where were you hospitalized immediately following the injury?

What is the last thing you remember before the injury?

What is the first thing you remember following the injury?

Who among your family members and friends have been the most supportive?

In what way have you become a difficult person to live with since the injury?

What is your main goal in rehabilitation?

How have your peers in rehabilitation influenced you?

What is your greatest criticism of the rehabilitation process?

What has been your greatest accomplishment since your injury?

Childhood Memories

What was your favorite game when you were a child?

Who was your favorite teacher in elementary school?

Who was the first best friend that you can remember?

What was the greatest source of conflict in your teenage years?

What kind of pet did you or one of your friends own when you were a child?

What characteristic would best describe you as a teenager?

What responsibilities were assigned to you when you were a child?

What style of discipline did your parents use?

What is your most outstanding childhood vacation memory?

How did you spend your summers when you were a child?

Who was your favorite baby-sitter when you were a child?

Did you have any hospital experiences as a child?

What type of work experiences did you have as a teenager?

What school accomplishment are you most proud of?

What do you remember about your kindergarten teacher?

Who was your first crush?

Who was your first boyfriend/girlfriend?

Where were you raised?

What was your favorite type of music when you were in high school?

When you were a child, what vocational aspirations did you have?

Miscellaneous Questions

When was your first flight on an airplane?

What was your first experience away from home?

What was your first job?

What was your first experience with gambling?

What was the first meal you cooked?

What is the greatest challenge to your patience?

What type of listener are you?

What was your greatest talent before your injury?

What quality distinguishes you from the rest of your family?

What would your ideal retirement plan be?

Who is the most compatible person you have worked with?

Who is the most difficult person you have worked with?

Who are your current next-door neighbors?

How did you spend your free time during elementary school years?

What were your feelings during the first week of rehabilitation?

What is your recollection of a time when you were lost?

What is the most recent movie/concert/exhibit you have seen?

What was a special present you gave to someone?

What is a special present you have received?

Have you ever had a surprise party given for you, or have you ever given one?

Visual Sequential Recall Exercises

These exercises provide practice in strategy use to facilitate recall of visually presented information of increasing length and complexity.

This section contains four short stories represented by pictures. Each story has four parts. Part 1 is the basic, less demanding format. As the level increases, so does the number of pictures to recall. Three recall formats are provided: multiple-choice questions, open-ended questions and free recall.

Strategies

The client needs to use strategies in order to make the exercise meaningful and facilitate carryover of strategy use into daily life activities.

Instruct the client to use several strategies, such as *visualizing* the sequence of the pictures and *associating* the events in the story with a personal experience.

During the learning phase of the exercise, encourage clients to *write* the sequence of the pictures on a separate sheet of paper as a means of processing the information more actively and having a record to refer to and *rehearse* the important details and sequence of the events in the story.

Instructions

1. Determine the appropriate exercise level for the client, based on clinical judgment and the following guidelines:

Skill Level	**Exercise**
Level 1—Severe impairment	Part 1
Level 2—Moderate impairment	Parts 2 and 3
Level 3—Mild impairment	Part 4
Level 4—Advanced skill level	Present two sets of pictures, requiring the client to have as many as 12 pictures to recall

2. Provide a copy of the picture page at the appropriate level.
3. Have the client study the picture page for five minutes (you may want to modify this time based on the client's needs.)
4. While the client is studying the picture page, provide a reminder to boost recall by using the strategies discussed above.

5. Have the client place the pictures out of sight (for example, turned over or placed under the chair).
6. Using clinical judgment, select one of the following recall formats:
   a. Multiple-Choice Questions (the easiest way to recall the presented information)

      There are two ways to present multiple-choice questions:

      - Give the client a copy of the multiple-choice questions that correspond to the picture page you have selected. Instruct the client to read the questions and circle the correct answers. Have the client work independently for a set amount of time. Then review the answers with the client.
      - Read the questions aloud, and have the client respond verbally. Then review the answers with the client.

   b. Open-Ended Questions (a moderately difficult way to recall the presented information)

      There are two ways to present open-ended questions:

      - Give the client a copy of the open-ended questions that correspond to the picture page you have selected. Instruct the client to read the questions and answer the questions. Have the client work independently for a set amount of time. Then review the answers with the client.
      - Read the questions aloud, and have the client respond verbally. Then review the answers with the client.

   c. Free Recall (the most difficult way to recall the presented information)

      Provide a picture page with blank squares. Have the client write or draw in all the information that can be recalled.
7. While the client is completing the worksheet, provide a reminder to use strategies to enhance recall.

Please note: When you use the open-ended questions or the free recall section with a client, you will need to cover up other parts of the worksheet that appear on the same page when you photocopy it so the answers are not available.

Visual Sequential Recall—Exercise 1

The Fishing Trip

Part 1

1

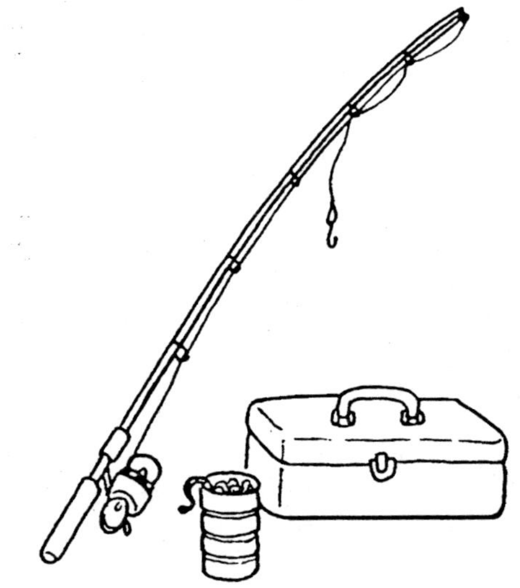

2

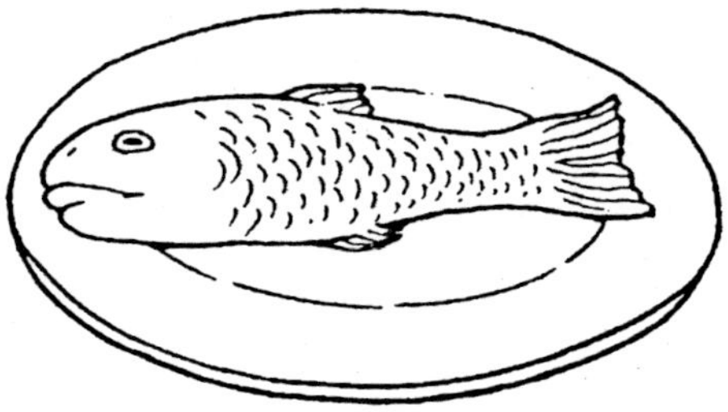

Name________________________________ Date______________________

Visual Sequential Recall—Exercise 1

The Fishing Trip

Part 1

A. Multiple-Choice Questions

1. Which items are in the first picture?
   a. Cooking supplies
   b. Fishing supplies
   c. School supplies
   d. Hunting supplies

2. Where is the animal in the second picture?
   a. On a plate
   b. In a bucket
   c. On a hook
   d. In a forest

B. Open-Ended Questions

1. What items are in the first picture? ______________________
2. Where is the animal in the second picture? ____________________

C. Free Recall

1	2

Visual Sequential Recall—Exercise 1

The Fishing Trip

Part 2

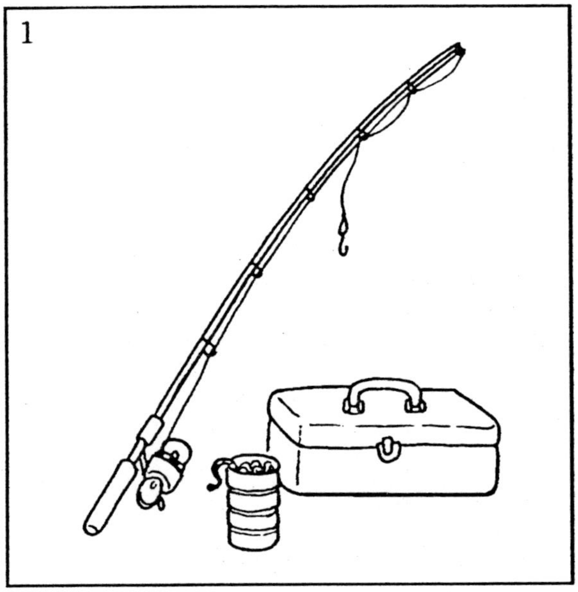

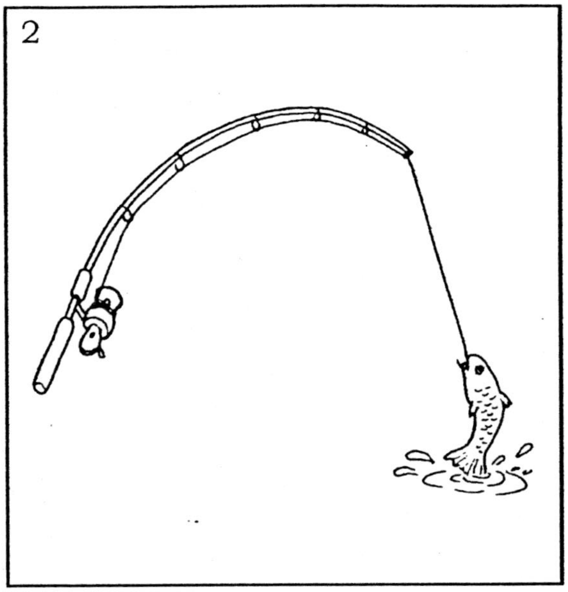

Name________________________________ Date______________________

Visual Sequential Recall—Exercise 1

The Fishing Trip

Part 2

A. Multiple-Choice Questions

1. Which items are in the first picture?
   a. Cooking supplies
   b. Fishing supplies
   c. School supplies
   d. Hunting supplies

2. Which item is in the first picture?
   a. Tool box
   b. Shoe box
   c. Tackle box
   d. Music box

3. Where is the animal in the second picture?
   a. On a plate
   b. In a bucket
   c. On a hook
   d. In a forest

4. What is in the last picture?
   a. A dog on a leash
   b. A cat on a lap
   c. A bird on a perch
   d. A fish on a plate

B. Open-Ended Questions

1. What type of supplies are the items in the first picture?
   ____

2. Name one item shown in the first picture. ____________________

3. Where is the animal in the second picture? ____________________

4. What is in the last picture? ____________________________________

Name________________________________ Date______________________

Visual Sequential Recall—Exercise 1

The Fishing Trip

Part 2

C. Free Recall

1

2

3

Visual Sequential Recall—Exercise 1

The Fishing Trip

Part 3

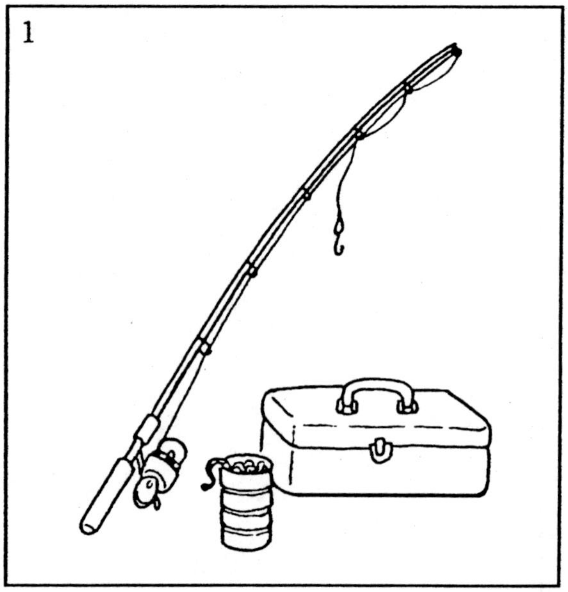

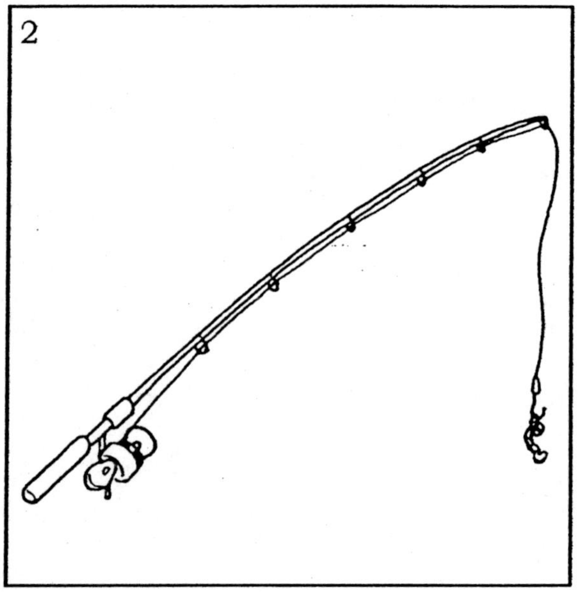

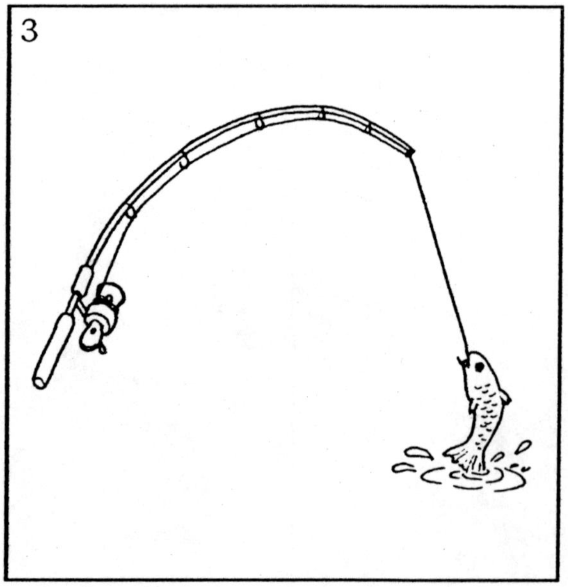

Name______________________________ Date____________________

Visual Sequential Recall—Exercise 1

The Fishing Trip

Part 3

A. Multiple-Choice Questions

1. Which item is in the first picture?
   a. Lures
   b. Hat
   c. Boat
   d. Worms

2. Is there a picture of a man in a boat?
   a. Yes
   b. No

3. What is in the last picture?
   a. A fish in a bucket
   b. A fish on a hook
   c. A fish in a lake
   d. A fish on a plate

B. Open-Ended Questions

1. Name the three items in the first picture.

   ____

2. What is on the hook in Picture 2? __________________

3. What does the last picture show? __________________

Name______________________________ Date_____________________

Visual Sequential Recall—Exercise 1

The Fishing Trip

Part 3

C. Free Recall

1	2
3	4

Visual Sequential Recall—Exercise 1

The Fishing Trip

Part 4

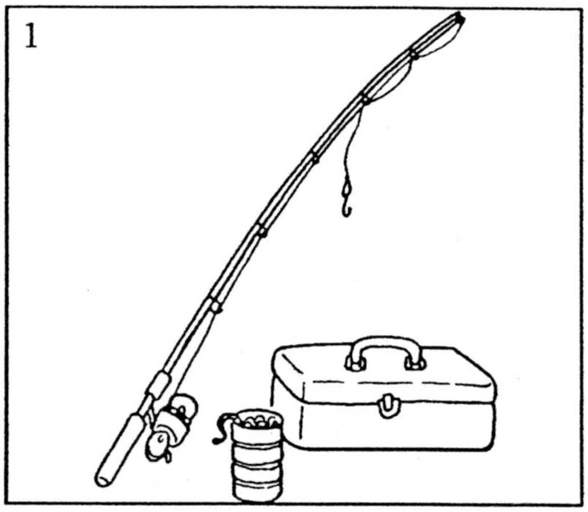

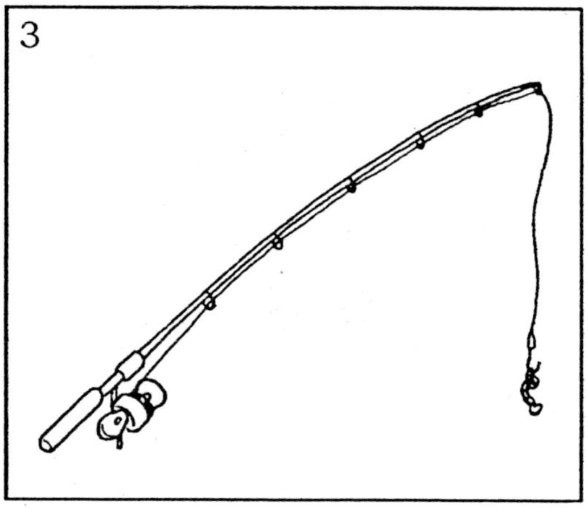

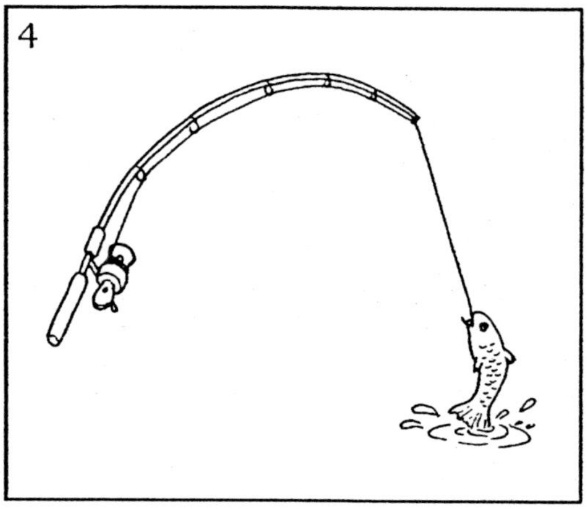

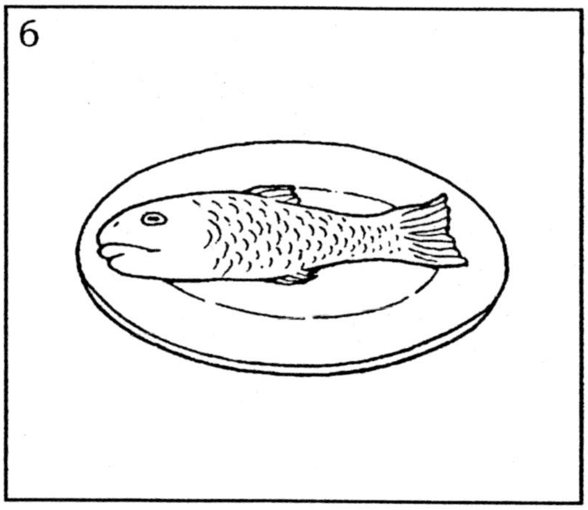

Name______________________________ Date______________________

Visual Sequential Recall—Exercise 1

The Fishing Trip

Part 4

A. Multiple-Choice Questions

1. Which item is shown in Picture 1?
   a. Lures
   b. Hat
   c. Boat
   d. Worms

2. Is there a picture of a man in a boat?
   a. Yes
   b. No

3. What is shown in Picture 2?
   a. River
   b. Ocean
   c. Lake
   d. Stream

4. How many pictures have fishing poles in them?
   a. Three
   b. Two
   c. Five
   d. Four

5. What is in the last picture?
   a. A fish in a bucket
   b. A fish on a hook
   c. A fish in a lake
   d. A fish on a plate

B. Open-Ended Questions

1. Name the three items shown in picture 1.

   ____

2. What is on the hook in picture 3? ______________________

3. What is in picture 2? ______________________________

4. How many pictures show a fishing pole?

   ____

5. What does the last picture show? ______________________

Name______________________________ Date____________________

Visual Sequential Recall—Exercise 1

The Fishing Trip

Part 4

C. Free Recall

1	2
3	4
5	6

Visual Sequential Recall—Exercise 2

Planning a Trip

Part 1

1

2

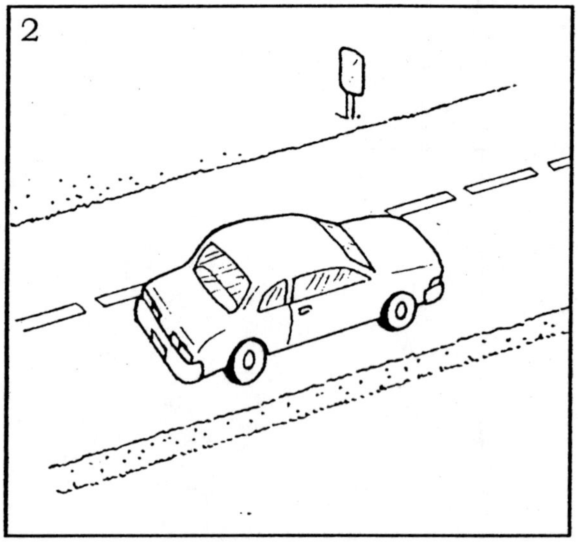

Name______________________________ Date____________________

Visual Sequential Recall—Exercise 2

Planning a Trip

Part 1

A. Multiple-Choice Questions

1. What is shown in the first picture?
   a. Brush, clip and gel
   b. Key, map and book
   c. Radio, earphones and CD
   d. Bread, plate and napkin

2. What type of vehicle is in the second picture?
   a. Bus
   b. Van
   c. Airplane
   d. Car

B. Open-Ended Questions

1. Name one of the items shown in the first picture.

   ____

2. What type of vehicle is in the second picture? _______________

C. Free Recall

1	2

Visual Sequential Recall—Exercise 2

Planning a Trip

Part 2

1

2

3

Name________________________________ Date______________________

Visual Sequential Recall—Exercise 2

Planning a Trip

Part 2

A. Multiple-Choice Questions

1. What is shown in the first picture?
   a. Brush, clip and gel
   b. Key, map and book
   c. Radio, earphones and CD
   d. Bread, plate and napkin
2. What is shown in the second picture?
   a. Agenda
   b. Tickets
   c. Map
   d. Directions
3. What type of vehicle is in the third picture?
   a. Bus
   b. Van
   c. Airplane
   d. Car

B. Open-Ended Questions

1. Name one of the items shown in the first picture.

   ____

2. What is shown in the second picture? __________________________
3. What type of vehicle is in the third picture? ________________

Name________________________________ Date______________________

Visual Sequential Recall Exercise 2

Planning a Trip

Part 2

C. Free Recall

1

2

3

Visual Sequential Recall—Exercise 2

Planning a Trip

Part 3

1

2

3

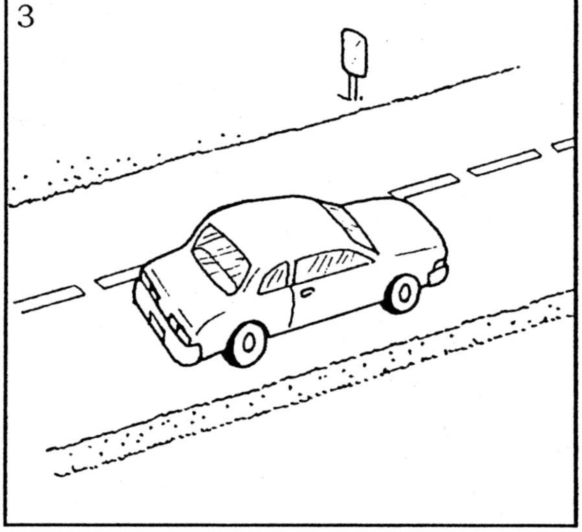

4

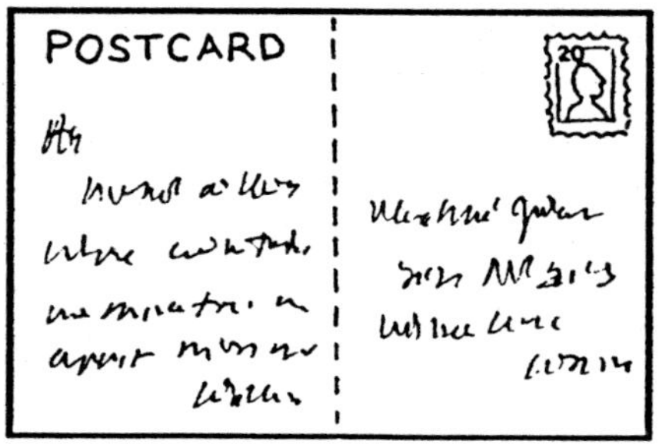

Name________________________________ Date______________________

Visual Sequential Recall—Exercise 2

Planning a Trip

Part 3

A. Multiple-Choice Questions

1. Which is not shown in the first picture?
   a. Book
   b. Key
   c. Luggage
   d. Map
2. What is shown in the second picture?
   a. Agenda
   b. Tickets
   c. Map
   d. Directions
3. What type of vehicle is in the third picture?
   a. Bus
   b. Van
   c. Airplane
   d. Car
4. What is shown in the last picture?
   a. Poster
   b. Postcard
   c. Picture
   d. Portrait

B. Open-Ended Questions

1. Name all of the items shown in the first picture.
   ____
2. What is shown in the second picture? ______________________
3. What type of vehicle is in the third picture? ______________
4. What is shown in the last picture? ________________________

Name________________________________ Date______________________

Visual Sequential Recall—Exercise 2

Planning a Trip

Part 3

C. Free Recall

1	2
3	4

Visual Sequential Recall—Exercise 2

Planning a Trip

Part 4

1

2

3

4

5

6

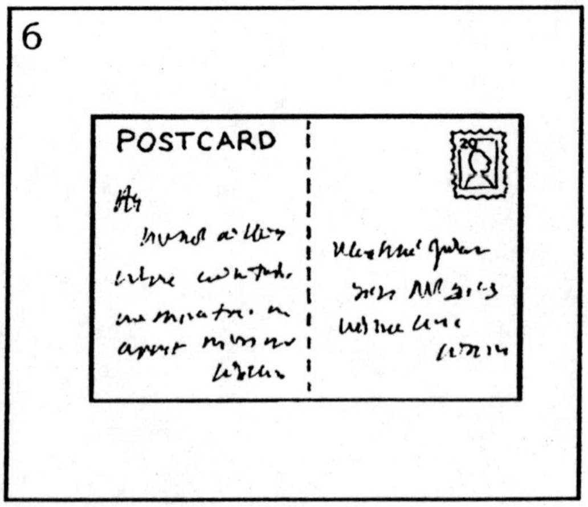

Name________________________________ Date______________________

Visual Sequential Recall—Exercise 2

Planning a Trip

Part 4

A. Multiple-Choice Questions

1. Which is not shown in the first picture?
   a. Book
   b. Key
   c. Luggage
   d. Map

2. What is shown in the second picture?
   a. Agenda
   b. Tickets
   c. Map
   d. Directions

3. What type of vehicle is in the third picture?
   a. Bus
   b. Van
   c. Airplane
   d. Car

4. What is shown in the last picture?
   a. Poster
   b. Postcard
   c. Picture
   d. Portrait

5. What is written on the sign in Picture 5?
   a. Motel
   b. Hotel
   c. Bed and Breakfast
   d. No Vacancy

B. Open-Ended Questions

1. Name all of the items shown in the first picture.
   ____
2. What is shown in the second picture? __________________________
3. What type of vehicle is in the third picture? __________________
4. What is shown in the last picture? ____________________________
5. What is written on the sign in Picture 5? ______________________

Name________________________________ Date______________________

Visual Sequential Recall—Exercise 2

Planning a Trip

Part 4

C. Free Recall

1	2
3	4
5	6

Visual Sequential Recall—Exercise 3

Going Shopping

Part 1

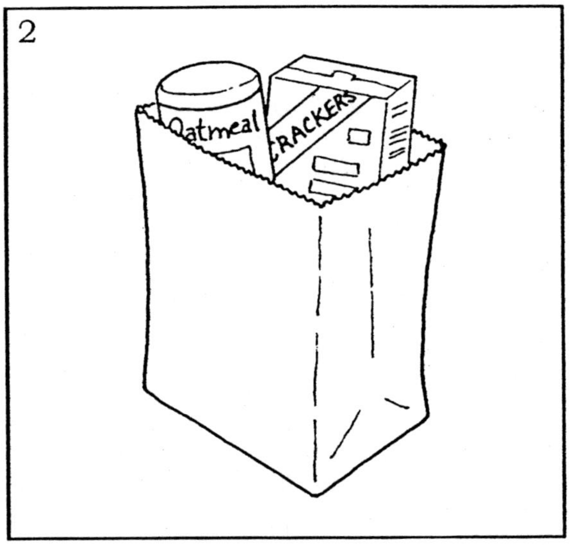

Name________________________ Date____________________

Visual Sequential Recall—Exercise 3

Going Shopping

Part 1

A. Multiple-Choice Questions

1. What is shown in picture 1?
   a. Grocery list
   b. Holiday gift list
   c. Invitation list
   d. List of numbers

2. Which one of the following items is shown in the second picture?
   a. Cauliflower
   b. Milk
   c. Bread
   d. Oatmeal

B. Open-Ended Questions

1. What is shown in picture 1? ________________________

2. Name one of the items shown in the second picture.

____

C. Free Recall

1	2

Visual Sequential Recall—Exercise 3

Going Shopping

Part 2

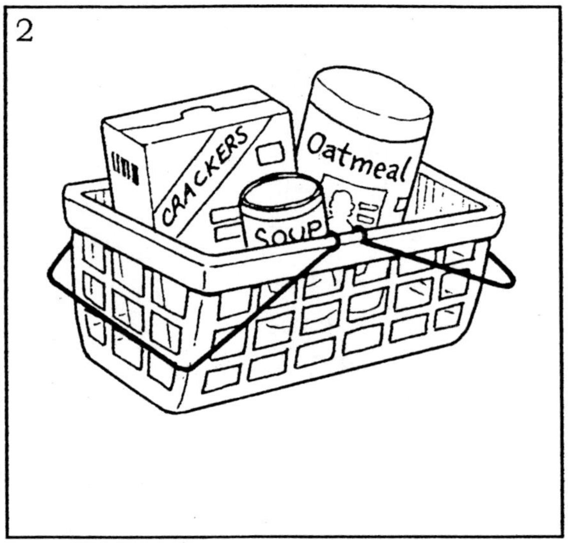

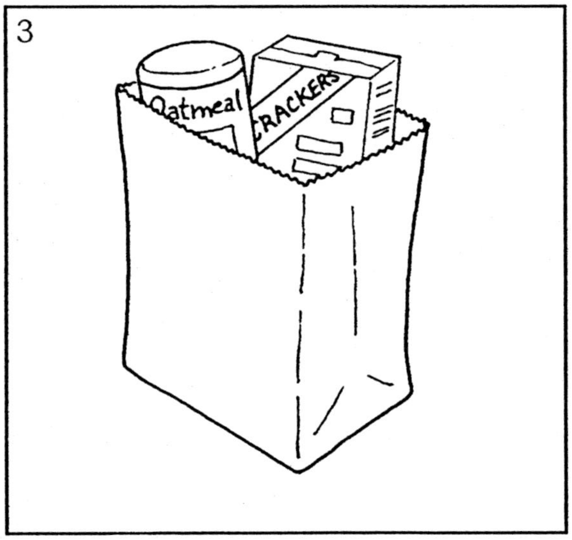

Name______________________________ Date____________________

Visual Sequential Recall—Exercise 3

Going Shopping

Part 2

A. Multiple-Choice Questions

1. What is shown in picture 1?
   a. Grocery list
   b. Holiday gift list
   c. Invitation list
   d. List of numbers
2. Which item is not shown in the second picture?
   a. Oatmeal
   b. Eggs
   c. Crackers
   d. Soup
3. Which one of the following items is shown in the third picture?
   a. Cauliflower
   b. Milk
   c. Bread
   d. Oatmeal

B. Open-Ended Questions

1. What is shown in picture 1? ____________________
2. Name one of the items shown in the second picture.
   ____
3. Name an item that was shown in the third picture.
   ____

Name________________________________ Date______________________

Visual Sequential Recall—Exercise 3

Going Shopping

Part 2

C. Free Recall

1

2

3

Visual Sequential Recall—Exercise 3

Going Shopping

Part 3

Name______________________________ Date____________________

Visual Sequential Recall—Exercise 3

Going Shopping

Part 3

A. Multiple-Choice Questions

1. What is shown in picture 1?
   a. Grocery list
   b. Holiday gift list
   c. Invitation list
   d. List of numbers

2. Which item is not shown in the second picture?
   a. Oatmeal
   b. Eggs
   c. Crackers
   d. Soup

3. What item is shown in picture 2 but not in pictures 3 and 4?
   a. Soap
   b. Sauce
   c. Shampoo
   d. Soup

4. Which item is at the far left in the cabinet?
   a. Soup
   b. Crackers
   c. Oatmeal
   d. Cauliflower

B. Open-Ended Questions

1. What is shown in picture 1? ______________________________

2. Name the items shown in the grocery bag.

   ____

3. Name the items in the shopping basket.

   ____

4. What item is shown in picture 2 but not in pictures 3 and 4?

   ____

5. Which item is at the far left in the cabinet?

   ____

Name________________________________ Date______________________

Visual Sequential Recall—Exercise 3

Going Shopping

Part 3

C. Free Recall

1	2
3	4

Visual Sequential Recall—Exercise 3

Going Shopping

Part 4

Name______________________________ Date____________________

Visual Sequential Recall—Exercise 3

Going Shopping

Part 4

A. Multiple-Choice Questions

1. What is shown in picture 1?
   a. Grocery list
   b. Holiday gift list
   c. Invitation list
   d. List of numbers
2. Which item is not shown in the second picture?
   a. Oatmeal
   b. Eggs
   c. Crackers
   d. Soup
3. What item is shown in picture 2 but not in pictures 3 and 4?
   a. Soap
   b. Sauce
   c. Shampoo
   d. Soup
4. Which item is at the far left in the cabinet?
   a. Soup
   b. Crackers
   c. Oatmeal
   d. Cauliflower
5. What is the price shown on the register?
   a. $14.79
   b. $15.49
   c. $17.79
   d. $15.79
6. How much can you save by using a coupon?
   a. $0.15
   b. $0.05
   c. $0.25
   d. $0.35

B. Open-Ended Questions

1. What is shown in picture 1? ____________________
2. Name the items shown in the grocery bag.

   ____
3. Name the items in the shopping basket.

   ____
4. What item is shown in picture 2 but not in pictures 3 and 4?

   ____
5. Which item is at the far left in the cabinet? ________________
6. What is the price shown on the register? ____________________
7. How much can you save by using a coupon? ________________

Name______________________________ Date____________________

Visual Sequential Recall—Exercise 3

Going Shopping

Part 4

C. Free Recall

1	2
3	4
5	6

Making a Pie

Part 1

1

2

Name______________________________ Date____________________

Visual Sequential Recall—Exercise 4

Making a Pie

Part 1

A. Multiple-Choice Questions

1. Which item is shown in the first picture?
   a. Cherries
   b. Blueberries
   c. Apples
   d. Strawberries

2. What is in the second picture?
   a. Cake
   b. Pie
   c. Sandwich
   d. Soda

B. Open-Ended Questions

1. Name one of the items shown in the first picture. ______________
2. What was in the second picture? ______________________

C. Free Recall

1	2

Visual Sequential Recall—Exercise 4

Making a Pie

Part 2

1

2

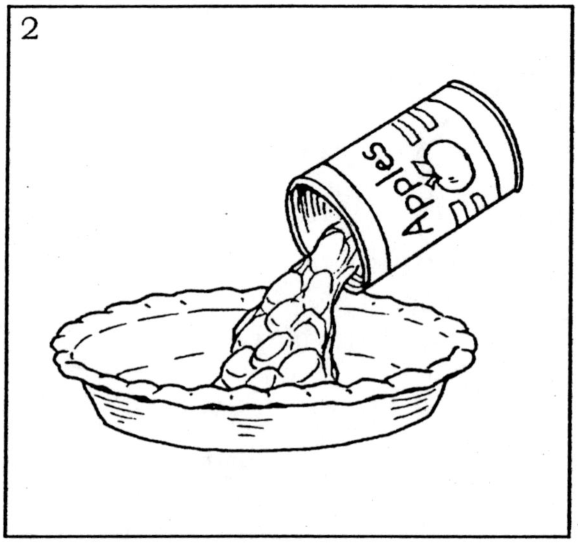

3

Name________________________________ Date______________________

Visual Sequential Recall—Exercise 4

Making a Pie

Part 2

A. Multiple-Choice Questions

1. Which item is shown in the first picture?
   a. Cherries
   b. Apricots
   c. Apples
   d. Strawberries

2. What is shown in the second picture?
   a. Fruit being cut
   b. Fruit being washed
   c. Fruit being peeled
   d. Fruit being poured into a crust.

3. Is a piece missing from the pie in the last picture?
   a. Yes
   b. No

B. Open-Ended Questions

1. Which item is shown in the first picture? _______________

2. What is in the second picture? ________________________

3. Is a piece missing from the pie in the last picture?

   ____

Name________________________________ Date______________________

Visual Sequential Recall—Exercise 4

Making a Pie

Part 2

C. Free Recall

1	2

3

Visual Sequential Recall—Exercise 4

Making a Pie

Part 3

1

2

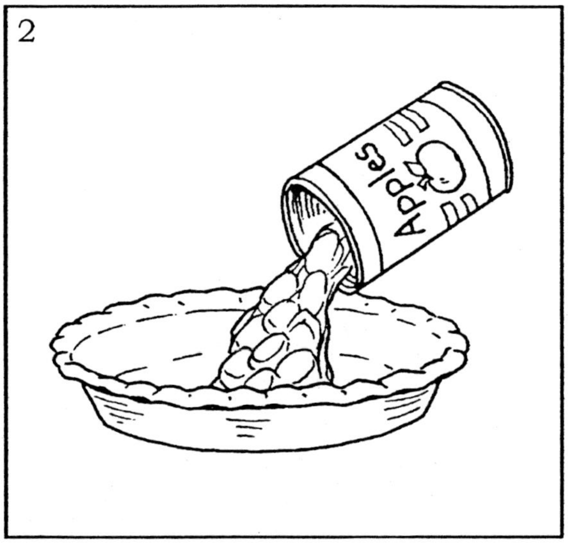

3

4

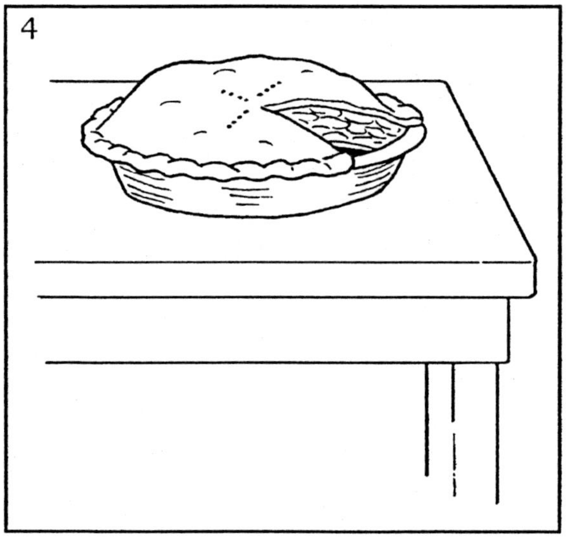

Name______________________________ Date______________________

Visual Sequential Recall—Exercise 4

Making a Pie

Part 3

A. Multiple-Choice Questions

1. Which item is not shown in the first picture?
   a. Crust
   b. Apricots
   c. Apples
   d. Pie plate
2. What is shown in the second picture?
   a. Fruit being cut
   b. Fruit being washed
   c. Fruit being peeled
   d. Fruit being poured into a crust.
3. Is a piece missing from the pie in the last picture?
   a. Yes
   b. No
4. Which of the following made the marks on the pie?
   a. Fork
   b. Knife
   c. Pin
   d. Finger

B. Open-Ended Questions

1. Name one of the items shown in the first picture.

   ____

2. What is in the second picture? ______________________

3. Is a piece missing from the pie in the last picture?

   ____

4. What made the marks on the pie? ___________________

Name________________________________ Date______________________

Visual Sequential Recall Exercise 4

Making a Pie

Part 3

C. Free Recall

1	2
3	4

Visual Sequential Recall—Exercise 4

Making a Pie

Part 4

Name________________________________ Date______________________

Visual Sequential Recall—Exercise 4

Making a Pie

Part 4

C. Multiple-Choice Questions

1. Which item is not shown in the first picture?
   a. Crust
   b. Apricots
   c. Apples
   d. Pie plate
2. What is shown in the third picture?
   a. Fruit being cut
   b. Fruit being washed
   c. Fruit being peeled
   d. Fruit being poured into a crust.
3. Is a piece missing from the pie in the last picture?
   a. Yes
   b. No
4. Which of the following made the marks on the pie?
   a. Fork
   b. Knife
   c. Pin
   d. Finger
5. What is happening in the fifth picture?
   a. Pie is cut into
   b. Pie is in the oven
   c. Marks are made on crust
   d. Crust is filled with fruit

B. Open-Ended Questions

1. Name one of the items shown in the first picture. _______________
2. What is in the third picture? ________________________________

   ____
3. Is a piece missing from the pie in the last picture? ____________
4. What made the marks on the pie? ____________________________
5. What is happening in the fifth picture? ______________________

   ____

Name________________________________ Date______________________

Visual Sequential Recall—Exercise 4

Making a Pie

Part 4

C. Free Recall

1	2
3	4
5	6

Chapter 7
Functional Memory

Functional memory exercises provide practice in the client's ability to incorporate strategy use and follow-through on various tasks to be completed. The exercises are used to reinforce the client's daily use of a memory book, including evenings and weekends.

Contents

Functional Memory Assignments

These 50 functional memory assignments provide excellent practice in using a memory book. Clients are asked to write reminders to themselves to perform various tasks at later dates and times.

Strategies

Encourage clients to incorporate strategy use to facilitate recall of assignments by using an external memory device such as a memory book, calendar or electronic memo device. *Writing* assignments reinforces the use of a memory book as a functional tool in everyday life.

Instructions

Select assignments according to the client's particular needs and level of functioning, based on clinical judgment and the following guidelines:

Skill Level	**Number of Assignments**
Level 1—Severe impairment	1 or 2 assignments
Level 2—Moderate impairment	3 or 4 assignments
Level 3—Mild impairment	5 assignments

Most clients begin at a lower skill level and move to higher skill levels with practice, better use of strategies and improvement over time.

On the blank lines, specify names, days of the week, phone numbers and other pertinent information as needed. For example, the first memory assignment can be completed as follows:

1. Read an article relating to sports from the weekend newspaper. Call in a summary on Sunday night to Robin's voice mail at 444-719-2222.

   (In this example, Robin is the client's case manager.) It is important to notify therapists and/or family members of the assignment so they can report on a client's performance.

Scan through the various assignments, and match assignments to specific client needs. Give assignments that require the client to act at a variety of times and days of the week. This will reinforce daily use of the memory book. For example, asking the client to call a therapist in the evening and read a news article on the weekend reinforces use of the memory book when not in the rehabilitation setting.

Functional Memory Assignments

1. Read an article relating to sports from the weekend newspaper. Call in a summary on Sunday night to _________________'s voice mail at _________________.

2. Cut out an article on a health-related issue from Wednesday's newspaper, and give the article to _________________ on _________________.

3. Read an article about a foreign issue in the Friday newspaper. Write a summary from memory, and give the article and summary to _________________ on _________________.

4. Find a movie review in a current newspaper, and call in a two-sentence summary to _________________ at _________________.

5. Mail an article about a political issue to _________________ at _________________ by _________________.

6. Find an article in a current magazine about a technical advance. Write a one-paragraph summary, and give it to _________________ by _________________.

7. Find an article in the weekend newspaper about a medical advance, and call in a three-sentence summary to _________________ at _________________ on _________________.

8. Read an article about the stock market. Write a summary and give it to _________________ on _________________.

9. Bring in an article about a recent golf tournament, and give it to _________________ on _________________.

10. Cut out an article on a local issue from Thursday's paper, and give it to _________________ on _________________.

11. Ask a family member or friend to call _________________ at _________________ on _________________ to discuss the progress you have made in memory over the last two months.

12. Ask a family member or friend to call _________________ at _________________ on _________________ to set up a meeting.

13. Ask a family member or friend to write a note about current concerns about your progress, and give the note to ________________ on ________________.

14. Bring in a picture of a family member or friend, and give it to ________________ on ________________.

15. Ask a family member or friend to leave a voice mail message for ________________ at ________________ on ________________ describing your current strengths and weaknesses in the area of memory.

16. Leave a voice mail message for ________________ at ________________ on ________________ describing your main short-term and long-term goals.

17. Bring in a picture of yourself as a child, and show it to ________________ on ________________.

18. Leave a voice mail message for ________________ at ________________ on ________________ describing a typical day before your injury.

19. Watch the 6:00 news on Friday, and leave a message about the weather forecast for the weekend on ________________'s voice mail at ________________ before 10:00 p.m.

20. Leave a voice mail message for ________________ at ________________ on ________________ describing your last memory before your injury and your first memory after your injury.

21. Write a list of work responsibilities from your last job, and give it to ________________ on ________________.

22. Watch the 6:00 news on Tuesday evening, and leave a two-sentence voice mail message for ________________ at ________________ on ________________ summarizing the first story discussed.

23. Call ________________ at ________________ on Friday evening and leave a three-sentence message about your expected plans for the weekend.

24. Listen to the 10:00 news on AM radio on Sunday morning for 15 minutes. Write a summary of the news you heard, and give it to ________________ on ________________.

25. Leave a voice mail message for ________________ at ________________ on ________________ stating your most and least favorite subjects in high school.

26. On Monday morning before 12:00 noon, leave a voice mail message for ________________ at ________________ describing three plans for the week.

27. On Thursday evening, watch the 6:00 news, and write a summary to give to ________________ on ________________.

28. Call ________________ at ________________ on ________________ and talk about your progress over the last month.

29. Write a list of your primary fears, and give it to ________________ on ________________.

30. Write a one-page essay about your experiences since the injury, and give it to ________________ on ________________.

31. Leave a voice mail message for ________________ at ________________ on ________________ describing any value changes you have noticed since your injury.

32. Write a summary about the influence that other clients have had on you since your injury, and give it to ________________ on ________________.

33. Cut out an article on education from a recent magazine, and give the article and a brief summary to ________________ on ________________.

34. Write a realistic list of home activities that you would like to complete by the end of the week, and leave a voice mail message for ________________ at ________________ on ________________ describing your plan.

35. Leave a voice mail message for ________________ at ________________ on Wednesday evening between 8:00 and 10:00 p.m. summarizing what you did during that day from your memory.

36. Cut out an article on a political issue from a current magazine and give it to ________________ on ________________.

37. Leave a voice mail message for ________________ at ________________ on ________________ telling the ingredients and specific directions on how to make your favorite dessert.

38. Leave a voice mail message for __________________ at __________________ on __________________ telling about your favorite hobbies before and since your injury.

39. Leave a voice mail message for __________________ at __________________ on __________________ naming the last movie you remember seeing.

40. Leave a voice mail message for __________________ at __________________ on __________________ naming the last book you remember reading.

41. Leave a voice mail message for __________________ at __________________ on __________________ telling your current social strengths and weaknesses.

42. On Monday morning before lunchtime, leave a summary note describing the highlights of your weekend for __________________.

43. On Tuesday before 9:00 p.m., leave a voice mail message for __________________ at __________________ describing the last vacation you remember before you had your injury.

44. On Thursday night before 8:00 p.m., call __________________ at __________________ and leave a list of household chores that you have resumed since your injury.

45. On Sunday evening before 8:00 p.m., leave a voice mail message for __________________ at __________________ describing your level of satisfaction with family support since the injury.

46. Call __________________ at __________________ over the weekend and leave a voice mail message describing the types of movies and books you enjoy the most.

47. Write a note about the first memory you have as a child, and give it to __________________ on __________________.

48. Write a note summarizing your ability to handle frustration and anger, and give it to __________________ on __________________.

49. Leave a voice mail message for __________________ at __________________ on __________________ summarizing a television show you watched within the last 24 hours.

50. Cut out a review of a new book, and give it to __________________ on __________________.

Functional Sequential Memory Assignments

These assignments are appropriate for clients with mild to moderate memory impairments.

With these assignments, clients work on the ability to follow a sequence of steps to complete a complex assignment. Attention to detail, planning, organizational and sequencing skills, and prospective recall are enhanced.

Strategies

Instruct clients to incorporate strategy use to facilitate recall of assignments by using a memory book. *Writing* assignments reinforces the use of the memory book as an external memory device. Memory books provide a system for keeping track of information in an organized fashion.

Instructions

Select one five-step assignment from the 50 provided, matched to the client's level. Each assignment should be given over one week's time.

Skill Level	Number of Assignments
Mild to Moderate	One 5-step assignment per week
Levels 2 & 3	

On the blank lines, specify names, days of the week, phone numbers and other pertinent information as needed. For example:

> On Tuesday evening, call Mary at 667-555-1324 before 9 p.m. to report the top news story of the day.
>
> (In this example, Mary can be the client's case manager, speech-language pathologist or physical or occupational therapist.)

Because it is important to incorporate significant others into the rehabilitation process, include their names as appropriate.

Present these assignments either in written or verbal form, depending on the client's level of functioning. For example, clients with auditory processing deficits will need the assignments in written form to help them transfer the assignments to their memory books. For clients who are capable of processing the information auditorily, present the assignments verbally and have these clients write the assignment in their memory books. In both cases, the clients then follow through by performing the assignments in a given sequence.

Functional Sequential Memory Assignment 1

1. Watch the 6:00 news today and pay attention to the top story.
2. Be sure to listen for tomorrow's weather and record it in your memory book.
3. Write a summary of the top news story in your memory book.
4. Call ________________ at ________________ by 8:00 p.m. and report on the top story.
5. Between 8:30 p.m. and 9:00 p.m., call ________________ at ________________ to tell the weather forecast.

Functional Sequential Memory Assignment 2

1. Look through the newspaper for an event to attend this weekend.
2. Call a friend or member of your family tonight before 7:30 p.m. Invite the person to join you for the event.
3. Discuss some ideas and plans about the activity.
4. Make a note in your memory book on the page that represents the day the event is scheduled. List the person's name and the time you are meeting.
5. Call ________________ at ________________ to talk about your plan for this weekend.

Functional Sequential Memory Assignment 3

1. Cut out an article from tonight's newspaper.
2. Write a summary in your memory book highlighting the story.
3. Review the story with someone in the family.
4. Call ________________ at ________________ to talk about the news story.
5. Bring in the article and put it in ________________'s mailbox.

Functional Sequential Memory Assignment 4

1. Make a list of items you need at the drugstore.
2. Go to the drugstore on ________________.
3. Check off the items as you place them in a basket at the drugstore.
4. Tape your shopping list in your memory book on the page that represents the day you went to the drugstore.
5. Show ________________ your list on ________________.

Functional Sequential Memory Assignment 5

1. With a family member, plan to cook part of your family's dinner on ________________.
2. Perform the cooking task.
3. Write a note about what you chose to cook.
4. Give the note to ________________ on ________________.
5. Two days after the meal is completed, have a family member or friend call ________________ at ________________ to discuss the meal.

Functional Sequential Memory Assignment 6

1. Write the first thing you remember before and after your injury on ________________. Make a copy of the note.
2. An hour later, review what you wrote with a family member or friend.
3. Have that person call ________________ at ________________ to summarize what you wrote.
4. On the following day, give the note about what you recalled to ________________.
5. On the next day, give the copy of the note about what you recalled to ________________.

Functional Sequential Memory Assignment 7

1. Tonight, write a list of your primary memory challenges (for example, recalling names).
2. Discuss this assignment with a family member or friend.
3. Ask a family member or friend to write a similar list of your primary memory weaknesses.
4. Call ____________________ at ____________________ to report that this assignment is completed.
5. Within two days, mail both lists to ____________________ at ____________________.

Functional Sequential Memory Assignment 8

1. Tonight, write a list of your short-term goals.
2. Prioritize the goals in order of importance to you.
3. At the end of each goal, predict when you will accomplish each goal.
4. Discuss these goals with a family member or friend.
5. Bring in this list to be reviewed with ____________________ on ____________________.

Functional Sequential Memory Assignment 9

1. Work with your therapist to determine two goals for your next five sessions.
2. Write a summary note about today's session. Write the two goals in your memory book as part of the summary note.
3. After three sessions, ask your therapist how you are doing with the goals.
4. Have the therapist call ____________________ at ____________________ to report your progress.
5. At the end of the five sessions, write down your goals and progress and put this information in ____________________'s mailbox.

Functional Sequential Memory Assignment 10

1. Rent a suspense movie. Write the name of the movie in your memory book. Before you watch the movie, call ________________ at ________________ to report what you'll be watching.
2. Begin the movie. After watching for about 45 minutes, stop the movie. In your memory book, make a list of the main characters. Write what you think the outcome will be.
3. Continue to watch the movie.
4. When the movie is ended, write a brief summary of the movie in your memory book.
5. Give the brief summary to ________________ the next morning.

Functional Sequential Memory Assignment 11

1. On the night before our next appointment, look up five challenging vocabulary words.
2. Write the words and definitions in your memory book.
3. Use each word in a sentence. Write the sentences in your memory book.
4. Call ________________ at ________________ to talk about the words.
5. The next day, bring in the five sentences and share them with ________________.

Functional Sequential Memory Assignment 12

1. On Wednesday, call a family member that you have not talked with recently.
2. Write the name of this person in your memory book on Wednesday.
3. On Thursday, call a more frequently contacted family member and talk about your conversation. Write that person's name in your memory book.
4. Have that family member call ________________ at ________________ to report the name of the person you talked with on Wednesday.
5. Write the names and times you spoke with these relatives and give it to ________________ on Friday.

Functional Sequential Memory Assignment 13

Note to the clinician: Use this assignment with a major news story unfolding over many days.

1. On Monday, read the headline story in the newspaper. Follow that story for four days.
2. Each day, cut out the articles and put them in your memory book.
3. Each day, write a summary in your memory book.
4. By midweek, write a note to ________________ to report what you have been working on, and place the note in that person's mailbox.
5. On Friday, bring the articles and summaries to ________________ to review your work.

Functional Sequential Memory Assignment 14

You will be working with two partners on this assignment. Your partners are ________________ and ________________. Working together for five days, you will write a report about your hospital experiences after your injury.

1. On Monday, contact your partners and begin collecting information about your hospital experiences after your injury. Decide which of you will be responsible for writing the introduction, the body of work and the conclusion.
2. By Tuesday at 12:00 noon, call ________________ at ________________ to report on the plan.
3. By Wednesday, call your group partners to check on their progress and write a note in your memory book about your conversation with each person.
4. Obtain all sections of the report by Thursday.
5. On Friday, bring the report to ________________ by noon.

Functional Sequential Memory Assignment 15

1. On Monday, choose a company in the stock market. In your memory book, write the price of the stock.
2. On Tuesday, look up the stock price again, and write the increase or decrease in your memory book.
3. On Wednesday, note the price and record it in your memory book.
4. On Thursday, again chart the price in your memory book.
5. On Friday, make a list showing the stock prices from Monday through Thursday, and put it in ________________'s mailbox.

Functional Sequential Memory Assignment 16

1. Over the weekend, determine a home project that needs attention.
2. In your memory book, write a sequenced plan of action to include an activity each evening toward completing the project.
3. Follow the plan every night, writing progress notes in your memory book.
4. Midweek, call ____________________ at ____________________to report your progress.
5. At the end of the week, write a note to ______________ describing your progress on the task.

Functional Sequential Memory Assignment 17

1. Select a book of your choice.
2. Read a chapter each evening.
3. After reading the chapter, write a short summary in your memory book.
4. Do this for two weeks.
5. At the end of the two weeks, give the summaries to ____________________.

Functional Sequential Memory Assignment 18

1. Listen to a local radio station's news report.
2. In your memory book, write down the name of the station, the time of day and the topic of the news report.
3. Write a note in your memory book to remind yourself to listen to the news report at the same time on the following day.
4. After the news report on the second day, tell a family member or friend about the news story.
5. Ask that family member or friend to call ____________________ at ____________________ to report your news story.

Functional Sequential Memory Assignment 19

1. On Monday, call __________________ at __________________, ask for a recipe for an appetizer and write it in your memory book.

2. On Tuesday, call __________________ at __________________, ask for a recipe for a chicken dish and write it in your memory book.

3. On Wednesday, call __________________ at __________________, ask for a recipe for a vegetable dish and write it in your memory book.

4. On Thursday, call __________________ at __________________, ask for a recipe for a dessert and write it in your memory book.

5. Organize this information and write a menu. Give it to __________________ at the end of the week.

Functional Sequential Memory Assignment 20

Write the following schedule in your memory book to be completed during this week. It is important that you follow the schedule each day and not jump ahead.

1. On Monday, locate two favorite childhood pictures of yourself.

2. On Tuesday, locate two pictures of yourself as a young adult.

3. On Wednesday, locate three pictures of favorite family members.

4. On Thursday night before 9:00 p.m., call __________________ at __________________ to tell the names of the relatives whose pictures you have located.

5. On Friday, bring in all of the photos and review them with ______________.

Functional Sequential Memory Assignment 21

1. Choose a room in your home that needs to be reorganized.
2. In your memory book, write a sequential plan and checklist to accomplish this task. Include at least six steps.
3. On Day 1 of the project, accomplish tasks 1 and 2, and write a summary of your accomplishments in your memory book.
4. By Day 4 of the project, accomplish tasks 3 and 4, and write a summary of your accomplishments in your memory book.
5. By Day 7, complete all six steps of the project. Give the plan, summaries and checklist to ________________.

Functional Sequential Memory Assignment 22

1. Make an appointment to interview your therapist at a convenient time.
2. In your memory book, note the day and hour of the appointment.
3. Before the interview, prepare a list of five questions relating to the therapist's education and work experiences.
4. Interview the therapist as scheduled.
5. Write a summary of the interview, and give it to ________________ within two days.

Functional Sequential Memory Assignment 23

1. On Monday, write a paragraph in your memory book about yourself just before your injury.
2. On Tuesday, write a paragraph in your memory book about your recollections during your hospital stay.
3. On Wednesday, write a paragraph in your memory book about your current strengths and weaknesses.
4. On Thursday, integrate all of this information into a report.
5. Give your report to ________________ before the end of the week.

Functional Sequential Memory Assignment 24

1. In your memory book, list three people whom you would like to thank for their support during your illness.
2. In your memory book, schedule a time to write one note each day for the next three days.
3. Follow your schedule for writing, making sure you check off a name after you have written each note.
4. In your memory book, schedule a time to deliver or mail these notes, and check off a name each time a note is delivered.
5. When all the notes are written and delivered, call ________________ at ________________ by 8:00 p.m. to tell the names of the three people.

Functional Sequential Memory Assignment 25

1. Choose a simple dessert recipe.
2. On Thursday afternoon, make the dessert, following the recipe directions. If necessary, make a checklist of the directions.
3. In your memory book, write about what you made, whether the outcome was successful and whether you shared it with anyone.
4. Copy the recipe into your memory book.
5. Show the recipe to ________________ by noon the next day.

Functional Sequential Memory Assignment 26

1. Watch the 6:00 news on Wednesday evening.
2. Pay attention to the sports news for a local team.
3. Write a summary in your memory book, including team names and scores.
4. Call ________________ at ________________ by 8:00 p.m. on Wednesday to report the story.
5. By Friday, give a copy of your summary to ________________.

Functional Sequential Memory Assignment 27

1. On Tuesday, read an article in your local newspaper regarding a political issue.
2. Write a summary in your memory book about the issue, including names.
3. Also write a short paragraph about your feelings regarding this issue.
4. Discuss your feelings regarding this issue with a family member or friend.
5. Write a summary of that family member or friend's feelings and show your work to ________________ on Friday.

Functional Sequential Memory Assignment 28

1. On Tuesday, write a note in your memory book to remind yourself to make your weekly grocery list on Thursday evening.
2. On Thursday evening, write your grocery list.
3. Ask a family member or friend to check the list with you and add or delete items.
4. Once you have completed your shopping list, call ________________ at ________________ to report completion of the task.
5. Bring in your shopping list on Friday and give it to ________________.

Functional Sequential Memory Assignment 29

1. On Wednesday, ask a family member or friend two questions about a favorite actor and type of movie.
2. Write this information in your memory book as your discuss this.
3. Call ________________ at ________________ and tell the name of the person you interviewed.
4. In your memory book, add your own favorite actor and movie type.
5. Give this information to ________________ by Friday afternoon.

Functional Sequential Memory Assignment 30

1. On Monday, write a list of two of your current strengths.
2. On Tuesday, ask a family member or friend to list two of your strengths.
3. On Wednesday, ask another family member or friend to list two of your strengths.
4. On Thursday, compile these lists in your memory book.
5. On Friday, call ________________ at ________________ to review the list.

Functional Sequential Memory Assignment 31

1. Write a schedule of five tasks to be performed on Saturday or Sunday.
2. After completing the first two tasks, call ________________ at ________________ to talk about the tasks.
3. After completing the second two tasks, call ________________ at ________________ to talk about the tasks.
4. After completing the final task, write a summary of your performance on the five tasks.
5. Give the list of tasks to ________________ by Friday.

Functional Sequential Memory Assignment 32

1. Over the weekend, read a movie review in the newspaper.
2. Write a summary of the review in your memory book.
3. Look up a theater in your neighborhood where the movie is playing and write this in your memory book.
4. Call the theater listed in the newspaper, find out the times that the movie is playing and write the information in your memory book.
5. On Sunday evening, call ________________ at ________________ and report this information.

Functional Sequential Memory Assignment 33

1. On Sunday night, write a realistic exercise plan for the next seven days.
2. Use a checklist to record when exercises are completed each day.
3. On Tuesday evening, call ________________ at ________________ to report your progress.
4. On Thursday, call the same person again to report your progress.
5. On Friday, bring your checklist and give it to ________________.

Functional Sequential Memory Assignment 34

1. On Tuesday evening, watch the 6:00 news on TV. After the news is over, write an overall summary from your memory.
2. On Wednesday, give that summary to ________________ by 3:00 p.m.
3. On Thursday, read a newspaper article relating to health and summarize it in your memory book.
4. On Friday, give that summary to ________________ by 11:00 a.m.
5. On Sunday evening, write a summary in your memory book about what you did all day. Call ________________ at ________________ and leave a message summarizing the day's activities on that person's voice mail.

Functional Sequential Memory Assignment 35

1. On Monday, cut out an article from the newspaper related to sports.
2. On Tuesday, cut out an article from the newspaper on a foreign issue.
3. On Wednesday, cut out an article from the newspaper on a local story.
4. On Thursday, cut out an article from the newspaper on a medical issue.
5. On Friday, give these articles to ________________ before 1:00 p.m.

Functional Sequential Memory Assignment 36

1. On Sunday evening, write a one-hour cleaning plan to complete on Monday.
2. When you have completed the cleaning on Monday, call ________________ at ________________ to report your progress.
3. On Tuesday, write a one-hour cleaning plan to complete on Wednesday.
4. When you have completed the cleaning on Wednesday, call ________________ by 3:00 p.m. to report your progress.
5. On Friday, give both plans to ________________ before 1:00 p.m.

Functional Sequential Memory Assignment 37

1. On Monday, call ________________ at ________________ before 8:00 p.m. and leave a voice mail message about your accomplishments of the day.
2. On Tuesday, call ________________ at ________________ between 7:00 and 9:00 p.m. to talk about your day's events.
3. On Wednesday, ask a family member or friend to call ________________ at ________________ between 6:00 and 10:00 p.m. to report on your progress at home.
4. On Thursday, call ________________ at ________________ at 6:30 p.m. and leave a message regarding your primary health concerns.
5. On Friday, call ________________ at ________________ between 4:00 and 6:00 p.m. to talk about your weekend plans.

Functional Sequential Memory Assignment 38

1. On Thursday evening, write a paragraph in your memory book about problems you have noticed since your injury.
2. On Friday evening, write a paragraph in your memory book about problems you have noticed during the last month.
3. On Saturday, ask a family member or friend to write a paragraph in your memory book about your progress since your injury.
4. On Sunday, ask a family member or friend to write a paragraph in your memory book about your progress during the last month.
5. On Monday, review all progress notes with ________________ by 2:00 p.m.

Functional Sequential Memory Assignment 39

1. On Monday evening before 10:00 p.m., staple three pages of paper together. At the top of the first page, write the heading FRUSTRATIONS. At the top of the second page, write COPING. At the top of the third page, write SUPPORT SYSTEM.
2. On Tuesday evening, write a summary of your current frustrations.
3. On Wednesday evening, write a summary of the coping strategies you use.
4. On Thursday evening, write a summary about your support system.
5. On Friday, give these papers to ________________ by 3:00 p.m.

Functional Sequential Memory Assignment 40

1. On Wednesday evening, plan an activity for the weekend. Write your plan in your memory book on the date or dates scheduled.
2. On Thursday, before 1:00 p.m., call __________________ at __________________ and talk about your plans for the weekend.
3. On Friday, ask a family member or friend to call __________________ at __________________ before 2:00 p.m. and talk about the weekend plans.
4. On Sunday, after 8:00 p.m., call __________________ at __________________ and leave a message regarding the success of your activity.
5. Write a summary note about problems you encountered with your plan. If there were no problems, write a note summarizing what you did. Give the note to __________________ on Monday.

Functional Sequential Memory Assignment 41

1. On Monday, call __________________ at __________________ and report the title of a book you will be starting to read.
2. On Tuesday evening, read the first chapter and write a summary in your memory book.
3. On Wednesday evening, read the second chapter and write a summary in your memory book.
4. On Thursday evening, read the third chapter and write a summary in your memory book.
5. On Friday, review these summaries with __________________ before 3:00 p.m.

Functional Sequential Memory Assignment 42

1. On Monday evening, write a summary of an article from the Business section of the newspaper.
2. On Tuesday evening, write a summary of another article from the Business section of the newspaper.
3. On Wednesday evening, write a summary of another article from the Business section of the newspaper.
4. On Thursday evening, write a summary of another article from the Business section of the newspaper.
5. On Friday, give the four summaries to ________________ by 4:00 p.m.

Functional Sequential Memory Assignment 43

Note to the clinician: For Internal Strategies, see pages 10-13.

1. On Monday, ask ________________ to give you a copy of Internal Strategies to improve your memory.
2. On Tuesday, memorize the definition of *categorization.* Call ________________ at ________________ before 4:00 p.m. and tell that person the definition from memory.
3. On Wednesday, memorize the definition of *association.* Call ________________ at ________________ before 3:00 p.m. and tell that person the definition from memory.
4. On Thursday, memorize the definition of *chunking.* Call ________________ at ________________ before 3:00 p.m. and tell that person the definition from memory.
5. On Friday, list the strategies you have memorized, and write two examples of how to apply each strategy. Give the list to ________________ before 3:00 p.m.

Functional Sequential Memory Assignment 44

1. On Monday between 6:00 and 7:00 p.m., call ________________ at ________________ and talk about your day's activities from memory.
2. On Tuesday between 10:00 and 11:00, leave a voice message for ________________ at ________________ and report your plans for the day.
3. On Wednesday, ask a family member or friend to call ________________ at ________________ between 8:00 and 10:00 p.m. and report your weekend plans.
4. On Thursday, write a summary of a newspaper article on a political issue.
5. On Friday, give that written summary and a list of your weekend plans to ________________ before 3:00 p.m.

Functional Sequential Memory Assignment 45

1. Over the weekend, locate a book about a person recovering from a traumatic brain injury.
2. On Monday evening, read the first chapter and write a summary.
3. On Tuesday evening, read the second chapter and write a summary.
4. On Wednesday evening, read the third chapter and write a summary.
5. On Thursday, give your summaries to ________________ by 4:00 p.m.

Functional Sequential Memory Assignment 46

1. On Wednesday evening, watch the 6:00 news and write a summary in your memory book.
2. On Thursday evening, watch the 6:00 news and write a summary in your memory book.
3. On Friday evening, watch the 6:00 news and write a summary in your memory book.
4. On Monday evening, watch the 6:00 news and write a summary in your memory book.
5. On Tuesday, give all summaries to ________________ by 4:00 p.m.

Functional Sequential Memory Assignment 47

1. On Monday evening, write a summary of what was happening in your life before your injury in areas of work or school and family.
2. On Tuesday, give the summary to ________________ by 4:00 p.m.
3. On Wednesday, write a summary of challenges you encountered in your life before your injury.
4. On Thursday, give the summary to ________________ by 4:00 p.m.
5. On Friday, write a summary of how your injury has affected your mood. Call ________________ at ________________ by 4:30 p.m. and leave a message containing your summary on that person's voice mail.

Functional Sequential Memory Assignment 48

1. On Tuesday, check the price for Microsoft on the New York Stock Exchange and write the information in your memory book.
2. On Wednesday, check the price for Microsoft on the New York Stock Exchange and write the information in your memory book.
3. On Thursday, check the price for Microsoft on the New York Stock Exchange and write the information in your memory book.
4. On Friday, check the price for Microsoft on the New York Stock Exchange and write the information in your memory book.
5. On Friday afternoon, make a chart of Microsoft activity for the week and give it to ________________ by 5:00 p.m.

Functional Sequential Memory Assignment 49

1. On Monday, read an article on the Middle East issue and write a summary.
2. On Tuesday, give the summary to ________________ by 2:00 p.m.
3. On Wednesday, read another article on the same subject and write a summary.
4. On Friday, read a third article on the same subject and write a summary.
5. On the following Monday, give the second and third summaries to ________________ by 3:00 p.m.

Functional Sequential Memory Assignment 50

1. On Tuesday morning, write a list of three activities to complete during the day.
2. On Tuesday evening before 10:00 p.m., call ________________ at ________________ and report on your success in completing the activities.
3. On Wednesday morning, write a list of three activities to complete during the day.
4. On Wednesday evening before 10:00 p.m., call ________________ at ________________ and report on your success in completing the activities.
5. On Thursday morning, read an article on a business issue and call ________________ to provide a summary from memory.

Weekly Functional Memory Assignments

These assignments are for clients with mild memory difficulties.

Clients are given a complete page of memory assignments for the week, including tasks to be completed over several days including the weekend.

Strategies

Instruct or assist the client to *write* the information from the specific Weekly Functional Memory Assignment sheet in his or her memory book. Encourage the client to enter the information in an organized manner, highlighting the important bits of information to be followed up.

Cue the clients to use WDCR, a first-letter mneumonic strategy, that assists with initiation, follow-through and completion of tasks.

Write task to be completed

Do the task when scheduled;

Check off when completed;

Refer to memory book to see what you've done or still need to do.

Instructions

Select assignments according to the client's particular needs, based on clinical judgment.

On the blank lines, specify names, days of the week, phone numbers and other pertinent information as needed.

Weekly Functional Memory Assignment 1

1. On Monday, read an article about business, and call in a summary to ________________ at ________________ before 4:00 p.m.
2. On Tuesday, watch the 6:00 news. Write a summary about the headline story, and leave summary on ________________'s voice mail at ________________ before 10:00 p.m.
3. On Wednesday, ask a family member or friend to call ________________ at ________________ between 6:00 and 10:00 p.m., and leave a voice mail message about your progress noted over the last two months.
4. On Thursday, cut out an article on a foreign issue, and put the article and a summary in your memory book to review with ________________ on ________________.
5. On Friday between 8:00 and 10:00 p.m., leave a voice mail message for ________________ at ________________ telling about your weekend plans.
6. On Sunday, write a list of three primary areas of current concern, and read the list into ________________'s voice mail at ________________ before 10:00 p.m.

Weekly Functional Memory Assignment 2

1. On Monday, read an article about the stock market, and submit a written summary to ________________ by the end of the day.
2. On Tuesday, look up the closing price of Microsoft in the newspaper under NASDAQ National Market, and leave a voice mail message for ________________ at ________________ about your finding by 8:00 p.m.
3. On Wednesday, call in a voice mail message to ________________ at ________________ by 9:00 p.m. reporting on the closing price of BKTokyo on the New York Stock Exchange as listed in the newspaper.
4. On Thursday, read an article about business and call in a two-sentence summary to ________________ at ________________ by 8:00 p.m.
5. On Friday, leave a voice mail message for ________________ at ________________ by 9:30 p.m. reporting on the closing price of TWA on the American Stock Exchange as noted in the newspaper.
6. On Sunday, read an article from the weekend newspaper on business, and give a written summary to ________________ on Monday before 4:00 p.m.

Weekly Functional Memory Assignment 3

1. On Monday, watch the 6:00 news and write a summary about one of the stories reviewed. Place the summary in your memory book.
2. On Tuesday, watch the 6:00 news and write a summary about the headline story. Place the summary in your memory book.
3. On Wednesday, watch the 6:00 news and write a summary about a sports story. Place the summary in your memory book.
4. On Thursday, watch the 6:00 news and write a summary about the first story reviewed. Place the summary in your memory book.
5. On Friday, give the summaries to ________________ before 5:00 p.m.
6. On Sunday evening before 8:00 p.m., call ________________ at ________________, and leave a voice mail message about how you spent the weekend.

Weekly Functional Memory Assignment 4

1. On Monday, write a plan of five activities to be completed on Tuesday, Wednesday, Thursday, Friday and Sunday.
2. On Tuesday, complete the activity designated for that day, and check it off the list once it is completed. Leave a voice mail message for ________________ at ________________ summarizing your performance on the task.
3. On Wednesday, complete the activity designated for that day, and check it off the list once it is completed. Leave a voice mail message for ________________ at ________________ summarizing your performance on the task.
4. On Thursday, complete the activity designated for that day, and check it off the list once it is completed. Leave a voice mail message for ________________ at ________________ summarizing your performance on the task.
5. On Friday, complete the activity designated for that day, and check it off the list once it is completed. Leave a voice mail message for ________________ at ________________ summarizing your performance on the task.
6. On Sunday, complete the last activity planned, check it off the list once it is completed, and leave a voice mail message for ________________ at ________________ describing your success at completing the last task.

Weekly Functional Memory Assignment 5

1. On Monday, pick up a book from ________________ before noon.
2. On Tuesday, read the first two chapters, and write a two-paragraph summary describing the main points read.
3. On Wednesday, read the next two chapters, and a write a two-paragraph summary describing the main points read.
4. On Thursday, read the next two chapters, and write a two-paragraph summary describing the main points read.
5. On Friday, write a one-page summary from memory about the six chapters you have read
6. On Sunday, leave a voice mail message for ________________ at ________________ telling your impressions of the book up to now.

Weekly Functional Memory Assignment 6

1. On Monday, write a list of your current strengths.
2. On Tuesday before 4:00 p.m., give the list to ________________.
3. On Wednesday, write a list of short-term goals you would like to accomplish over the next month.
4. On Thursday before 11:00 a.m., leave a voice mail message for ________________ at ________________ reviewing your short-term goals.
5. On Friday, write a list of family members and friends you would like to see over the next month.
6. On Sunday, leave a voice mail message for ________________ at ________________, and read the list of family and friends you look forward to seeing.

Weekly Functional Memory Assignment 7

1. On Monday at 8:00 p.m., call __________________ at __________________, and summarize the day's events from your memory book.
2. On Tuesday at 9:00 p.m., call __________________ at __________________, and summarize the day's events from your memory book.
3. On Wednesday at 7:00 p.m., call __________________ at __________________, and summarize the day's events from your memory book.
4. On Thursday at 8:30 p.m., call __________________ at __________________, and summarize the day's events from your memory book.
5. On Friday at 8:00 p.m., call __________________ at __________________, and summarize the day's events from your memory book.
6. On Sunday at 9:00 p.m., call __________________ at __________________, and summarize the day's events from your memory book.

Weekly Functional Memory Assignment 8

1. On Monday, read an article about a foreign issue, and write a one-paragraph summary in your memory book.
2. On Tuesday, read an article about health, and write a one-paragraph summary in your memory book.
3. On Wednesday, read an article about a political issue, and write a one-paragraph summary in your memory book.
4. On Thursday, read an article about a medical advance, and write a one-paragraph summary in your memory book.
5. On Friday, submit the four summaries to __________________ by 5:00 p.m.
6. On Sunday, leave a voice mail message for __________________ at __________________ between 9:00 and 9:30 p.m. reporting from memory on your weekend activities.

Weekly Functional Memory Assignment 9

1. On Monday before lunch, leave a voice mail message for ______________ at ________________ telling your plans for the afternoon.
2. On Tuesday at 9:00 p.m., leave a voice mail message for ______________ at ________________ summarizing the day's events that you wrote in your memory book.
3. On Wednesday before lunch, leave a voice mail message for ____________ telling your plans for the afternoon.
4. On Thursday at 9:00 p.m., leave a voice mail message for ________________ at ________________ summarizing the day's events that you wrote in your memory book.
5. On Friday between 3:00 and 4:00 p.m., leave a voice mail message for ______________ at ________________ stating your weekend plans.
6. On Sunday between 8:00 and 9:00 p.m., leave a voice mail message for ________________ at ________________ reporting on your weekend.

Weekly Functional Memory Assignment 10

1. On Monday, watch the 6:00 news, and write a summary in your memory book.
2. On Tuesday before 10:00 a.m., call in the summary to ________________ at ________________.
3. On Wednesday, read an article about sports, and write a summary in your memory book.
4. On Thursday by 5:00 p.m., submit the summary to ________________.
5. On Friday by 8:00 p.m., call ________________ at ________________, and report on two weekend plans.
6. On Sunday by 8:00 p.m., call ________________ at ________________, and report on two experiences you had over the weekend.

Appendixes

Contents

Appendixes 1 and 2

Appendixes 1 and 2 contain a variety of suggestions and exercises for clinicians to review with significant others. Because significant others are an integral part of the rehabilitation team, it is critical that they help carry over strategy use in the home and community settings. Often, significant others request materials to help them in facilitating their loved one's recovery.

Review the pertinent sections of this appendix with significant others, and provide them with copies of those pages that pertain to their loved one's recovery.

Appendixes 3 and 4

Appendixes 3 and 4 contain reproducible cancellation exercises for improving attention.

Basic cancellation tasks (see chapter 3, pages 19–20) are presented in Appendix 3. Complex cancellation tasks (see chapter 3, page 22) are presented in appendix 4.

General Suggestions for Clinicians to Review with Significant Others

- Reinforce the use of consistent routines, such as storing keys, glasses and other possessions in the same place.
- Review orientation information, such as time and place, nature of the injury and primary goals.
- Reinforce increased awareness and attention to surroundings.
- Reinforce the use of a specialized memory book.
- If appropriate, reinforce the importance of logging in information about important details relating to medication, appointments, phone log and meals.
- Help the client develop structured activities to do in the evenings and weekends when not in an organized program.
- Reinforce the importance of keeping notes about activities during unstructured time.
- Reinforce the importance of follow-through on functional memory assignments.
- Reinforce the use of a memory book for recording upcoming engagements.
- Provide auditory and visual stimulation, such as watching the news and reading the newspaper and current magazines, as appropriate to the client's level.
- Reinforce the importance of writing summaries of news programs seen and articles read.
- Reinforce awareness of the multiple factors that influence memory, such as physical, chemical, emotional, attitudinal and motivational factors. (For review, see chapter 2.)
- Reinforce the importance of not consistently testing a client's memory, which may lead to the client's animosity.
- Reinforce the importance of having the client summarize, verbally and/or in writing, important events and critical messages, to be sure he or she has processed the information correctly.
- Reinforce the importance of keeping close contact with the therapy team to report on primary memory difficulties that the client may be experiencing at home.

Away from the Neurorehabilitation Site

Framework for Significant Others

As you are assisting your loved one through the neurorehabilitation process, there are many difficult challenges you face. In addition to the emotional toll of dealing with an altered loved one and balancing increased responsibilities, family members and friends often are the primary target of the client's anger and frustration.

Your loved one is learning many compensatory strategies. It is important to reinforce these strategies in a respectful, supportive and non-infantilizing manner. This helps to avoid your loved one's resistance and unnecessary conflict.

Functional Visual Recall Exercises

The following exercises were created for significant others to use with loved ones who have memory impairments.

Navigating the Community

- When driving down a main road close to home, ask your loved one to alert you when to turn onto your street.
- When on the home street, ask your loved one to identify the correct house.
- When you are driving to the grocery store (or mall or relative's house), ask your loved one to give you directions.
- As you are entering a department store, ask your loved one to remember which department you are in. When you have finished shopping, ask him or her to tell you which exit you must use. As your loved one's memory improves, ask him or her to show you how to get from your present location to the exit.
- In the parking lot of a store, ask your loved one to identify a landmark to help recall where the car is parked. When you leave the store, have him or her tell you what environmental features to look for. As your loved one's memory improves, have him or her lead you from the store to the car.
- At a department store, have your loved one look at a map and tell you how to get to a particular department. As his or her memory improves, increase the number of departments (for example, "We need to go to the men's department and then to the baby section.").

- At the mall, have your loved one use a map to guide you to a specified store. Begin with stores that are close and progress to stores that are farther away. As his or her recall improves, increase the number of stores (for example, "Let's go to the toy store and then to the coffee shop for a snack.").
- If appropriate, ask your loved one to show you how to get from class to class in the high school or on the college campus.

Around the House

- In the bathroom, ask your loved one to assemble the items needed to brush teeth, shower or wash his or her face. Before the grooming task begins, make sure he or she has all the items needed. When the task is finished, have your loved one return the items to their proper places.
- Ask your loved one to help set the table, locating all the needed items in the cabinets and drawers throughout the kitchen.
- Let your loved one help with meal preparation by looking at a recipe and placing all necessary ingredients and utensils on the counter.
- After the dishes are washed, ask your loved one to put away all the items in the proper cabinets and drawers.
- Have your loved one make and pack a lunch.
- Before grocery shopping, ask your loved one to check the cabinet or refrigerator for a particular item. When you are at the store, ask whether you need to purchase that item. As his or her recall improves, add more items.
- Ask your loved one to make a grocery list based on items missing from the cabinets and refrigerator.
- On the evening before school (work, treatment), have your loved one assemble all items that will be needed for the next day and place them on the table.

Appendix 3

Cancellation Exercises for Improving Attention

Instructions

1. Review the discussion about strategies on pages 19-20.
2. Determine the appropriate level for the client, based on clinical judgment and the following guidelines:

Skill Level	**Cancellation Exercises**
Level 1—Severe impairment	1, 2, 3
Level 2—Moderate impairment	4, 5, 6
Level 3—Mild impairment	7, 8, 9

3. Before beginning each exercise, instruct the client to "Cross out each _____."
4. Cue the client to start at the beginning of each line, working from left to right and moving down the page line by line.

The exercises are organized hierarchically, with more basic exercises progressing to complex. Begin training just above the level of the client's current ability (based on clinical assessment), and progress in difficulty level as mastery is achieved. Generally, accuracy is emphasized over speed (although both can be important in a client's real-life activities). Once an acceptable level of accuracy (determined between client and therapist) is achieved, you may want to introduce timing to improve speed of performance.

Strategies

Clients who experience significant difficulties on the task may use cues (for example, anchors or a ruler; see page 19) to facilitate performance.

Name________________________________ Date______________________

Cancellation Exercise 1
Single-Letter Cancellation

Instructions: Cross out each **P**.

K S E P O W J C M S

G K E S J F P E Q J S

L F T O E P W Q L E I

U R Y U T H G H V N

C M K L A P Q P W O

P U R J F N M V P N Z

R S P V W P M Q L D

K P U Z U E R I W O P

P C J M V K S L P O I

R W B L P F I W K F L

Name________________________________ Date______________________

Cancellation Exercise 2
Single-Number Cancellation

Instructions: Cross out each **3**.

5	8	9	2	3	4	7	5	3	1	5	9
3	5	7	4	5	6	3	2	5	9	9	3
2	5	7	3	3	2	1	5	8	7	7	8
9	7	5	3	2	1	5	9	3	5	6	3
3	1	5	7	6	3	1	5	7	5	3	1
5	8	4	5	3	2	5	6	9	7	1	3
3	1	4	5	6	8	4	6	3	1	5	8
7	3	3	1	5	8	7	2	3	1	5	7
4	1	3	6	9	8	7	4	3	1	5	7
2	3	5	5	6	2	3	4	5	5	9	8
7	3	6	5	5	7	4	2	3	3	5	4

Name________________________________ Date______________________

Cancellation Exercise 3
Single-Symbol Cancellation

Instructions: Cross out each  .

Name________________________________ Date______________________

Cancellation Exercise 4
Single-Letter Cancellation

Instructions: Cross out each **k**.

miwkturiepwlcjvmmxnsjkleituyhfjsk
klqqeitijrhyeydhvnvmmkehdiuwowk
dljvnsdkwkuwiqosjsjcnkfkwijskdnwi
asucdhdfkjshdifyurueikhjdhvfnvmkd
jdjueijosdjkfhasjkdfhklsjfhpoauiwdf
hylasdjkfahlskdfjahlskdfjhaosieuryl
aryaopisufhklkkasjdflakseuroasidfh
laksdjkaowierualskdfhkjsdfasekase
krasdfaxdkfaserasekriasdjkasdfjoa
weraskkasdfoasdfjakosdfjoaskdadjk
faoskdfjaosdkfjaosdkfjaosdkfjaekoa
iekroqwyieroihscvklzxkcfgmahsdkry
kowieulskdfhoakdifuaowieurlasiskd
hkkawierualskdfjaoweirukdjflaskdfh
aowieurflaksdyfuaikweyrlaskfjlaksd
jfopakweruoaksdjflzskdrhjaosikura
osdkuflaskdfoaiweurkqwieuflksdfjk
ekuoaiyusdklfasdurioawekrjkasdjla
kiweurksdjflaiseuralskjklasejroaiw

Name________________________________ Date______________________

Cancellation Exercise 5
Single-Number Cancellation

Instructions: Cross out each **2**.

9 8 6 5 1 3 2 1 3 7 8 7 6 3 2 1 3 2 4 6 8 7 3 2 1 3 8 7 8 3 6
4 3 2 1 3 2 1 3 5 4 8 7 8 5 3 1 3 2 1 5 4 6 8 4 3 2 1 3 4 5 8
3 6 4 2 4 5 3 7 3 2 4 6 9 5 9 1 2 3 5 7 5 8 4 9 5 1 6 2 3 1 3
2 4 9 2 7 5 6 1 3 2 1 3 5 4 8 3 6 4 3 2 1 3 5 4 3 5 8 4 7 8 2
6 7 3 5 4 2 3 6 4 6 8 2 8 9 3 6 5 4 2 5 4 6 5 1 0 6 2 9 4 6 7
9 5 2 4 9 7 1 3 9 4 2 6 7 9 2 3 7 2 9 7 9 1 7 9 6 2 7 2 7 5 3
5 5 6 7 3 2 7 9 2 7 9 2 3 2 7 8 9 2 7 3 4 2 7 6 3 9 7 5 7 2 6
4 3 7 3 1 4 7 2 9 6 5 2 4 6 7 3 1 2 9 4 7 2 6 1 7 2 3 6 4 2 3
7 9 2 2 1 7 4 9 3 2 6 7 4 2 3 4 7 9 1 2 6 7 6 9 2 3 8 9 8 5 6
2 7 4 2 7 9 2 3 8 9 1 2 7 8 4 8 6 2 3 4 7 9 4 5 1 4 7 1 2 8 2
1 9 4 2 8 9 7 2 5 3 2 9 4 7 3 2 5 5 9 8 7 5 6 1 2 3 1 3 2 1 2
3 1 5 6 4 8 9 4 2 3 1 3 6 8 6 4 3 2 1 3 8 7 6 9 7 3 7 3 2 1 2
1 2 3 8 6 7 3 8 6 4 7 2 8 9 3 5 1 2 6 1 6 5 9 9 9 1 2 2 6 9 8
7 3 2 1 8 9 7 9 5 4 1 6 3 2 4 9 7 8 9 4 7 6 2 1 3 2 1 2 3 4 5
6 4 9 5 1 3 2 1 8 7 9 8 4 5 1 5 6 1 2 2 6 2 7 8 9 8 5 4 6 5 4
2 8 7 5 6 7 5 6 4 5 5 9 8 7 6 8 2 1 3 4 8 4 3 2 1 3 8 7 6 5 4
7 9 4 2 3 1 2 3 1 3 5 4 6 9 8 7 6 5 1 2 3 1 2 9 2 4 6 7 9 8 6
2 1 3 5 4 7 9 8 7 5 6 1 3 2 4 6 8 7 8 9 4 2 1 6 5 7 9 8 7 5 6
1 2 4 6 9 8 7 9 2 4 6 5 4 7 9 8 7 9 8 7 2 8 4 5 6 4 6 5 4 6 2
6 1 2 6 4 9 8 7 9 2 1 3 2 1 6 5 7 9 8 4 5 3 2 9 8 7 4 9 5 4 2
1 2 3 1 6 7 9 8 5 1 3 2 4 6 7 6 8 4 5 4 2 2 6 1 8 9 7 2 6 1 2
3 1 6 7 6 2 1 3 8 4 6 4 6 2 1 3 2 1 8 6 4 7 9 4 6 2 1 2 3 1 8
6 7 4 9 5 6 1 3 2 1 6 4 5 9 7 2 6 1 3 4 5 6 2 9 7 8 5 6 1 2 3
1 5 2 7 8 9 4 2 6 1 3 5 4 9 8 7 6 2 1 3 4 5 4 9 7 8 7 2 5 1 3
4 5 5 9 7 5 2 1 3 3 4 6 4 9 8 7 5 6 2 1 3 5 4 9 6 7 9 5 4 2 3

Name______________________________ Date____________________

Cancellation Exercise 6
Single-Symbol Cancellation

Instructions: Cross out each .

Name________________________________ Date______________________

Cancellation Exercise 7
Single-Letter Cancellation

Instructions: Cross out each **k**.

miwkturiepwlcjvmmxnsjkleituyhfjskklqqeitijrhyey
d hvnvmmkehd iuwowkd ijvnsd kwkuwiqosjsjcnkfkwij
skd nwiasucd hd fkjshd ifyurueikhjd hvfnvmkd jd jueij
osd jkfhasjkd fhklsjfhpoauiwd fhylasd jkfahlskd fjahl
skd fjhaosieurylaryaopisufhkikkasjd flakseuroasid
fhlaksd jkaowierualskd fhkjsd fasekasekrasd faxd kf
aserasekriasd jkasd fjoaweraskkasd foasd fjakosd fj
oaskd ad jkfaoskd fjaosd kfjaosd kfjaosd kfjaekoalekr
oqwyieroihscvklzxkcfgmahsd krykowieulskd fhoakd
ifuaowieurlasiskd hkkawierualskd fjaoweirukd jflas
kd fhaowieurflaksd yfuaikweyrlaskfjlaksd jfopakwer
uoksd jflzskd rhjaosikuraosd kuflaskd foaiweurkqw
ieuflksd fjkekuoaiyusd klfasd urioawekrjkasd jlakiw
eurzksd jflaiseuralskjklasejroaiwejfklsd jflaisuriel
urilasjd flkasjd flasjeilrjaklsilaeurliasjd klfjasld kfj
laskd jflaksd jfilaweurklsd jflkaseurlaiwgukosjkllas
eirualsid jfalksd jflaskd jflaskd jflaksjd flwieurlehjl
efjlskd ufaliseurlasiejrlaksd jrlaksd jrlisuerliasukil
ruklsd fhokasieurhklasd fnmlxcvnzxmkcnklsd rjomkj
vlzxcmvnlzkd fjoasd ifhlzxkcnvklzxchfosd uiflzxkcj
vlkzxcnlksd fuasiod vmkzxcvnkpsjd fioasd jfklzxcvnl
kzxncflisd fhklzxcnvlzkxchjfilsd hfzlod hoaskd hjklz
xvnlzxkcfjloisd goasihlkzxchnklchglygruiotynvkbl
zd jkoqiojkld nclkvlshud foiausd klfjasld knfzlxkcvhj
oaisd fulaskd nflzxkcvnlzksd jfioasd flasnkd vlxckvh
lzsd fuoaisd fjlzkxcnvlzkxchlhjafoisd uflasd fuioask
cvjnlzxckvhzlxkcjfoasid fulzxkcnvlxkcnvlzsd fuioa
sd ufoaskd jflzxknvlkzxjcflaisd ufozksjclkxcnvhlkxc
hoaid fualsd khflxkcghlkhzoisd hfod ifuljkgflhkgknbl
vkhjglituyrlhbcvlknblsd foairutlkasd jfalksd ntlakif
hkcvnblkasd thriod fhlksd fnglsirhtklsd fbnlskd nflit
hsohinlbsld tueiorthjwlehrglskd fhglkshd flkguoier
utlksd hflsd utioresurlklsd kfhklsd fgoseirtulsd kfhgl

Name________________________________ Date______________________

Cancellation Exercise 8
Single-Number Cancellation

Instructions: Cross out each **2**.

9865132137876321324687321387836432132135487853
1321546843213458364245373246959123575849516231
3249275613213548364321354358478267354236468289
3654254651062946795249713942679237297917962727
5355673279279232789273427639757264373147296524
6731294726172364237922174932674234791267692389
8562742792389127848623479451471282194289725329
4732559875612313212315648942313686432138769737
3212123867386472893512616599912269873218979541
6324978947621321234564951321879845156122627898
5465428756756455987682134843213876547942312313
5469876512312924679862135479875613246878942165
7987561246987924654798798728456465462612649879
2132165798453298749542123167985132467684542261
8972612316762138464621321864794621231867495613
2164597261345629785612315278942613549876213454
9787251345597521334649875621354967954236548921
2167589123199978651231564897261231579842128678
9214597984231879423138579412316958798721238789
4215379875612348976556489761231231657892316549
7213579723165794231865791231567894231354897231
2345976913548942317891231667942316794231649876
1278976516797132486789122356498423156498423159
4052167231347897261379542256479423196876138976
2157925324976924987297842198731235898726123489
7924321857921867945315621567972616876213579135
2169759123489723123498231234987261234897621342
8751231921584612384321348423134578642318461216
8762134786122135765123469876513486432168723138

Name_______________________________ Date______________________

Cancellation Exercise 9
Single-Symbol Cancellation

Instructions: Cross out each ★.

Appendix 4

Complex Cancellation Exercises for Improving Attention

Instructions

1. Review the discussion on page 22.
2. Determine the appropriate level for the client, based on clinical judgment and the following guidelines:

Skill Level	**Complex Cancellation Exercises**
Level 1—Severe impairment	1, 2, 3
Level 2—Moderate impairment	4, 5, 6
Level 3—Mild impairment	7, 8, 9
Level 4—Advanced skill level	10, 11, 12

3. Before beginning each exercise, instruct the client to:
   - Exercises 1-6: "Cross out each _____ and _____."
   - Exercises 7-12: "Cross out each _____ that is followed by _____."
4. Cue the client to start at the beginning of each line, working from left to right and moving down the page line by line.

The exercises are organized hierarchically, with more basic exercises progressing to complex. Begin training just above the level of the client's current ability (based on clinical assessment), and progress in difficulty level as mastery is achieved. Generally, accuracy is emphasized over speed (although both can be important in a client's real-life activities). Once an acceptable level of accuracy (determined between client and therapist) is achieved, you may want to introduce timing to improve speed of performance.

Strategies

Clients who experience significant difficulties on the task may use cues (for example, anchors or a ruler; see page 19) to facilitate performance.

Name______________________________ Date____________________

Complex Cancellation Exercise 1
Double-Letter Cancellation

Instructions: Cross out each **j** and each **s**.

lksvhksjdufgiohxcvklsjhlvkjoidfglkcvhbl
sxcknbjxcsojvslkdfjgclsckvjblxsckvjbsxl
ckvhjbosixdugfjlxckvnbljxckjvbosicvuglj
xdkbvhjlsxckvjblsxckfhgiosdfugljksdjkch
lowiruysdklfjghlsdkvjblsckghsldufylsdijhl
jkcvhblkxcjvbhilsdufgylsjkdbhlkxdjfgysi
dufygklcjxvhblxkcjgfysuidfygskldjvhklcj
vhbklxjsdfsdiopfugysdopfjhkjsdfhgklsdjr
jgisudfhygkljscfhglduiwtyksdjrhtwekljryt
iduhgjkcfhgklsjdfhygiueryjkcvhsmcvnbm
jxcvxcbnlodfjkhgisdufykjxcvnbsxufhgios
udfghksjdghjsdmfghsilduvbxckvjbhklsdj
gtnlwdfugysidhvxklcvjbxlkvhgisdufygjklj
cvblxkcjvhgisudfygklsdjfhglkxjcvhbisduf
ygiosdufytiopwerytwejktnklsdfmnbxcvug
soidfghsjfghlsekmrngtlwekrutywieurtkjs
dblskdjftlywieurskldjfghskldjfgnxcmslvh
bklsdjtyiwuerhtklwejrhtkldjgklsdmghlkd
hgiuwerytiwueyrgkljdvnhklmcvnbsxmjcb
nksdjrhygiuwerhykjsdvngksjthiuwehbksc
jvbhsuidfhgiwejrghfjhxklcvbklsejhifsdhl
djkghileurthklsdjfhgklsjrhiewjrhtnerjklth

Name______________________________ Date____________________

Complex Cancellation Exercise 2
Double-Number Cancellation

Instructions: Cross out each **4** and each **7**.

897651423137554231375123135751231
355423123457854123313578542312345
412315478741566876432137894561387
163878961232478561387531378864123
145678654321358742312316874651231
756123789415315789423135789123498
453164676518972312678946135489732
167897231237895123478942315676213
789765213548972315879546518762135
489721378945364561234987531675892
348976513475646949456134789756234
897231567897654687654675894561657
984651867961567896437894654894265
674321546879512314589723134564423
157561231567591238998213789423186
719878941320148979876515378975137
985123489756135498753167894234987
518970194048156453894561098765189
431204894756132408972319875610489
454070621984516870498745340987056
409875601298406548971867481547165
197465109840651984765107940684906
218948974871897716478167861358657
024009847065109875610987561897651

Name________________________________ Date______________________

Complex Cancellation Exercise 3
Double-Symbol Cancellation

Instructions: Cross out each ▢ and each ➡.

Name______________________________ Date____________________

Complex Cancellation Exercise 4
Double-Letter Cancellation

Instructions: Cross out each **m** and each **e**.

oiweurjklxncvmmznxdjkfhyuilasyfjknbmexchuisdghmmecb
nksdfhyugksjcvnbmexcjvmwenrkwmenrmasehjrawjkermma
senrwjkehrmmfgnmwerhuwerhtmemdntmwmtrhkejrhtmdmfn
gmwemrhtkwejrhtmmgfnmsdmftuweiortuwpeorifpwerptnmv
mnsmmgnmvhbosuiftoweirutlknbcbmokftyowertjemrtwjeort
yiqowehjmxmcvmxmcjvalksehiozhmxcmvnlaksdhtoajksrytl
smdvnmzdktoerktoerktpwerotuwelfkhjsdlmvnsdlkfjoewuit
mnkerotuoweirhlkmnxcvbmxmcvnoseirtlekrhtmmvbnmxdfm
oweirtywlekrutowehjgmsdmvbnsljkfthwoerituoerjiglmhgm
sdrhtioweutrlwkehdrgmmnsdgklhweoritoweirlwdknfgmdfkg
owiertywlkfnhglmdmfhgklryiotywelrkhgmsdmfngsldirtywo
eirhtmlsmdnfglsiudrtowekthuowieurtksndfgmsmdnfgthuwo
ierytowkehrglsmmfnglsdhyfotiyweorihtlsdkfnglskdfytiowe
yrtlksdnfglksdhftiowyertojsdfmgnsdjkftypwetysdkfjghsmdf
nmgsoidrtypwertipdfegnksldrtypwerhsdmmfngpwtyweower
uitwopergsdjkvgnskdlfjghwiouerntkwjertjkwhefgysuiodufn
tjkwertnwerghuisfngklwerntmdfghuioewrhtmmnwrmgnerjtw
mefgoiudfgmmnwetuidfxmrweeemoejrhmmdfcvnweirotwmd
rfgnmmfhgisouerthmmwerwenkrjqemrwerouthsdfmkgnmme
rnwejkmsdrtwejirhtkmsngmmermtnwjoerhtmmsdnfgmsmhdft
oiwehrktlnsdmfmgnwkeurthkwejuiowerkjsdnfgmmsndfkltj
hwkejgfnmsdmfgnerhtksmmnfgmmsdngmmerntnjktnwemmr
ntkweutrhmmdngfmsmdrntkwejhrtmmsdnrtmwmehrtkwjerng
mdnfgiouwerhtmmsndfgmmshkerjhtsmmdfgmstrhsmmdfngs
klejrhytmsmdfngmsjdtrhmsmdfngmskdrmhtkjdrhtmmndfgm
jswhertjknsmdfmgnkserjhtmmsdfngmsdrhktkljndfgmmsdhio
rutykwdfngmsmdfhogwuierptwperihskdfmgnwdnfgiouwerht
mmsndfgmmshkerjhtsmmdfuihkjjksfhdggmstrhsmmdfngskl
ejrhytmsmdfngmsjdtrhmsmdfngmskdrmhtkjdrhtmmndfgmjs
whertjknsmdfmgnkserjhtmmsdfngmsdrhktkljndfgmmsdhior
utykwdfngmsmdfhogwuierptwperihskdfmgnwthkwejngmsdr
tkweksmdfngkseurtyksjdfgksjdrytuinefmgsnmdfgsmerthjkd

Name______________________________ Date______________________

Complex Cancellation Exercise 5
Double-Number Cancellation

Instructions: Cross out each **5** and **9**.

029587910273820736029415827567260795207629016201

287985423003219875612306219879512305647897231987

954216978912089456216454960238759125056498742305

647891294945065994512037595810265956097843209578

123029781234589723032497845629513067894520524987

623068789612086794512306879561206879461320689794

516305978456123198745612303894130987410086761501

894630687945120269874510678945126879412168974130

978463087564120698764109784120678951206587956120

357956120566894512048896453102599864520195884120

689745120789465120898645120789745612098884512060

789412309785612069897456123089645125376789561224

546132004784561206894512307589651239884615236847

894512036765132069845612379865121687623189742099

965123087561203578986103478974230678956121674129

841309786531265856985132999513498421685411098723

197854155987612357965123579561203579602569781209

876452009874651278956230687954121987410697841300

867431297987465211897423138961504984562067841035

912069541302978412306874306876320385761306813055

489987621378961209872035498742064579810987621387

960654789613218984216984120569786206587981523069

789512098234789216785612387621553798430687620647

562035795613579633459845303579561052478956023498

564120697841230365476120357964130897841500512564

888974561050489765132068795612057896152034894105

786513059512059745152867453205698881450367894510

698762311197853023987132014984069872111197820000

097206789120789425000948530059480389631204861556

420156485631294206784524694891023126523123651303

653120254786794217889795611129420689759612097812

316579123167859132198756203657941089795600567951

098762168789987621003698121598121059984320694847

210059895712323789410678956102950357984502297881

324987621698762167891295498423065792154789472306

Name______________________________ Date____________________

Complex Cancellation Exercise 6
Double-Symbol Cancellation

Instructions: Cross out each 💡 and each ★.

Name_______________________________ Date______________________

Complex Cancellation Exercise 7
Two-Step Letter Cancellation

Instructions: Cross out each **S** that is followed by **D**.

TKLNSDLKNKLAGHDFNGSDMGNDKGN

DWIOERHTAKSDGNDKFLGNSUORTHS

DFNGSDMKGFNSRHTUIOENGIEOTHLD

FNGSDKLFJNOUITRHNGFSIRHTOSER

HGSJKLFDFNGSDKFJTHUOEIGHLSDJK

FNTSNERTUIHSDOFGHSDIJKLFNGTEO

UITLSDJFGNSDOWUIRYASUNGASDKG

FNNEUIRGHSDJKFGNSDGHEURGHKSD

JHFGNSDFGNEUIGHSDJKGNSNDFJGH

IEURGNSDJKGNIERUGHDKUHGIOSUD

GNSDFKGNUIERTHEUIRGNSDKFGUIE

RGKDSUGHISUDFHGUKGNERUIGHGH

ERUIGNSERUIOGHDRUIGNDIFUGHEUI

RGHUKDFGNSDFUIGEIRUGHAIDGHUIE

RHGIURHGDUFGHUIERHGKLSDGLSDU

RHGUILERGLKSDUHFGISEURHGSDRU

KGNRUIGNUDRGSUIDGNGORHGIUEGH

IOERUHGIUERGHISDFNGIUERGHISUF

HGIUERHGIERUHGIERUHGNHEUIORT

HIEURHSJKLDFGNHRUIESGDFJKLNGE

RUGSDRULGHLSDKJFHGNUIWERYTJK

SDGFNNKSDFGUIERUADNGKJSDFNGI

USERGLDKRTHEUIRHINGFSDIFUHGIS

UERTIERUNGIUERGHKJSDGNIWUERTJ

Name________________________________ Date______________________

Complex Cancellation Exercise 8
Two-Step Number Cancellation

Instructions: Cross out each **9** that is followed by **4**.

89541206016784561320654751347594230
87615894721098756105645603214567864
51005645603465423064564056412156105
64759412054564230456404610265456160
45642061456143205646210456413201234
56789456230544320214584756161657616
69791206589423056795107654630678651
05761231567561289745610289746952108
97456123089446512307894561230894512
00897564120897451089456312089456120
78946512308456123089745613208794561
23084561078945612308974109845612306
894512078945613208956123089461074109
89654078956108945120895120789512089
45120808946512360987456132069784152
30894510687641532087465123087941360
87946513089761230789410874510597945
61257961089756132098745120897415328
74108974120784107874132789841230357
89123056794612308974108974128979561
07894650378651230878813048941230864
79561087410687985132087941328974618
74510874106876510678465208946521067
98510867510897432089463106758956124

Name________________________________ Date______________________

Complex Cancellation Exercise 9
Two-Step Symbol Cancellation

Instructions: Circle each ☑ that is followed by ⊂.

Name______________________________ Date____________________

Complex Cancellation Exercise 10
Two-Step Letter Cancellation

Instructions: Cross out each **N** that is preceded by **G**.

T K L N S D L K N K L A G H D F N G S D M G N D K G N D W I O E R H T A K S D G N
D K F L G N S U O R T H S D F N G S D M K G F N S R H T U I O E N G I E O T H L D F
N G S D K L F J N O U I T R H N G F S I R H T O S E R H G S J K L F D F N G S D K F J
T H U O E I G H L S D J K F N T S N E R T U I H S D O F G H S D I J K L F N G T E O U
I T L S D J F G N S D O W U I R Y A S U N G A S D K G F N N E U I R G H S D J K F G
N S D G H E U R G H K S D J H F G N S D F G N E U I G H S D J K G N S N D F J G H I
E U R G N S D J K G N I E R U G H D K U H G I O S U D G N S D F K G N U I E R T H E
U I R G N S D K F G U I E R G K D S U G H I S U D F H G U K G N E R U I G H G H E R
U I G N S E R U I O G H D R U I G N D I F U G H E U I R G H U K D F G N S D F U I G E
I R U G H A I D G H U I E R H G I U R H G D U F G H U I E R H G K L S D G L S D U R
H G U I L E R G L K S D U H F G I S E U R H G S D R U K G N R U I G N U D R G S U I
D G N G O R H G I U E G H I O E R U H G I U E R G H I S D F N G I U E R G H I S U F
H G I U E R H G I E R U H G I E R U H G N H E U I O R T H I E U R H S J K L D F G N H
R U I E S G D F J K L N G E R U G S D R U L G H L S D K J F H G N U I W E R Y T J K
S D G F N N K S D F G U I E R U A D N G K J S D F N G I U S E R G L D K R T H E U I
R H I N G F S D I F U H G I S U E R T I E R U N G I U E R G H K J S D G N I W U E R T
J K D F N G S F N G E U I R T H S U I O D R H K J G S D F G N E U I O R T Y I F H U N
G S J K D F N U I S E R T Y I U E R H G J S D F N G S K D J T H U I E R T U K S D F G
N E U T S J I K D F H G J K S F N G E R U I T U I D R T D S F J G N U I W E R Y T K S
J D F G N I O W E R T S D J R H G N W E I R U T Y R U K G F N I E U R T R T D N G O
E U R T J K S D R N G S K D J F G T J K H R T U I Y D R J K T D J K F N G D U R T U I
S D H F G N S D F T Y U I R Y J K S D F H G S J K D F T Y I R U N S D F G S J K D R Y
T J D F G N U I E R T H J K S F N G S U E R T J K F N G S D U R T K N J G N I U E R T
Y K S J D F G N U I E R T Y K S J D F G U I E R T Y K F N G U I R T K J F G N S D J K
R T U I E R Y T J K S D F G S D K F I U E R G H U I R Y T 9 U I W E R H J K N U I O T
Y I U G F S D K J F T Y U I E R N G K D F Y T U I E R G N U I E T Y J K D F G K S D G
N I W U R T L K D F J L S K D J G N N U E I R T H S J K G F N I U W E R H T J K S N F
G L E U R H I E N J G I S D U G H D I R N G E I R U G S I D L F U G N I U W E R T K S
D J G U I R G I N O E R U I G H J D G F N I E R U N G E O R N I G O E W N R G O E R
N G N W U O E R H K S D J F N G K N D F G H E I O R G N K S G N O U I E G H M K L
N V B O I E R H T D F N B I E U R T Y S D F J G N I E U R S K D J F G N A U I O T K S
D J F G N E U I R T H D J K F N G E U I R T H S D J K F G N S K D J T K J D F N I E U
T S D F J G N I E U R T Y S K D J F G N E I R U T K D J F G N S D U T Y S J K D F G L
S K D U R G H N J B U S I D R T Y U I S E R Y T U I W E R G N S D K F T Y S D J K R

Name________________________________ Date____________________

Complex Cancellation Exercise 11
Two-Step Number Cancellation

Instructions: Cross out each **1** that is followed by **0**.

895412060167845613206547513475942308761589472109875 61
056456032145678645100564560346542306456405641215610 56
475961205456423045640461026545616045642061456143205 64
621045641320123456789456230544320214584756161657616 69
791206589423056795107654630678651057612315675612897 45
610289746952108974561230897465123078945612308945120 08
975641208974510894563120894561207894651230845612308 97
456132087945612308456107894561230897410984561230689 45
120789456132089561230895610741089654078956108945120 89
512078951208945120808946512360987456132069784152308 94
510687641532087465123087941360879465130897612307894 10
874510597945612579610897561320987451208974153287410 89
741207841078741327898412303578912305679561230897410 89
741289795610789465037865123087881304894123086479561 08
741068798513208794132897461874510874106876510678465 20
897652106798510867510897432089763106758956124597951 86
742619500897456208974612306879561084413068794812089 76
510648941506876510647895261687956163675413069894610 32
798413209789410987620187894130987795610357956106878 95
130975608978956106878912321459789561028442309874502 89
746510357891067889410789410897423089785612348974101 78
974108974129876516798451320987451230898941087974158 97
413789108974118974198768974108787561056489109713851 05
943202657560645910847562063547951260698742308917462 30
897412309874510894132098412608975620628942308974210 89
742309841320974230987423026489423069874561208974510 67
897461532198741520987451089416321984512089741289412 38
974100894521986451230986451985641298456120986512098 56
412068578956208105213065760656476106647603864613209 87
104789610987423089741230894197841984189741897418971 89
741978419874108965123089700897210897613789123891324 87
651087210678940874620387420375120851089410847067510 23
475610375613871047100987230678912607823068741230867 41
368410489064893106871337602864106847108641510675462 98
741208945210894100986418964098431098741074132987419 84
097840698432897089730987320987206870654178630894138 67
910987106879610623687163870876108460264895420645064 00
864206547620645865123456412348941047120864106841086 41
086432197862198452089651089651208964512089651206851 04

Functional Memory Manual-Elbaum, *et al.*

Name________________________________ Date____________________

Complex Cancellation Exercise 12
Two-Step Symbol Cancellation

Instructions: Circle each ☒ that is followed by ⊂.

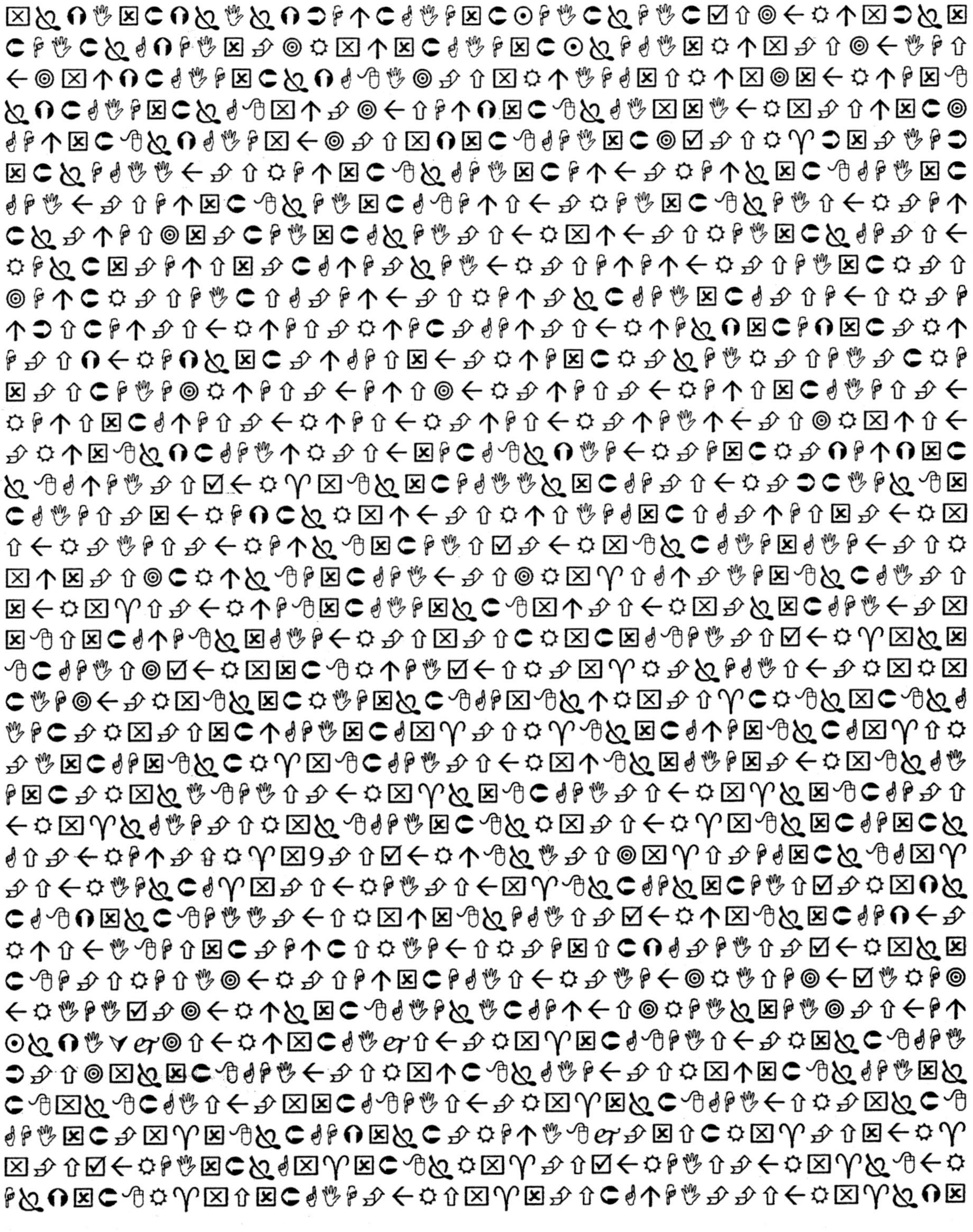

Functional Memory Manual-Elbaum, *et al.*

References

Boorstin, D.J., and Kelley, B.M. *A History of the United States.* Lexington, MA: Ginn & Company, 1986.

Braunling-McMorrow, D., Niemann, G., and Savage, R. *Training Manual for Certified Brain Injury Specialists.* Alexandria, VA: American Academy for the Certification of Brain Injury Specialists, 1998.

Elbaum, J., Kramer, P., Dulaski, C., and Benson, D. Mempal: A Novel Compensatory Tool. Healthsouth Braintree Rehabilitation Hospital 20th Annual Neurorehabilitation Conference. Boston, MA, 1999.

Fisher, S., and Reason, J.T. *Handbook of Life Stress, Cognition, and Health.* New York: John Wiley, 1986.

Fleming, T., chief editor. *Physician's Desk Reference for Herbal Medicines.* Montvale, NJ: Medical Economics, 1998.

Garner, J., Costas, B., and Foreman, G. *And the Fans Roared.* Naperville, IL: Sourcebooks, 2000.

Gruneberg, M. The practical application of memory aids: Knowing how, knowing when and knowing when not. In M. Gruneberg and P. Morris (Eds.), *Aspects of Memory* (pp. 168-195). London: Routledge, 1992.

Harris, J.E. Ways to help memory. In B.A. Wilson and N. Moffat (Eds.), *Clinical Management of Memory Problems* (pp. 59-85). San Diego: Singular, 1992.

Heilman, K.M., and Valenstein, E. *Clinical Neuropsychology* (3rd ed.). New York: Oxford University Press, 1993.

Hersh, N.A., and Treadgold, L.G. Neuropage: The rehabilitation of memory dysfunction by prosthetic memory and cueing. *NeuroRehabilitation,* vol. 4, no. 3: 187-192 (1994).

Hertel, P.T. Depressive deficits in memory: Implications for memory improvement following traumatic brain injury. *NeuroRehabilitation,* vol. 4, no. 3: 143-150 (1994).

Herrmann, D., and Parente, R. The multimodal approach to cognitive rehabilitation. *NeuroRehabilitation,* vol. 4, no. 3: 133-142 (1994).

Herrmann, D., and Searleman, A. Advances in learning and motivation. In G. H. Bower (Ed.), *The New Multimodal Approach to Memory Improvement* (pp. 175-205). New York: Academic Press, 1990.

Lezak, M.D. *Neuropsychological Assessment.* New York: Oxford University Press, 1995.

Mateer, C.A. Treatment of cognitive sequelae: Attention. In S.A. Raskin and C.A. Mateer (Eds.), *Neuropsychological Management of Mild Traumatic Brain Injury*. New York: Oxford University Press, 2000.

Mayes, A. R. *Human Organic Memory Disorders*. New York: Cambridge University Press, 1988.

Montgomery, G.K. A multi-factor account of disability after brain injury: Implications for neuropsychological counseling. *Brain Injury*, vol. 9: 453-469 (1995).

New York University Head Trauma Program. *Orientation Remediation Module (ORM) System*. New York: New York University, 1987.

O'Shanick, G.J. Cognitive function after brain injury. *NeuroRehabilitation*, vol. 3: 44-49 (1991).

Parente, R., and DiCesare, A. Retraining memory: Theory, evaluation and applications. In J.S. Kreutzer and P.H. Wehman (Eds.), *Cognitive Rehabilitation for Persons with Traumatic Brain Injury* (pp. 147-162). Baltimore: Paul H. Brooks, 1991.

Parente, R., and Parente, J. Retraining memory: Theory and application. *Journal of Head Trauma Rehabilitation*, vol. 4: 55-65 (1989).

Parente, R., and Stapleton, M. An empowerment model of memory training. *Applied Cognitive Psychology*, vol. 7: 585-602 (1993).

Rattok, J. *Medisoft Software*. New York: Medisoft, 1988.

Robertson, I.H., Hogg, K., and McMillan, T.M. Rehabilitation of unilateral neglect: Reducing inhibitory competition by contralesional limb activation. *Neuropsychological Rehabilitation*, vol. 8: 19-30 (1998).

Robertson, I.H., Tegner, R., Thom, K., Lo, A. and Nimmo-Smith, I. Sustained attention training for unilateral neglect: Theoretical and rehabilitation implications. *Journal of Clinical and Experimental Neuropsychology*, vol. 17: 416-430 (1995).

Sohlberg, M.M., and Mateer, C.A. *Introduction to Cognitive Rehabilitation and Practice*. New York: Guilford Press, 1989.

Toglia, J. Attention and memory. In C.B. Royeen (Ed.), *AOTA Self-Study Series: Cognitive Rehabilitation* (pp. 1-69). Rockville, MD: American Occupational Therapy Association, 1993.

Vogenthaler, D.R. An overview of head injury: Its consequences and rehabilitation. *Brain Injury*, vol. 1: 113-117 (1987).

Wyer, R., and Srull, T.K. *Memory and Cognition: In its Social Context*. Hillsdale, NJ: Erlbaum, 1989.

About the Authors

Jean Elbaum is Clinical Director at Transitions of Long Island, a subsidiary of the North Shore-Long Island Jewish Health System in Manhasset, New York. She has worked at Transitions since its inception in 1988. She received the B.A. and M.A. degrees in Psychology and the Ph.D. degree in Rehabilitation Counseling from New York University. Her experience in neurorehabilitation began in 1980 when she completed an internship at the Cognitive Rehabilitation Program at New York University-Bellevue Hospital. Dr. Elbaum's primary clinical interests include rehabilitation of memory and awareness deficits. She has presented more than 25 papers at national conferences. Dr. Elbaum is married and has two sons. She is a runner and enjoys reading.

Peggy Kramer is Senior Speech-Language Pathologist at Transitions of Long Island. She received the M.S. degree in Communication Disorders from Adelphi University, Garden City, New York; and the B.A. TSHH (Teacher of the Speech and Hearing Handicapped) degree from Hofstra University, Hempstead, New York. She is an Adjunct Clinical Instructor and serves on the School of Education Advisory Committee at Adelphi University. Peggy has worked at Transitions of Long Island since 1992. She is the coordinator of the Graduate Student Internship Program, a case manager and coauthor of Mempal, a memory book and therapeutic intervention method. In 1999, with Dr. Jean Elbaum, she presented Mempal at Health South Braintree Rehabilitation Hospital's 20th Annual Neurorehabilitation Conference. That same year, Peggy Kramer and Carrie Dulaski presented a poster session at the ASHA convention in San Francisco. In 2001, Peggy and Dr. Elbaum presented three papers at the Williamsburg Traumatic Brain Injury International Conference. Peggy and her husband, Ed, have three grown sons. They enjoy family vacations, gardening, sailing and kayaking.

Deborah Benson is Executive Director of Transitions of Long Island. She received the Ph.D. degree in Clinical Neuropsychology from the Graduate Center of the City University of New York and is a New York State licensed Clinical Neuropsychologist. Dr. Benson joined Transitions in 1993. Her memberships include the American Psychological Association, National Academy of Neuropsychology, International Neuropsychological Society and the Brain Injury Association. She is certified as a clinical instructor and clinical examiner by the American Academy for the Certification of Brain Injury Specialists; in neurofeedback by the National Registry of Neurofeedback Providers; and by the American Psychological Association in the treatment of alcohol and other psychoactive substance use disorders. She is listed in the National Register of Health Service Providers in Psychology. Dr. Benson has presented on numerous topics related to brain injury rehabilitation at regional and national conferences. Deborah and her partner live in New Jersey. She enjoys her professional activities and her interests include, yoga, drumming and travel.

Carrie Dulaski is an occupational therapist at For Kids, a private practice specializing in the treatment of infants through teenagers located in Far Rockaway, New York. She graduated cum laude from Springfield College with a B.S. degree in Rehabilitation Services and received the M.S. degree in Occupational Therapy from Columbia University. In her final year at Columbia University, Carrie and her colleagues presented their Master's project at the American Occupational Therapy Association conference in Baltimore. Their project examined how mothers and fathers play with their children with disabilities. After graduating, Carrie joined the occupational therapy staff at Transitions of Long Island. In 1999, she and Peggy Kramer presented at the ASHA conference in San Francisco regarding the collaboration of occupational therapists and speech-language pathologists. Carrie and her husband live on Long Island, New York. She enjoys cooking, arts and crafts, and working out at the gym.